Developing Computer-Based Information Systems

Information Sciences Series

Joseph Becker and Robert M. Hayes:
INFORMATION STORAGE AND RETRIEVAL

Charles P. Bourne:
METHODS OF INFORMATION HANDLING

Harold Borko:
AUTOMATED LANGUAGE PROCESSING

Russell D. Archibald and Richard L. Villoria:
NETWORK-BASED MANAGEMENT SYSTEMS (PERT/CPM)

Charles T. Meadow:
THE ANALYSIS OF INFORMATION SYSTEMS, A PROGRAMMER'S
INTRODUCTION TO INFORMATION RETRIEVAL

Launor F. Carter:
NATIONAL DOCUMENT-HANDLING SYSTEMS FOR SCIENCE AND
TECHNOLOGY

George W. Brown, James G. Miller and Thomas A. Keenan:
EDUNET: REPORT OF THE SUMMER STUDY ON INFORMATION
NETWORKS CONDUCTED BY THE INTERUNIVERSITY COMMUNI-
CATIONS COUNCIL (EDUCOM)

Perry E. Rosove:
DEVELOPING COMPUTER-BASED INFORMATION SYSTEMS

Robert M. Hayes:
MATHEMATICS OF INFORMATION SYSTEMS (IN PREPARATION)

Developing Computer-Based Information Systems

Perry E. Rosove

Education Systems
Advanced Systems Division
System Development Corporation

John Wiley and Sons, Inc.   New York · London · Sydney

Library of Congress Catalog Card Number: 67-21331
Printed in the United States of America

CONTRIBUTORS

Jack Jaffe

J. J. Connelly

L. A. Friedman

H. Sackman

Information Sciences Series

Information is the essential ingredient in decision making. The need for improved information systems in recent years has been made critical by the steady growth in size and complexity of organizations and data.

This series is designed to include books that are concerned with various aspects of communicating, utilizing, and storing digital and graphic information. It will embrace a broad spectrum of topics, such as information system theory and design, man-machine relationships, language data processing, artificial intelligence, mechanization of library processes, non-numerical applications of digital computers, storage and retrieval, automatic publishing, command and control, information display, and so on.

Information science may someday be a profession in its own right. The aim of this series is to bring together the interdisciplinary core of knowledge that is apt to form its foundation. Through this consolidation, it is expected that the series will grow to become the focal point for professional education in this field.

Preface

This book attempts to describe selected aspects of the process by which computer-based information systems are developed. These aspects of the development process tend to be neglected in the published literature, although they are critical for successful system performance. Many books have been written about computer technology, computer programming, systems engineering, systems design, and systems analysis but few have been written about the human factor in the conception, design, production, installation, operations, and evolution of systems. The focus of this book, then, as distinct from others of the genre, is on the human factor and the interdependence of this human factor with other elements in the system development process. Systems have gone awry in the past and they will flounder again in the future. The computer hardware may be off-the-shelf and the programs may be impeccably debugged, but the critical element, the human factor, will remain for some years to come the source of less-than-desirable system performance. In this book it is contended also that the human factor is a critical variable at *all* stages of the development process, from the initial notion that an information system may be the answer to a problem to the handover of the system to the user.

The book has been written to meet a need often expressed by the buyers, administrators, and users of information systems. Too often they have been confused, if not overwhelmed, by the complexities of the systems they have bought, administered, or used. In particular, they have not always understood their own role in the development process. The systems engineers and computer programmers occasionally confess that they might be able to design better hardware, better systems, or better computer programs if only they understood the human factor more than they do. This book attempts to satisfy these varied needs both by its review of the development process and by its focus on the human factor in that process.

In order to describe the information system development process in a meaningful way the chapters in the book are presented in a sequence that reflects a model of the process from the initial determination of the system user's goals and objectives to the handover of the physical components of the system to the user. In view of the focus in this book on the human factor, however, the design of hardware is not considered as a separate topic. One chapter is devoted to computer programming. Technical and managerial problems commonly encountered during the course of development efforts are reviewed.

In a field as new as computer-based information processing there is no consensus as to *the* appropriate way to develop an information *system,* nor is there widespread agreement on the nature and content of a model or pattern of the development process. Furthermore, there is no commonly accepted terminology with which to describe the information system development process. Concepts such as "systems," "information systems," "software," "personnel subsystem," "system training," and so on are subject to misunderstanding and controversy. Inevitably, therefore, there will be disagreement with the positions taken in this book and with its particular terminology. We offer no assurance that the several contributors to this book agree with one another on all issues or that the careful reader will not find some inconsistencies in the use of technical jargon in different chapters. We take the position that this is inevitable at this time; it reflects the dynamic nature of the technology with which we are dealing. Debate on these subjects and the publication of alternative approaches and terminology will, it is hoped, contribute to progress in the field.

The book is written by personnel of the System Development Corporation who have worked as pioneers in the development of the first generation of military, large-scale, computerized information systems. The individual chapters are based either on first-hand experience with such systems or on corporation documents and reports written by first-hand participants which describe their design and production. These systems include the Semi-Automatic Ground Environment (SAGE) System, the Strategic Air Command Control System (SACCS), the North American Air Defense Combat Operations Center (NORAD COC), and the Department of Defense Damage Assessment Center. Other corporate experience reflected in this book includes the development of the Back-Up Interceptor Control (BUIC) System, The NORAD Space Detection and Tracking System (SPADATS), the Navy Space Surveillance System (SPASUR), and the Air Force Satellite Control System.

In addition the contents of this book reflect the experience and knowledge acquired by personnel of the System Development Corporation in such areas as medicine, education, law enforcement, the administration of justice, air traffic control, and civil defense.

The review of the information system development process and the model of that process contained herein have also drawn heavily on the published literature that deals with information system development in the industrial sphere.

Many specialists who represent different disciplines cooperate in the development of the typical, large-scale, computer-based information system. It is not surprising, therefore, that a book about the system development process, such as this one, should require the efforts of several authors. It is appropriate, then, for me to express my appreciation to the other writers who contributed chapters to the book: Jack Jaffe, John Connelly, Lee Friedman, and Harold Sackman. Without their patience, dedication, and hard work, this book would never have seen the light of day. Their contributions have provided the book with a range and depth that would have been otherwise impossible.

It would be difficult for me to express my appreciation to all my colleagues and associates at the System Development Corporation during the last decade who in ways large and small contributed to the preparation of this book. I am indebted particularly to W. C. Biel and J. R. Champion.

The System Development Corporation generously freed me from my other duties so that the book could be written and provided the secretarial assistance necessary to prepare the manuscript for publication.

The opinions of the writers of this book are their own and should not be interpreted as representing in any way a corporate point of view.

PERRY E. ROSOVE

Santa Monica, California
June 1967

Contents

Chapter One

Introduction

P. E. Rosove

1.1 THE INSTITUTIONAL CRISIS

Many contemporary organizations and institutions are in a state of crisis. This book is concerned with the means whereby these organizations and institutions are attempting to resolve the difficulties which beset them. In their efforts to survive and adapt in a world of rapid and incessant change, these enterprises are turning increasingly to the use of the new "information technology" exemplified by, but not limited to, the electronic digital computer. Unfortunately the application of a new, dynamic technology as a means to overcome crises generates its own unique problems. These problems include creating an efficient process for the development of systems employing the new technology, and dealing with the effects of the new development process on existing management orientations and organization. This book deals with both types of problems.

In the second half of the twentieth century we are witnessing an extraordinary growth in the size and complexity of governmental, military, and business organizations. Whether we look at public institutions, military commands, or business corporations, we see an increasing division of labor and more intensive task specialization, a growth in the number of employees, personnel, or clients serviced, an

1

increasing diversification of operational functions, a proliferation of organizational components, and a growth in the geographical scope of operations. A contemporary enterprise may be characterized as a vast maze of interconnected and interdependent elements, all, presumably, organized and operating to achieve a common objective or related objectives, whether this goal be producing a product, defending the United States against air attack, or serving the needs of the public.

As governmental, military, and business enterprises grow in size and complexity, and as they attempt to adapt to rapidly changing environments or changing threats in their environments—missiles, competitors, or the population explosion—the need of government administrators, military commanders, and business managers to be able to receive, process, and use large volumes of information rapidly becomes increasingly critical to the successful operation of the enterprise. The sheer number of data which must be utilized in the typical institution of the contemporary period is in itself overwhelming. One has only to think of the burgeoning population data handled by the Bureau of the Census, or the weapons and materials inventories dealt with in the military and business realms. Furthermore, the division of labor, technical specialization, and departmentalization characteristic of contemporary large-scale institutions call for a degree of coordination and, therefore, an exchange of information among interdependent operational units never before equaled in human history. In addition, events and operations within interrelated organizational units occur so rapidly that the unaided human mind is no longer able to keep abreast of the course of events with a speed sufficient to comprehend and control them.

There is abundant evidence that existing methods and procedures for handling and using information in contemporary large-scale enterprises are failing to keep up with the needs of public administrators, business managers, and military commanders. As a result of this situation, there has emerged in recent years the specialized study and development of "systems" for the transmission, processing, and utilization of information.

1.2 THE ROLE OF INFORMATION

To conduct some rationally conceived endeavor, means and ends must be logically related. Information constitutes an essential link between means and ends. Information is needed about the environment of the enterprise and about the condition of the enterprise itself. This information must be obtained somehow and transmitted to a central location, usually the headquarters of the leader of the enterprise, and to other levels of the operation. At these various locations the information is studied, analyzed, summarized, organized, and stored for future reference or displayed for immediate use. On the basis of this information processing and a consideration of other relevant factors, such as the institutional goals, the leader of the enterprise formulates his plans and makes his decisions. Directives and orders are then transmitted to the component units and personnel involved to administer, direct, coordinate, and control their activities so that the stated ends can be accomplished. At each lower level of the enterprise, information is also used for similar types of activities relevant to that level. The handling and use of information in an enterprise is thus analogous to the functioning of the nervous system of an organism. It is not the organism; it is the mechanism which coordinates and controls the components so that the organism, as a whole, can survive in and adapt to its environment.

1.3   WHAT IS INFORMATION?

This book is about *information* as distinct from data. A datum is a fact in isolation. Information is an aggregate of facts so organized or a datum so utilized as to be knowledge or intelligence. Information is meaningful data, whereas data, as such, have no intrinsic meaning or significance.

Information is the concept relating data which are otherwise meaningless to some specified human purpose or objective. From this point of view, "data processing" is a set of activities which transforms data into information. This distinction between data and information emphasizes what needs to be stressed. It focuses attention upon the uses we intend to make of data, rather than upon data-processing tools as such. A radar operator in a system of air defense who is tracking an unidentified aircraft regards radar returns from clouds as noise, not information; but to a meteorologist attempting to forecast weather, radar returns from clouds are not noise—they are the information he needs to achieve his objectives.

The different uses of data within a system and the form in which they are displayed also illustrate the distinction between data and information. The same data in a system are used in a variety of ways. The processing of the data after they are received or at some point in time after they have been stored in the system's files or memory changes these data into a variety of forms useful to different people. They are displayed at different positions in the system where they are used to fulfill a variety of functions. As an example, data may be reduced and summarized before display for a military commander as information relevant in deciding whether to move aircraft from one base to another as a result of a weather condition; these same data may be organized in a separate file in a computer's memory where they will be used by long-range planners for statistical analyses to optimize aircraft assignments to bases. It is this process of organizing data for specific uses which transforms them into information. The importance of displays in the design of systems is dependent upon the presentation of information with regard to format, location, and timing so that they are optimally useful to particular system personnel. For these reasons the design of appropriate display formats for system users is an important feature of system development.

1.4   DEFINITION OF INFORMATION SYSTEM

An information system is the formal or rationally planned means whereby managers receive and transmit information. Hence it is more than an automatic data-processing system. It may include automatic data processing as one aspect of the information-handling apparatus assisting management, but it may also include oral briefings. Every large man-made enterprise depends upon and has an information system of some kind. It is essential to differentiate between an information system as such and the particular technology which, in a given time and place, is utilized as one feature of the system. This is important because there is a tendency to classify types of systems by technological characteristics rather than by the characteristics of information systems.

A word needs to be said about the personnel who use the system. In a large-scale organization there is a hierarchy of personnel who make decisions, conduct operations, and develop plans of various kinds. An information system, therefore, must not be conceived merely as a tool of management at the highest level of the organizational hierarchy. If we think of a typical large-scale organization as composed of top managers, middle managers, supervisors or foremen, and operators, or, if we define their various roles functionally as policy planners, operations planners, operations controllers, machine operators, clerks, etc., then a properly designed system will serve the needs of all these persons for information. It follows from this concept that the development of an information system should be focused, not upon technology, but upon the informational needs of the system users. The foundation of information system development is the analysis of the need for information at all levels and for all functions in the enterprise. This analysis must precede commitment to a particular type of equipment.

In the years since the electronic digital computer was first applied it has been put to use in over 600 different ways.[1] One of the major difficulties in attempting to define what is meant in this book by an information system is the state of terminology and classification of computer-based systems in current use. Applications of computers are usually classified along functional lines such as "scientific," "commercial," and "military command and control systems." Some classification schemes differentiate "real-time" from "non-real-time" systems or "on-line" from "off-line" systems. Much of this usage of terminology and classification seems to be the result of an historical process in addition to technical design issues. For example, the first electronic computers were developed to carry out scientific computations, while nonscientific applications followed at a later period. Similarly, the development of large-scale, "real-time" control systems appeared in the military area, before they emerged in business.[2]

To avoid the confusions inherent in a terminology derived in large measure from the history of computer applications, we shall include under the rubric of information systems all the varied uses of computers referred to in the previous paragraph insofar as such uses are found in particular systems. Thus a system may include the use of a computer complex for "off-line" scientific research, the handling of payroll information, or "real-time" production control. By the term "information system" we shall subsume both business and military applications since the fundamental task of *management* is the same in both fields. Business and military managers alike must receive information about their organization and its daily operations; both must control these operations; and both must conduct short-range and long-range planning. R. J. Rhine, who has participated as a manager in the development of both military and nonmilitary information systems, makes this point very clearly:[3]

"Military command and control systems are often larger and more expensive than the typical automated management system; nevertheless the functions they serve are in fact management functions. And the basic properties of these systems, shorn of all frills, details, and complexities, are identical to those found in management systems. . . .

"What has been learned the hard way about the development of complex command and control systems can be applied to the development of management systems for decision making. And as a matter of fact, the command and control technology for which the military establishment can take a lion's share of the credit, was developed to support certain general functions which are at the very foundation of management theory."

We should also note that management experts assert that the principles of management in business are applicable to the military realm.[4]

Our major point in this chapter, then, is that integrated information systems, regardless of their particular functions, have more in common than is usually believed. The development and management of such systems will be made more efficient to the extent that we can isolate and clarify the nature of these common features. The second point to be made here is that information systems should be classified by their degree of integration, that is, the extent to which they are "total" systems. This is related to the variety of functions that any particular system may be required to perform. As managers in industry gained experience with computerized systems, their purposes tended to shift from the use of computers in a limited area, such as payroll preparation or inventory control, to broader applications related to profit making at a company-wide level. As the purposes of management changed, the system boundaries changed (more functions—production scheduling, marketing analyses, sales forecasts, etc.—were automated) with the result that systems became subsystems of a still larger system. The dimensions of change were (1) laterally to incorporate different functions at the same organizational level, and (2) vertically to incorporate different levels of the organizational hierarchy.

Lateral Integration

Large-scale organizations in business, government, and military spheres have been composed traditionally of relatively independent and functionally differentiated areas such as personnel, accounting, production, and research. These functionally differentiated areas have been linked together by formal and informal information networks. However, the integration of compartmentalized functions, which are usually assigned to subunits of the organization such as departments, divisions, or branches, has always been a problem. The phenomenon of identification with and loyalty to a department rather than to the organization as a whole has been discussed in the management literature at considerable length. The inadequacies of the formal mode of information transmission have also received much attention. A large proportion of the energy and skill of management has been devoted to ensuring the smooth flow of information laterally across departmental lines. As J. W. Forrester points out, the education of managers in industry has followed the same lines as this organizational compartmentalization; that is, it has been fragmented. He writes, "Manufacturing, finance, distribution, organization, advertising, and research have too often been viewed as separate skills and not as part of a unified system."[5] This educational specialization of the manager is then followed by practical experience which perpetuates the same influence. But a compartmentalized and fragmented management technique which was adequate for the nineteenth century and the first half of the twentieth cannot cope with the problems of the present day.

As business, governmental, and military organizations increase in size and complexity, familiarity with the operations of parts of the organization by top managers no longer ensures successful and efficient over-all functioning. The manager's tasks are complicated by the fact that he must concern himself with a large variety of variables which affect his organization in nonlinear fashion. As a result of these factors, Forrester concludes that "in management, as in engineering, we can expect that the interconnections and interactions between the components of the system will often be more important than the separate components themselves."[6]

The evolution of many business and industrial applications of digital computers from isolated functions such as payroll and accounting to plant-wide and company-wide computer-based systems is now history. Figure 1.1 suggests this lateral shift in perspective from point A, which represents the unintegrated perspective, to point B, which represents lateral integration at the plant or company level.

Vertical Integration

The linkages which make up an information system in a business, in the military sphere, or in government may occur laterally, as described in the previous section, or vertically. Vertical integration means the linking of different levels of the organizational hierarchy from the

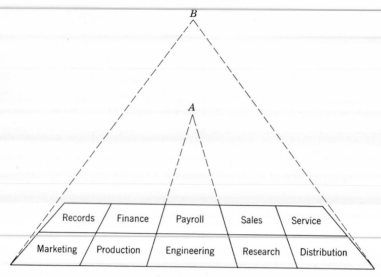

Figure 1.1   Lateral integration—company level.

production or operational "line" at the lowest level to the highest managerial level. In general, three levels can be distinguished: (1) production, servicing, or operational; (2) control; and (3) long-range planning. Note that these levels reflect distinctive functions associated with the various organizational levels. Figure 1.2 illustrates the vertical perspective in a management information system.[7] The figure shows the functions on the left and the organization on the right.

The differentiation of the three levels of a management system as shown in Figure 1.2 indicates that an integrated system may include *both* real-time and non-real-time operations. Management control of

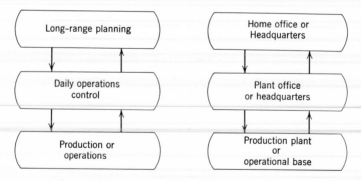

Figure 1.2   Vertical integration of a management system.

daily operations and the control of production are on-line, real-time functions, as these terms are usually defined. Long-range planning, on the other hand, is not carried out in real time or on-line.

In the development of large-scale computer-based systems for the military services, much has been made of the distinction between command systems and control systems. However, an information system may be composed of both command and control functions. The information system which is used by the North American Air Defense Command (NORAD), for example, is composed of two integrated elements—SAGE and the NORAD Combat Operations Center (425L). SAGE is essentially the control element, whereas COC is a command center.

The progressive integration of computer-based systems in the lateral and vertical dimensions has developed to the point where integration is occurring not only plant- or organization-wide, but also on a multiplant and an industry-wide basis. These latter forms of integration are no respecters of national boundaries. The long-range trend toward integration in which computerized information systems are playing an important technological role is well expressed by R. A. Brady:[8]

"The inner logic of the newer technology (automation) sets certain broad limits on how it may be most efficiently managed and directed. Through its application, processes are being linked to processes, plants to plants, firms to firms, and even industries to industries in such a way, and under such ordering disciplines of integration and synchronization, that the relating plans and management procedures must keep in step on pain of crippling breakdowns, any one of which may threaten to ramify endlessly throughout the system."

For our purposes, we can distinguish five levels of integration as follows:

LEVEL 1. Functional level—integration of a.single function, for example, payroll.

LEVEL 2. Plant or department level—integration of several functions, for example, payroll, finance, sales, marketing, and production control.

LEVEL 3. Company or organization level—integration of several plants, departments, offices, and geographical regions; the military command.

LEVEL 4. Intercompany or interorganizational level—integration of several affiliated or unaffiliated but functionally interdependent companies; integration of several military commands.

LEVEL 5. Industrial level—integration of several unaffiliated companies in a given business field, such as defense industry or banking; NATO illustrates this level in the military sphere.

United Air Lines provides us with an example of integration at the company level—level 3. (See Figure 1.3.) In this company's plan-

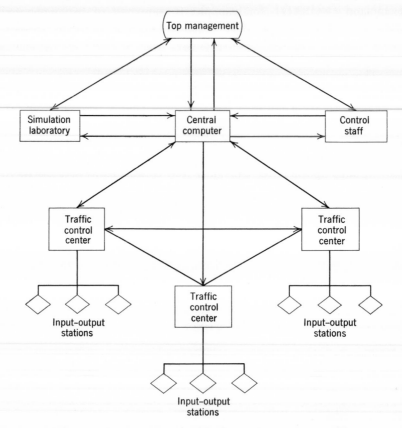

Figure 1.3   Integration of a typical information system.

ning, inputs originating in reservations offices, overhaul shops, storerooms, flight dispatch offices, etc., will flow through data control centers into a central computer, which will be linked, on the one hand, to a corporate laboratory for model experimentation and, on the other hand, to a staff group responsible for control of regular, daily operations. At the top of the system hierarchy is management, to be linked via a communications network to the central computer, the corporate laboratory, and the control staff.[9]

When we look at the historical development and evolution of information systems, particularly in the business realm, it becomes evident that classification schemes based on such criteria as "scientific," "commercial," "real-time," and "off-line" are too narrow for our purpose and too specific to particular technical design issues. In the latter part of the 1960's, the typical information system at levels 2, 3, and 4 is neither "scientific" nor "commercial," neither "real-time" nor "non-real-time." The typical information system which is organization- or corporate-wide encompasses some combination of these features. Similarly, the military command and control system may use its computers for scientific computations, inventory control, long-range planning, gaming, training, or deriving displays for status reports and command decision making. Thus, as integrated systems incorporate both "real-time" and "non-real-time" aspects, the use of "realtime" as a criterion for classifying information systems loses its value. For the purposes of this book, therefore, we shall define an information system as *an integrated, multiple-purpose, geographically dispersed, computer-based configuration of people, procedures, and equipment designed to satisfy the informational needs of a user.* Our concern throughout this book is with information systems at levels 2, 3, and 4 as specified above.

1.5   THE SYSTEM ORIENTATION

Systems Engineering and Operations Research

H. H. Goode and R. E. Machol[10] describe the emergence of a systems orientation in the field of engineering. They point out that early efforts to develop large-scale equipment systems, such as the telephone system, applied methods and an approach which had worked well in the design of small-scale systems. This approach, however, was not successful since the components of the large-scale systems did not work when they were joined together. Out of these early failures there emerged new concepts and new methods, and the name "system engineering" was given to the field. The type of man required is the engineering scientist or scientific generalist, and the method is the interdisciplinary team approach. "We are led to the concept of the system-design team . . . ," Goode and Machol write. "The technique has been variously called the *systems approach* or the team development method."[11]

According to A. D. Hall, the first formal attempt to teach systems engineering "probably" occurred in 1950 at the Massachusetts Institute of Technology.[12] To Hall, the "evolutionary forces" which resulted in the development of systems engineering as a field in the 1950's were increasing system complexity and the growth of modern technology, which broadens the range of possibilities and alternatives. Hall defines what he means by the "systems point of view" when he discusses the ideal characteristics of the systems engineer as distinct from traditional concepts of the engineer as a type. The systems point of view means that "the systems engineer is not concerned primarily with the devices that make up a system, but with the concept of the system as a whole —its internal relations and its behavior in the given environment."[13]

Whereas some specialists in operations research have emphasized the task of analysis as the distinguishing feature of this field, other specialists have stressed the "systems approach" as its central feature. C. W. Churchman has gone so far as to assert that operations research should equal "systems science."[14]

Operations research emerged as a separate field of activity during World War II. The application of operations research techniques in industry took hold in the United States during the decade of the 1950's. A standard textbook on the subject attributes the rapid growth of operations research to the "increased differentiation and segmentation of the management function. . . ."[15] As a consequence of the increasing division of labor in industry "a new class of managerial problems began to appear . . . executive-type problems." The fragmentation of large-scale industrial organizations into departments resulted in the emergence of departmental objectives which differed from the objectives of the organization as a whole. Thus operations research is defined as an effort to apply scientific method to managerial problems brought about by the increasing complexity of industrial organization. A central orientation to the solution of such problems is the "systems approach," since the industrial organization is regarded as an interconnected complex of functionally related components. The business organization is conceived as "a social or man-machine system."[16]

As in the case of systems engineering, operations research utilizes the team approach in the search for the solution to managerial problems in industry. The problems under investigation are new, and no single existing science possesses all the techniques necessary to resolve them. Furthermore, since the problems investigated are "system" problems, many factors are involved in their creation, and no one science is capable of dealing effectively with every one of these causative factors. Thus, in an organization composed of people as well as machines, a psychologist should be a member of the operations research team in addition to an engineer. A typical team might consist of one man who is familiar with the operations of the organization under study, a physical scientist, an engineer, a mathematician or statistician, a logician or specialist in scientific methodology, and a behavioral scientist.

"Integrated" and "Total" Systems in Business

The application of computer technology in the business sphere during the 1955-1964 decade shifted rapidly toward a "total systems" orientation.[17] But the relationship between the trend toward the development of "total systems" and "integrated data-processing systems" in business and the theoretical work in systems theory and cybernetics is not clear at this point in time. Operations research and systems engineering had an impact on business, of course, but relatively little direct influence on information systems development. Although the system concept existed as early as the 1940's, the development of integrated information systems in business appears to have been the result of a trial and error process. The historical accounts of various industries which have made extensive applications of computers suggest that the traditional profit motive and competitive pressures, rather than any abstract concept or theory, were the compelling forces behind the evolution of integrated systems. The extent to which various companies approached their problems with an integrated orientation varied, depending upon such diverse factors as the size of the company, the type of industry, the degree of decentralization, and the extent of integration of the productive process. Thus the Atwood Vacuum Machine Company, a relatively small organization, began its approach to computer applications with an integrated or systems viewpoint, whereas the Standard Oil Company of New Jersey proceeded to introduce computer technology on a piecemeal basis.[18]

In most industrial applications the computer was utilized, at least to begin with, in a direct and simple way. By automating the payroll operation, for example, clerical staffs were reduced in size, and costs were thereby lowered. Similar savings were achieved by automating accounting and inventory control operations. But as management gained experience with the use of computers in routine computations and clerical functions, the utility of the computer for solving more general problems became apparent. The managers of some companies began to ask themselves whether the computer could handle everything from customer order to product shipment. The computer could handle complex computations and control the processing of chemicals, petroleum, cement, and steel, but could it assist managers in the control of the entire company operation, including the planning of production from sales forecasts?

The Monsanto Chemical Company, for example, initially applied computers to accounting problems. As an "afterthought" the computer was also used to solve mathematical problems. It then became evident to company management that, although accounting records were used primarily for financial purposes, they were also an excellent source of marketing information, better than any other source available. Out of such experiences there gradually emerged the notion that a "central computer system" could serve the needs for detailed and summary records of several departments simultaneously. Thus, in this case, it was not by design that information system integration at the plant level became an operational reality. The Monsanto case also illustrates how the first relatively simple computer applications gradually evolved in the direction of taking over more sophisticated decision making at the lower-middle management level. Once the computer had been programmed to calculate freight rates, it was "but a small step from there to the point that the computer figures the rates for alternate ways of shipping and selects the lowest cost carrier. . . ."[19] Similarly, in the function of inventory control, the computer keeps track of inventory levels and decides when it is necessary to reorder stock which falls below a given threshold.

In many instances it was not the intent of a company which purchased a computer to undertake a complete overhaul of its operations. But the very nature of computers, in conjunction with the profit motive, forced company after company to integrate functions which had formerly been independent. It was simply a question of the most effective utilization of computer technology. Thus the Martin-Marietta Corporation began its computer applications with the basic objective of obtaining information in greater depth about the operations of its decentralized and geographically dispersed plants in Denver, Orlando, and Baltimore. Centralized control was mandatory to this corporation because of the interrelated nature of its productive operations. The installation of computers in three different locations, however, could not be made effective without first standardizing procedures at each location. An inventory system for all plants in the company could not work until all units used a common code for stock items. In this way computer technology determined the emergence of an integrated information system at the company level in spite of the absence of an a priori total systems orientation.[20]

The International Shoe Company, by contrast, began its computer applications as a result of an organizational crisis precipitated by basic changes in the shoe industry. The company was experiencing increasing inventories of finished goods, higher costs, and rapidly changing shoe styles. Each department and operating division of the company had been attempting to solve these problems independently. There was little coordination, with the result that merchandizing departments could not share information with procurement departments since estimates were made in different ways and in different time spans. The need for standardization on a company-wide level was therefore recognized by management at the outset. The company faced the fact that it could no longer operate efficiently with each of nineteen selling divisions functioning as a separate entity.[21] As a company spokesman put it, the company began its reorganization with the idea of "true integrated data processing. Consequently, we ruled out any single application, such as payroll or accounts receivable. We decided that the computer could best be used as an instrument of communication and co-ordination. . . ."[22] It was felt that the nature of computer operations was such that the company would profit most from applications which showed the impact of one transaction in a particular area upon transactions in all other areas. The computer would be used to link together sales and inventories; it would relate sales estimates with estimates for raw materials and labor requirements; and the sales data would be used for determining production schedules.

Notable technological improvements between 1955 and 1960 made it possible to apply computer technology to more sophisticated management problems. These technological developments included increases in the speed of internal computer operations and in storage capacities. Even more important from a management point of view was the development of ferrite magnetic core storage, which made it possible to go directly to addresses in the computer's memory (random access) instead of using the older method of searching the length of a magnetic tape for a particular address. This feature also makes it possible to create business, as well as military, computer applications which operate in "real time," that is, the results of computer processing are displayed for managers as they happen so that they can maintain control over operations. Other technological developments which contributed to sophisticated applications were improvements to the input and output devices which linked the human members of the system with the computer. However, it is evident from the emergence of actual integrated computerized systems in industry that organizational and conceptual traditions had to be overcome before the technical promise of computerized information-processing systems could be realized.

The history of the early applications of electronic information-processing equipment in industry has some interesting implications for the relationship between basic concepts and a given technology. It has been pointed out that, in its inherent characteristics, the electronic computer is completely and unquestionably integrative. The techniques of electronic equipment impose inherent notions of how operations should be conducted—and these notions only gradually become the operating concepts of the people who use the equipment. One writer puts it this way:[23]

"The multiplicities and speeds of electronic techniques are so great that they can perform great numbers of tasks on great numbers of inputs involving great numbers of varying factors to provide great numbers of outputs with so near a simultaneity that, from the human standpoint of evaluation, we can call them simultaneous. The former segregations of information by barriers of time and space have been removed, the prime requisite for integration."

The writer concludes that contemporary nonintegrated approaches to applications of information technology are purely temporary. As familiarity with the capabilities and potentialities of the technology of high-speed digital computers increases, the nature of the equipment will "force" an "integrated system concept of management control" in business applications.[24]

At the present time, the systemic orientation is gaining as a philosophic concept—as a world-view or a way of looking at things in general, as indicated in the various fields we have reviewed. For those who work in the information system field, however, the systems point of view has not yet prevailed in an operational, day-by-day sense.

1.6 THE INFORMATION SYSTEM DEVELOPMENT PROCESS

By system development for information systems we mean the creation of a new or a replacement system which is designed to accomplish the objectives or mission of a particular user. This definition of system development incorporates system design as merely one aspect of development. System development is concerned with the entire history of a particular information system, including the study and analysis of its manual or semimanual predecessor; the initial conception of the replacement system; the analysis of existing user objectives and the creation, in consultation with the user, of new objectives; the definition of the new system's operational requirements; the design of the system; the specification of its physical components; and the production of these physical components. System development includes provision for the human components of the system, that is, personnel and organizational design. It includes the creation of training programs and capabilities for system testing and system evaluation. And, given the concept of system evolution, system development must also include over-all, long-range planning for the evolutionary replacement of each system configuration by subsequent ones.

Phases of System Development

In the course of its development every large-scale information system must pass through a sequence of five stages in its life history. What shall we call the five phases? The criteria which should be used in the selection of terms for these phases include (1) descriptive suitability for the primary process or function which occurs within the phase; (2) simplicity and clarity of denotation; and (3) widespread usage. In meeting the first two criteria we do not want to disregard terms which are enjoying wide acceptance as, for example, "requirements." This term, although lacking the denotation of "production," is so commonly used with reference to the first phase of system development that it seems appropriate to retain it. We propose, then, to name the five phases of development as follows:

Phase I   — Requirements
Phase II   — Design
Phase III — Production
Phase IV   — Installation
Phase V   — Operations

Figure 1.4 shows the temporal sequence of the phases of system development. The feedback arrows indicate that the development history is a closed-loop cycle. This reflects the process of system evolution. Note also that the arrows between the phases indicate that knowledge acquired and decisions made in later phases are fed back to earlier phases. The feedback loops reflect the iterative problem-solving process. The overlapping of the phases in the figure illustrates concurrent development activities.

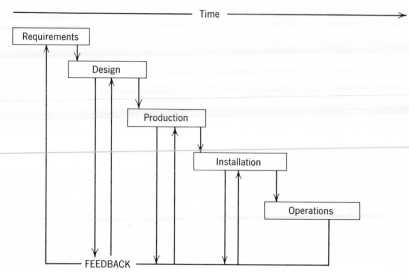

Figure 1.4   The sequence of development phases.

The use of the term "phase" in the context of system development should be qualified. Only at a high level of abstraction can we assert that there are five distinguishable phases of development and that they represent a logical and temporal sequence. In some cases, the primary process within a phase which gives that phase its name, such as requirements or design, is also an activity or function which is performed in other phases as well. The system requirements, for example, must be determined before the initial design activity, but the determination of requirements does not terminate at any specific phase. Throughout the course of the development of a system, old requirements are constantly undergoing refinement while more detailed requirements are being generated. When the system first becomes operational, actual experience with it may give rise to new requirements. Changes in the system's environment or in technology may also result in the creation of new requirements. Similarly, system design, in addition to serving as a name for a logical and temporal phase which follows the requirements phase, is also a function which is carried out repetitively at different levels of the system development process.

Parallel Development Processes

Several processes in the development of large-scale systems normally occur simultaneously. Initial determination of system requirements and design activities are focused upon the system as a totality. Then the major breakout of the system development effort occurs with the splitting off, at the subsystem level, of the "hardware" and "software."

There are few words in any language that do not have varying connotations to different users. In the case of technical jargons, there is an even greater problem in obtaining consensus on the meaning of terms. The term "software" is no exception. At one extreme "software" has been used to refer exclusively to the utility programs which computer manufacturers provide for the user of one of their machines. At the opposite extreme, the term has been used to designate everything which is not hardware, including, for example, the reports and data which a producer of equipment generates during his production activity. According to this usage, the alpha-numeric symbols displayed on a console, or the output of an automatic printer, could also be labeled software.

We do not conclude from these various meanings of "software" that it has no usefulness anymore than we would discard the term "hardware" because it fails to differentiate between different kinds of equipment. In general, "software" is valuable as a rubric for focusing attention, as we must in this book, on those aspects of information systems which are *not* hardware. We need some such term as a shorthand device to establish balance—as a counterpoise for those who tend to think about information systems in terms of gadgets, black boxes, and machines.

It is granted, of course, that, for the purpose of contracting, each item of software needs to be identified so that appropriate management accounting and controls can function. However, the requirements of management oriented to the acquisition of hardware should not be allowed to obscure the fact that there are justifications for the use of a general term.

The problem is to clarify why a general designation like "software" is important. A term is needed which brings out the interdependent nature of the major critical components of an information system—user objectives, system requirements, design documentation, computer programs, personnel, and operational procedures. It is a particular configuration of these interdependent elements which transforms the *same* computer or computer complex into a custom-made system which will serve the needs of a particular user. From this point of view, the hardware (specific computers and peripheral devices) is a constant, and it is the software which is the variable. But most important is the fact that an effective information system depends upon the *integration* by system designers of the computer programs, the personnel, and the operational procedures. Whereas machines can be designed as independent elements on the basis of deterministic principles and will meet their operational specifications when linked together into a system, such is not the case with nondeterministic information systems. Ideally, therefore, the computer programs, the personnel subsystem, and the operational procedures should be designed as an integrated unit, just as they must function in the operational environment.

For practical reasons, in a large-scale development effort, the software developer must fragment the task and assign various pieces, such as the computer program design, to specialists. This is precisely why the development of an information system is so difficult, and why the end results are so frequently disappointing. Following existing work practices (span of control, specialization, delegation of authority, etc.), we fragment a task which by its nature does not lend itself easily to this treatment.

In this book we shall use the term "software" as it has been widely employed within the System Development Corporation over the past several years. Software items are produced at all stages of the development process; they include the conceptual definitions and requirements documents prepared during the initial stages of system development, as well as the innumerable reports, data, and card decks produced during the final stages of the development effort. The term refers to the reports, products, and data resulting from the activities of system designers, computer program designers, and programmers. Software includes the procedures manuals, operator handbooks, and training program materials produced by technical writers, human engineers, psychologists, and human factors personnel. This definition will probably satisfy very few readers, but it will suffice, for the purposes of this book, as a basis for communication.

As we have noted, once the subsystem level is reached, developmental processes continue in parallel. Frequently, hardware and software development are the responsibilities of different contractors. Within each of the major subsystem divisions, additional areas of specialized activity are broken out at the component level, and within each of these component areas parallel developmental processes are carried out. The functions of requirements determination and design are repeated at each level and for each line of development. In the case of the software components, for example, while the requirements for the computer programs are being determined, they are also being defined for training, operational procedures, operator handbooks, and personnel manning and organization. When this requirement phase is terminated, the next phase, design, is conducted for each component area. While these development processes are being accomplished in the software subsystem, the same processes are being carried out, at the same time, in the hardware subsystem.

Throughout the component development process, since each of the components must eventually operate as an interdependent element of a system, it is necessary to plan and coordinate activities across the parallel lines of development. The responsibility of management, at the subsystem and component levels, is to ensure that such planning and coordination does, in fact, take place. After the components have been built as integrated entities, it is management's responsibility to guarantee that the subsystems are also integrated and, finally, that the total system operates as a single entity. Planning for and coordinating these manifold concurrent activities is one of the most difficult problems management faces.

Reintegration of Parallel Developmental Processes

The transition from the production to the installation phase is characterized by the process of integration and testing to ensure that each component meets the requirements that have been specified for it, that the components operate according to their requirements when they are linked together as subsystems, and that, finally, the entire system functions according to the requirements for it. It is during the installation phase that the system equipment, the computer programs, and the operations personnel are brought together for the first time to be "shaken down" and evaluated to determine whether the system does what it was designed to do. As soon as the entire system has been tested against the system requirements and has been accepted by the system user, the operations phase begins. It should be emphasized that the initial operations phase is not necessarily an end point but rather may be merely the termination of the first development cycle of the planned evolution of the system. In such cases, the initial operational system performs the function of the prototype—it is an experimental system upon the basis of which modifications will be made. During this initial phase of operations change proposals can be expected to be numerous. They are fed back to all the preceding phases. Initial operations may indicate that better integration of hardware and software is essential during the production phase, that a longer period of personnel orientation is needed during the installation phase, etc.

The organization of this book follows the distinctions made here among development phases, the parallel development processes, and the reintegration of the processes. Thus Chapter 3 deals with the system requirements phase; Chapter 4 reviews the system design phase; and Chapters 5, 6, 7, and 8 cover the parallel development activities of computer program production, personnel and organizational design, design of procedures, and design of the training program, respectively. Chapter 9 on the installation phase and Chapter 10 on system testing and evaluation are essentially concerned with the reintegration process.

1.7   SUMMARY

Many contemporary institutions are in a state of crisis and are turning to information system technology to solve their problems. In this chapter we have pointed out the role of information, as distinct from data, in meeting organizational objectives; we have defined "information" and attempted to define "information system." We have shown that efforts to classify computer-based systems have failed to keep up with the pace of change. Today's "integrated" information system may contain "scientific," "commercial," "command," "control," "real-time," "non-real-time," "on-line," and "off-line" elements. As information systems in business, government, and the military spheres have progressively integrated their automated elements in both the lateral and vertical dimensions, it has become increasingly irrelevant to classify an information system as "real-time" in terms of the attributes of one of its components, such as a control process. The integration of multiple-purpose information-processing elements into larger systems on company, intercompany, and industrial levels has become commonplace. There is, therefore, no simple definition of any information system. We have used the United Air Lines integrated information system plan to illustrate what we mean in this book by an information system. But it is obvious, from the many other examples cited in this chapter, that no simple definition will do justice to the complexities of the subject. Basically, an information system of the type considered in this book is a multiple-purpose, geographically dispersed, computer-based configuration of people, equipment, and procedures designed to meet the informational needs of a user.

We briefly discussed system orientation as it has emerged in systems engineering and operations research. The growth of an "integrated" or "total systems" approach to information systems in business was reviewed, but it was noted that system orientation did not play a key role in the early evolution of business systems.

A brief overview of the information system development process was presented. This subject was discussed in terms of the phases of system development, the breakout of parallel development processes, and the reintegration of these parallel processes. After distinguishing the "hardware" and "software" subsystem components, a working definition of "software" was presented. With the exception of the next chapter, the organization of the book follows, in a rough fashion, the sequence of development phases—requirements, design, production, installation, and operations—differentiated in this chapter. Chapter 2 deals with the typical management problems encountered in the development of a large-scale, computer-based information system.

REFERENCES

1. Neil Macdonald, "Over 600 Areas of Application of Computers," *Computers and Automation*, **XII**, No. 6 (June 1963).
2. For an example of some of the current controversies over definitions of terms in the technical literature see the articles by T. B. Steel, Jr., N. J. Ream, W. A. Bauer and S. Simmons, and H. van Gelder in *Datamation*, March 1964.
3. R. J. Rhine, *Development of an Operational Management System*. Santa Monica, Calif.: System Development Corporation, SP-1175, April 16, 1963, pp. 2-3; and, by the same author, "Command-and-Control and Management Decision Making," *Human Factors*, 6, No. 1 (February 1964), 93–100.
4. H. H. Albers, *Principles of Organization and Management*, 2nd ed. New York: Wiley, 1965, p. 3.

5. J. W. Forrester, *Industrial Dynamics*. New York: Wiley, 1961, p. 2.

6. *Ibid.,* p. 6.

7. For an example of this vertical perspective see D. P. Chrystal et al., "Allis-Chalmers Manufacturing Company: Applying Control Concepts to an Organization," *Total Systems*, A. D. Meacham and V. B. Thompson (eds.). Detroit: American Data Processing, 1962, p. 111.

8. R. A. Brady, *Organization, Automation, and Society*. Los Angeles: University of California Press, 1961, p. 4.

9. Figure 1.3 and this review of the United Air Lines information system are adapted from W. E. Alberts, "United Air Lines," *Management Organization and the Computer*, G. P. Shultz and T. L. Whisler (eds.). Glencoe, Ill.: The Free Press, 1960, pp. 175–177.

10. H. H. Goode and R. E. Machol, *System Engineering: An Introduction to the Design of Large-Scale Systems*. New York: McGraw-Hill, 1957, pp. 7–8.

11. *Ibid.,* p. 8.

12. A. D. Hall, *A Methodology for Systems Engineering*. Princeton, N. J.: Van Nostrand, 1962, p. vii.

13. *Ibid.,* p. 16.

14. C. W. Churchman, *Does Operations Research = Systems Science?*, Symposium on Operations Research. Santa Monica, Calif.: System Development Corporation, March 27, 1963.

15. C. W. Churchman et al., *Introduction to Operations Research*. New York: Wiley, 1957, p. 4.

16. *Ibid.,* p. 7; see also J. W. Forrester, Ref. 5, pp. 1–9.

17. D. J. Axsmith, "A Management Look at Data Processing: Promise, Problem, and Profit," *Total Systems*, Ref. 7, pp. 7-15; for an application of the "total systems" approach to the Pittsburgh Steel Company see *Business Week*, May 4, 1963, pp. 142–46.

18. For accounts of the experiences of these two companies with information systems see *Management Organization and the Computer*, Ref. 9.

19. W. A. Clark, "Monsanto Chemical Company: A Total Systems Approach to Marketing," *Total Systems*, Ref. 7, p. 135.

20. "Martin-Marietta Corporation: Centralized Operations Control," *Total Systems*, Ref. 7, pp. 148–160.

21. L. F. Vogt, "The International Shoe Company," *Management Organization and the Computer*, Ref. 9, p. 137.

22. *Ibid.,* p. 138.

23. A. O. Mann, "A Publically Regulated System of Management Control Services," *Management Control Systems*, D. G. Malcolm, A. J. Rowe, and L. F. McConnell (eds.), New York: Wiley, 1960, p. 247.

24. *Ibid.*

Chapter Two

Management Problems in the Development Process

P. E. Rosove

2.1 INTRODUCTION

The Purpose of the Chapter

The purpose of this chapter is to describe the more salient management problems associated with the development of information systems. Many of these problems are derived from three closely interrelated sets of conditions: (1) the widespread lack of familiarity of managers and administrators with the development process for information systems; (2) the use of an irrelevant model of hardware system development for the management of the information system development process; and (3) the incompatibility between existing management organization and administrative procedures and the unique nature of the information system development process.

In recent years there has been increasing concern at the highest governmental and industrial levels with system management problems as distinct from scientific and technological problems. This concern with management is reflected in such events as the National Advanced-Technology Management Conference held in Seattle, Washington, on September 4-7, 1962. The major concern of the conference is stated in the published proceedings:[1]

"Many have suggested that innovations in planning, organizing, and controlling have lagged. A cultural lag exists between scientific and technological achievements and our abilities to organize and manage the human and physical resources necessary to utilize these advancements effectively. We have not been able to invent new social organizations necessary to keep up with scientific and technological progress."

Much evidence suggests that, although there are many problems associated with the *technical* task of designing and producing large-scale information systems, the overriding difficulties in the development of such systems are the problems associated with the *management* of the development process. John Diebold, writing about the applications of computers in industry, makes a similar observation:[2] "It is ironic that this magic new resource is passed up by management, not because of the limitations of the technology—for information technology has already far outstripped our apparent ability to apply it—*but because of our organization structure itself.*" Too frequently the responsibility for information system development is assigned to the office of the "assistant controller," an office, as Diebold puts it, "buried too deep in one leg of the business."[3]

The position taken in this chapter, a position derived independently for computer applications in industry by John Diebold, Gilbert Burck, and many others, is that the revolution in information systems means "management will never be the same again." This applies with equal force to the management of operations and the management of the information system development process. In this chapter our concern is limited to the latter.

Organization of the Chapter

Our procedure will be, first, to list in Section 2.2 the basic activities in the system development process which must be accomplished by someone. (See Table 2.1.) Although the activities are the same in each case of development, there are no hard and fast rules pertaining to the individual, agency, or organization which should perform each or several of these activities. Second, in Section 2.3 we shall indicate that many contemporary management problems are consequences of lack of familiarity at this level with information systems—their technology and processes of development. Third, we shall systematically compare in Section 2.4 the basic differences between the relatively new computer-based information systems and the more traditional weapons and/or equipment systems. This comparison will serve to highlight the problems which result from using the traditional hardware-acquisition management structure and administrative procedures for the design and procurement of a very different type of system.

2.2 THE BASIC SYSTEM DEVELOPMENT ACTIVITIES

The basic system development activities which must be carried out in the creation of typical information systems are listed in Table 2.1. The activities are shown in the left-hand column of the table, with the name usually given to the individual, agency, or organization having responsibility for each activity shown in the right-hand column.

Table 2.1
System Development Activities

Activities	Organization
1. Establishing the system's objectives	1. The user
2. Defining the system requirements	2. The system designer, the system engineer
3. Procuring the system	3. The procurement agency
4. Technical management of the development effort	4. The technical manager
5. System design	5. The system designer, the system engineer
6. Designing and producing the hardware	6. The hardware developer
7. Designing and producing the software*	7. The software developer
8. Designing and producing the facilities	8. The facilities developer

* The term "software" is defined in Chapter 1 of this book.

In the development of any specific system, the manner in which responsibility for these various activities is assigned will show considerable variation. A major management responsibility which the non-military user must normally discharge involves deciding who will carry out the tasks. The management problem is simplified if all the necessary activities are carried out in-house, that is, by the user himself, or by a small number of external organizations closely supervised by in-house agencies. The problem of management control is compounded to the extent that the number of external organizations grows. In this latter situation, the problems of control and coordination increase geometrically. In the case of industrial systems it is common to find the activities distributed among a very few organizations. Typically, the technical staff of an industrial user performs the tasks of establishing the system's objectives, system procurement, system design, technical management, and facilities and software development with the aid of consultants from management counseling firms and the hardware developer. In military system development, by contrast, each of the activities listed in Table 2.1 may be the formal responsibility of a different external agency or organization.

To ensure understanding in the following sections, the terms which appear in the right-hand column of Table 2.1 opposite the activities to which they are related in the information system development process are briefly defined in the following paragraphs.

"User" refers, as the term implies, to the organization or institution which will make operational use of the new information system. We would like to make a distinction here between the users of the system and the system operators. By users we mean the persons whose needs for information are served by the system. An operator, by contrast, is a component of the information system. He merely transforms or transmits the information so that it can be used by others.

The "procurement agency" is the organization or institution that is responsible for acquiring a system for a user. In the United States Air Force, for example, the Electronic Systems Division of the Air Force Systems Command acquired the 465L SAC Control System for the Strategic Air Command, and in this case SAC is the user. The procurement organization or agency is responsible for such items as the statement of work, contract monitoring, contractual changes, and the funding of the new system.

The term "technical manager" refers to the organization that is responsible for the technical management of the system development effort. In the case of military systems, a special project management office is usually created for this responsibility. Such organizations as The MITRE Corporation and Aerospace Corporation conduct technical management for many military systems.

The distinction between the procurement agency and the technical manager is derived from the fact that, whereas the former supplies the funds for the new system, it may not have the capability to provide technical guidance for the development effort. Hence, a separate organization may be necessary to perform the technical management task.

The technical manager is distinguished from the "system engineer" and the "system designer" since the activities of system engineering and system design may be performed by the technical manager and also by personnel in the hardware and software developers' organizations. The distinction between *system* engineers and designers and other types of engineers and designers is that the former are responsible for the engineering and design of the system conceived as a total operating entity. H. H. Goode and R. E. Machol[4] distinguish the system engineer by emphasizing the fact that he is a "generalist," not a specialist. The system engineer is concerned with large-scale, complex systems made up of many different kinds of components. It is the function of the engineer as a generalist to see that all the components contribute to the optimal performance of the system as a whole, whereas sub-system engineers and designers are concerned with optimizing sub-systems or components.

The term "developer" refers to the organization or agency that is responsible for system and/or subsystem design and for production or manufacture of particular subsystems. We shall differentiate between two types of subsystem developers—the hardware and the software developer.

2.3 MANAGEMENT UNFAMILIARITY WITH INFORMATION SYSTEMS

The alienation of the user from the design, production, and maintenance of the artifacts of everyday use which has taken place in the area of mass production of basic goods has also occurred with respect to information systems. Before the advent of the electronic computer, the top management of a large-scale enterprise designed and built its own system to keep itself informed of the status of its operations so that appropriate decisions could be made as needed. Normally, such information systems began simply but grew to keep pace with the enterprise. This direct and sole involvement of the user is becoming passé for information systems. Complex and national or world-wide operations call for sophisticated information systems which make the most of an equally sophisticated technology. Today the user of an information system must go to the specialist to develop a system for him.*

What has been disconcerting to the users of the first generation of information systems is their cost, the length of time which has been required, in most instances, to design and build the systems, and the fact that they must continue to rely upon external development organizations (when these have been used) not only during the system design and production phases *but also during the operations phase.*[5]

An information system is not designed to specifications that are geared to unchanging physical conditions. It is intimately dependent upon user goals and objectives and reflects a specific set of environmental and user requirements. An information system is dependent, therefore, on the clarity and precision with which the user's goals and objectives are stated. Furthermore, an information system is peculiarly susceptible to change—change in its environment and in its user's requirements. Thus, during the era of the Cold War, administrators of military command and control systems have been faced with a difficult dilemma. Changes in national policies, military strategies, tactical doctrines, weapons systems, military organization, and the allocation of military missions among the services have been frequent and profound in nature. Under such conditions, the goals and objectives of a particular information system user cannot be stated readily with clarity and precision; and system requirements undergo repeated changes during the course of the creation of specific information systems. Similar problems have been described for industries acquiring computer-based information systems.[6] The unfortunate combination of the user's lack of technical knowledge, the difficulty of obtaining clearly stated user goals and objectives, and the rapidly changing environment have all served to thwart preconceived and mistaken notions that (1) information systems could be designed and produced on rigid, predetermined schedules despite frequently changing system requirements, and (2) the user would be able to maintain and adapt his information system without the help of the developer after the system attained operational status.

It is understandable that users and administrators, lacking understanding of information system technology and the development

---

* As this book goes to press, so-called "general purpose" systems using natural English terms are beginning to appear. However, these new "data management" systems are still limited to the manipulation of large data bases—they are not large-scale systems as defined in Chapter 1.

process, have utilized a familiar but irrelevant model—a hardware model—in their efforts to plan for and to control the design and production of information systems.

2.4 PROBLEMS IN THE USE OF A HARDWARE MODEL FOR SOFTWARE DEVELOPMENT

When new technologies appear on the scene, as they do with increasingly disconcerting frequency, it is to be expected that existing management organizations will acquire and apply these new technologies. In some situations, if the new technology is radically different from any previous one, the existing management organization will prove to be unsuited to the application of the new technology. This is, in fact, what has happened with respect to the management of the first generation of large-scale information systems. The management organization which has been applied to the design and acquisition of the first generation of military systems evolved over the years with respect to the design and procurement of weapons, primarily aircraft and missiles, and other types of hardware systems. Experience in the past decade has revealed this management structure and its procedures to be inadequate for the task of developing information systems. In the case of quasi-public and commercial enterprises which have sought to develop computer-based systems, the management structure to oversee and direct the task either did not exist or, as in the military establishment, experienced considerable difficulty in adapting existing organizational structure to the requirements of the task.[7]

Although the management organization for the development of information systems in industry and government is very different from that in the military, traditional experience with the acquisition of hardware systems influences and pervades both areas. To bring out as forcefully as possible how this influence occurs and the management problems derived thereby for the development of information systems, the rest of this chapter is based on a comparison of the basic characteristics of weapons systems with those of information systems. This, of course, represents the extreme case since the development of weapons systems by the military occurs under conditions of unusual uncertainty, by contrast with nonmilitary hardware systems, and in the context of a highly formalized managerial structure and process.[8] However, in many subtle ways contemporary nonmilitary management organization, principles, and concepts, derived as they are from ex-

Table 2.2
Basic Differences between Weapons Systems and Information Systems

Weapons Systems	Information Systems
1. Weapons systems are not normally limited to a single user (the same missile can be used by more than one service and more than one nation).	1. An information system is custom-made to fit the needs of a single user, such as a military commander and his staff or management in industry.
2. Many-of-a-kind. Normally a weapon system is mass-produced after the production of a prototype model.	2. One-of-a-kind. Only one information system is built to meet the needs of the user. A full-scale prototype would be equivalent to the system per se.
3. Model changes. The basic weapon evolves through a series of incremental modifications as technology improves, but the final model could not be conceived when the program began. Each model is a complete replacement of the previous model.	3. Planned evolution. The system evolves through a planned series of stages or phases each of which includes the *addition* of new functions which were conceived from the inception of the plan. The final system incorporates all earlier phases; it does not replace them as is the case with weapon models.
4. Hardware° state of the art is critical. The hard sciences, such as physics, chemistry, cryogenics, are relevant. Man plays a non-existent or minor role in system performance.	4. Hardware state of the art is much less critical. The "soft" sciences, such as psychology, human factors, human relations, management science, are relevant and critical. Man is a major component of the system and affects system performance.
5. High cost/effectiveness ratio. Cost is high because of rapid obsolescence and utilization of untried technologies. (The budget in FY 1963 for the Polaris System alone was $2 billion. And this is only one element of the Strategic Retaliatory Forces.)	5. Low cost/effectiveness ratio. Cost is low since the system utilizes better known hardware and will assist the user indefinitely. Its life-span is equivalent to the user's, since it is designed to change as the operational requirements change.
6. Independent capability. The weapon system is self-sufficient and self-contained. Integration requirements, if any, may be limited to a ground support system.	6. Functional and technical integration with other systems (interface) is a major aspect of operations. The system is not self-sufficient or self-contained but is interdependent with other systems.

° In weapons systems, software, as in the case of the guidance computer programs in a missile, supports the effective functioning of hardware; in information systems, hardware supports the effective functioning of human beings and computer programs.

32

perience with the production of hardware, have unfortunate consequences similar in nature to those found in the military realm. The comparison drawn in this chapter between weapons systems and information systems, therefore, should be useful in indicating typical managerial problems which pervade the nonmilitary as well as the military area.

In Table 2.2 we present a listing of the basic differences between weapons systems and information systems.[9] It should be borne in mind that this list is highly simplified for the sake of the following explication. We can deal here only with the more obvious differences. In point of fact, there are many additional differences in such areas as system testing, quality control, and maintenance, the cumulative effect of which has important implications for the management of the system development effort. It would require another book, however, to explore fully the ramifications of these implications.

Bearing in mind the basic differences between weapons systems and information systems as shown in Table 2.2, we can begin to consider the consequences of applying a management organization and principles geared to the development of weapons systems to the development of information systems. The identifying numbers of the following sections correspond to the numbers in the table.

1. The Information System Is Custom-Made to Fit the User

The same weapon or hardware system can be used equally effectively by a variety of users. A strategic missile can be employed by different services within the same country or by different countries. The same statement is true of automobiles or ships. Such is not the case with information systems. An information system is tailor-made to fit the needs, objectives, and requirements of a unique user. Each military command and each industrial enterprise needs information of a special kind. It is true that in the industrial realm one can speak of classes of computer applications such as payroll accounting, inventory control, production control, or airlines reservations, or of applications in the fields of banking, insurance, transportation, etc. But an examination of the details of these applications in similar areas would still show basic differences—for example, differences in computer programs, in the format and content of displays and reports, in the construction of the data base, in the relationships among system components, and in the use of human beings as elements of the system.

Since each information system is custom-made to meet the special needs of a single user, the developer must study the operations of the current system, assuming there is one, in order to clarify the user's problems, to determine his needs and objectives, and to establish preliminary system requirements. The difficulty in such a study is obtaining complete and accurate information on all relevant areas of system operations. Equal in importance to the study of the user's current system is *the study and analysis of the system's future requirements.*

One of the most important problems facing the software developer in analyses of operations and requirements studies is essentially this: *who is the official spokesman for the users?* Depending upon whom the investigator queries about system operations, he may obtain different interpretations about what the system does, what is wrong with it, and what it ought to do in the future. Each of these interpretations may be valid from the point of view of the individual informant and also inconsistent with one or more of the other viewpoints. This can place the developer in an extremely awkward and difficult position if there is no authority to resolve the issue. The nature of this problem can be brought out by noting that the Commander-in-Chief of the Strategic Air Command is one of the prime users of the 465L SAC Control System. Needless to say, the commander of SAC is an extremely busy individual. He may not be available, although he should be, to discuss operational details with development personnel. Presidents of corporations are also very busy people. If an effective information-processing system is to be designed, however, the software developer *must* obtain from such high-ranking individuals or their designated representatives their requirements for information, both current and future, since they are best qualified to say what these needs are. If this is not done, the developer obtains a set of requirements from unqualified subordinates, who necessarily provide their *interpretation* of what they think the commander or the president wants.[10]

What has frequently happened in the past as a result of such situations is that the developer will design the system in terms of statements made by informants at an available echelon of command only to find later that personnel higher in the organizational hierarchy had something else in mind. It is essential, therefore, to resolve this problem. The software developer cannot guarantee that the user will obtain a satisfactory information system unless the latter (1) identifies an *official* spokesman to represent the user's point of view, (2) makes sure that the official spokesman has access to the highest levels of personnel in the organizational hierarchy, and (3) *guarantees that the information given by the spokesman to the developer is authoritative.*

The designation of an authoritative spokesman by the user will help, but it will not resolve the issue. The necessity will still remain for the *frequent* and *regular* briefing of the commander or the company president on the status of the developing system's capabilities. It is his responsibility to ensure that the system, when it is completed, will actually meet the needs and objectives of the ultimate user.

It is not enough, in other words, merely to establish an in-house project office or appoint an external technical manager and to assume that such a project office or manager can satisfy the needs of the developer for information in the absence of direct contact with the ultimate user of the new system, which is normally the top rung of management in both military and nonmilitary systems. When such an authoritative voice is not established, what may happen, for example, is that displays will be designed on the basis of requirements as defined by personnel who will not be the users of these displays. When the ultimate users eventually see the display plans, they may reject them as not meeting their information requirements as *they* visualize them, with the result that a major overhaul of the design effort is necessary. Such situations account for many of the cost overruns, schedule slippages, and cases of management disillusionment encountered in information systems development.

The problem of identifying an authoritative spokesman is likely to be more difficult to accomplish in governmental institutions than in the military establishment. In the development of an integrated information-processing system for state law enforcement agencies, for example, the diffusion of authority may be a much greater obstacle to orderly and efficient progress and the acquisition of operational information than is the case with highly centralized military organizations. Similarly, a decentralized industrial organization in which department managers have equal authority may pose a special problem in the identification of a single authoritative spokesman representing the ultimate system users.[11]

Where the user is responsible for such functions as system procurement and technical management, the problem of identifying a single authoritative voice still exists but can be minimized; in situations where the user, the procurement agency, and the technical manager are all separate organizations, the difficulty of specifying one authoritative spokesman for the new system is compounded several times over. It is apparent, for example, that a technical manager cannot understand the user's requirements for information as clearly as the user himself. Nevertheless, frequently in military system development more than one organization may stand between the user and the software developer. In a system such as the NORAD Combat Operations Center (425L), for example, the 425L System Program Office of the Electronic Systems Division is the program manager, The MITRE Corporation is the technical manager, and NORAD is the user. It is quite possible for each of these organizations to have different interpretations of the user's needs. The software developer in such a situation is caught in a requirement cross fire. Whatever he does he will be unable to meet some of the demands levied against him. The energies of the developer are then dissipated in attempting to obtain a set of requirements which are acceptable to all the organizations involved.

As a result of the fact that many different individuals, agencies, and organizations have to approve a decision, even a minor one, before it can be implemented by the developer, excessive and unnecessary time is lost before a decision is officially approved. Meanwhile the developer, in order to meet his scheduled commitments, has proceeded in a direction that is subsequently reversed, or he may simply wait and do nothing. In either case the end result is cost overruns and schedule slippages.

2. Many-of-a-Kind/One-of-a-Kind

Many basic differences in weapons and software systems which have a profound impact on management stem from the fact that weapons systems, with some notable exceptions, are usually produced in large numbers from a prototype model. Information systems are one-of-a-kind, that is, only one operational system is ever developed from the design. The information system is not a mass-produced article. In regard to contemporary weapons systems, it is true that with increasing technological sophistication, with the advent of satellites and space vehicles, and even with ·more conventional weapons systems such as nuclear submarines and bombers, fewer items are being produced from a common design than heretofore. This may be attributed to the increasing cost of such systems and the fact that each vehicle is a carrier of much more destructive firepower. But the fundamental difference we are discussing here between weapons systems and information systems remains—current management organization and concepts are geared for the most part to a tradition of mass production, not the production of one-of-a-kind items.

A major consequence of mass production of an item in contrast to the production of a single item is the fact that a complete prototype of a weapons system can be built before full-scale mass production at a fraction of the total cost of the project. The purpose of building a prototype, of course, is to test the design, to ensure that the performance specifications have been met, and to check out new technological concepts and new materials. Modifications to the prototype can be made at a fraction of the total project cost in the event that it fails to live up to engineering expectations, since the bulk of the funds needed in weapons system acquisition are earmarked for production. Once the prototype model succeeds in meeting all user requirements, the design is frozen and production is started. By contrast, the creation of a complete prototype for an information system would be equivalent to producing the operational system per se; hence the cost of prototype construction is prohibitive.

In the development of large-scale information systems, two alternative procedures to the construction of prototypes are usually followed. One approach is the construction of a test facility in which the basic concepts of the new information system are tried out for feasibility. This test facility is completely separated from the operational system and is never used as part of it. A second approach is to create an initial operational capability which is small in scope compared to the final system but is designed in modular fashion so that additional and more sophisticated capabilities can be added to the original foundation.

The creation of a test facility before the construction of the information system itself is illustrated by the SAGE system of air defense. A working model of SAGE, called the Cape Cod System, was built in 1953 through the combined efforts of the Lincoln Laboratory of the Massachusetts Institute of Technology and the Air Force's Cambridge Research Center. The Cape Cod System was composed of several radars in and around Boston which transmitted data to the Whirlwind I Computer at the Massachusetts Institute of Technology. This system proved the feasibility of automating radar surveillance operations. The Cape Cod System with a new computer, the AN/FSQ-7, which was specifically designed for the job of air defense, evolved into what became known as the Experimental SAGE Sector. Although the Experimental SAGE Sector was hardly a model of the entire SAGE system, it did provide a test-bed for the development of basic features of SAGE automation, operations, and training.

The use of a test-bed approach, as in the case of SAGE, however, is not as satisfactory as the construction of a prototype weapon which represents the complete system. At best, a test-bed information system can only represent a truncated version of the operational system. The proof of this lies in the fact that large-scale development efforts were still needed to create a working SAGE system after its feasibility was demonstrated in the Cape Cod test-bed.

Because of the untried and untested nature of the automation of radar operations utilizing a digital computer, funds were provided to create the Cape Cod System and, later, the Experimental SAGE Sector. But management may miss the point that such an experimental test-bed *or an equivalent alternative* is an essential ingredient of the development of any large-scale information system during the contemporary stage of computer technology. It was not a unique requirement for SAGE.

Information systems may vary considerably in the degree to which they utilize well-established computer-programming concepts in association with off-the-shelf computer equipment. For a system using off-the-shelf technology and equipment there may be no requirement for research activities, for an experimental prototype system such as the Cape Cod System, for simulation facilities, or for "exploratory" and "advanced" development as these terms are used in hardware acquisition. On the other hand, many of the first-generation computer-based information systems developed for the military and for commercial uses did require the creation of new computer-programming concepts for extremely complex information-processing functions which had not been automated previously.[12] For the next generation of information systems it can also be expected that at least some proportion of them will require the creation of new computer-programming concepts and a continuing pressure to advance the software state of the art. Thus appropriate managerial and funding arrangements must be made to provide for those aspects of information systems which are exploratory in character. To accomplish this goal the mental set imposed by experience with hardware acquisition must be broken.

The many-of-a-kind/one-of-a-kind dichotomy holds many other dangers for management if the basic differences are not kept in the foreground. The circumvention or elimination of these dangers frequently involves spending relatively large sums of money, as in the case of the test models for SAGE already discussed. For military information systems the issue of survivability is especially crucial. An information system, such as a command and control system, is the nerve center of the command's operations. When the information system is disrupted, the command is in jeopardy as an operating entity. Such is not the case with weapons systems. Both SAGE and SAC can lose many weapons without ceasing to exist as command entities. But they would cease to exist if their information systems built around digital computers were destroyed. Thus, the issue of survivability, of continuous around-the-clock operations regardless of conditions in the environment, is of crucial importance to the management responsible for the development of these types of systems. How much time, manpower, and money should go into the design and construction of hardened sites? How much should go into the design and production of redundant communication lines, computers, consoles, input/output devices? How much should go into the design and production of an alternative or backup system to take over in the event that the primary system is destroyed? An interminable series of critical questions of this type derives from the fact that the information system is the nerve center of the command, and it may be the only nerve center the command has.

These issues are not only relevant to military command and control systems, as one might at first suppose. Many types of nonmilitary systems that have already been built, are in the process of being built, or may be built in the near future also include requirements for survivability, redundancy, alternate modes of operations, and backup capabilities. Examples are air-traffic control systems, space surveillance systems, space-vehicle tracking and recovery systems, air-sea rescue systems, weather forecasting systems, fire warning and control systems, law enforcement systems, etc.

It follows, from the vulnerable nature of the military information system and the special requirements of the other nonmilitary systems mentioned, that more time, manpower, and money should be devoted to the conceptual phase of such systems and the creation of a test facility than is now the case. It is reasonable to expect that, if only one system is going to be built, a relatively larger proportion of the total development effort should go into the earlier phases of the effort than into the later production phases. If we are producing scores of nuclear submarines or hundreds of bombers, most of the available funds must be allocated to production activities. But if we are creating *one* information system, it is foolhardy to proceed into production without allotting adequate resources to determine if the requirements are the right ones, if the design is the best one possible, and if the design will fulfill the requirements.*

A different attitude toward system testing is demanded of the

---

* Some system designers believe that the sooner one creates an operational system the better, on the assumption that an adequate set of requirements cannot be obtained in advance of actual operations. It would be impossible to do justice to this argument in the space available.

manager because of the inherent differences between hardware systems and information systems. It is true that weapons systems can be reduced to obsolescence by technological advances. But as rapid as technological change is, no one will claim that it occurs on a daily basis. In any case, the physical environment for which the weapons system was designed does not change. Thus, it is possible to subject the weapons system to rigorous tests under controlled conditions to determine its reliability and design validity. Such is not the case for information systems. The information system must be tested for the full range of operational possibilities in an environment which may be undergoing change on a daily basis. The ability of the information system to adapt to such changes is, in itself, a test variable. To provide adequately for such system testing requires, first, understanding the need and, second, allotting the necessary resources to do the job.

The one-of-a-kind information system poses many special problems for training which do not exist for many-of-a-kind systems. Training must be conducted for the one-of-a-kind system without interfering with on-going operations. It is necessary to design a simulation capability into the operational system in such a way that both operations and training can be conducted simultaneously. Since realistic system training may require the participation of major elements of the total system, training designers are hard pressed to find the computer storage capacities to handle both operational and exercise data simultaneously. Similarly, data processing and the display of operational data and exercise data may have to be performed concurrently. Appropriate programming must be designed into the system so that, in the event of an emergency, the system can revert from an exercise mode to a full-scale operational mode without loss of needed data and with minimum delay.

Finally, we must mention with respect to the many-of-a-kind/one-of-a-kind differentiation the managerial headache, shared with the developer, of phasing in the new system to assume operational responsibility without interfering with on-going activities. Few operations, military or nonmilitary, can afford to close up shop for a period of time, however short, in order to make the shift from one system to another. Must the user suffer through a period of degraded operational capability while the new system is being phased in and the old one phased out? In the one-of-a-kind system this is a major managerial dilemma. Thus, the phase-over period is a critical one, involving both training and operations, which calls for much research, exploratory effort, planning, and design in order to ensure a smooth transition.

It is the manager's responsibility to provide the resources and to schedule the time needed to carry out this vital aspect of the development process.

3. Model Changes/Planned Evolution

Another basic difference between hardware systems and information systems is to be found in the nature of their change and replacement through time. Weapons systems proceed through what is called "model" changes, whereas we can refer to changes in information systems as "planned evolution." In the case of weapons systems, the initial weapon, if it changes at all, undergoes a series of incremental modifications as technology improves or requirements change, but the final model could not be technically implemented when the program for the weapon began. Each model is a complete replacement of the previous one, although earlier versions may continue to be utilized in the weapons inventory. A typical example of model changes is provided, in the case of aircraft, by the series of B-52 bombers: B-52A, B-52B, B-52C, ... Similarly, for missiles we have the series of Atlas A, Atlas B, Atlas C, etc. Each subsequent model incorporates improved capabilities of various kinds—range, speed, altitude, reliability, or load capacity.

By contrast with weapons systems, information systems are evolutionary in that they are designed and implemented in several iterations to perform information-processing functions for a continuing enterprise. The information system evolves through a planned series of stages or phases each of which includes the addition of new tasks and functions which may have been conceived and regarded as feasible from the inception of the plan. It is also possible that functions not conceived during the original planning may be added at a later date, but these should be integrated with the long-range plan. The system as it exists at any stage or phase incorporates earlier phases; it does not replace them, as is the case with weapons systems, although the same functions may be performed by more efficient computer programs or better allocations of tasks among men and machines.

The term "evolution" is appropriate for information systems also in that they are adaptive to their environment. An information system has the capacity to adapt itself to changing situations and the capacity to learn from experience. These capacities are provided by its human components, who are themselves adaptable and capable of learning. Modifications to the system are made through an on-going dialogue between system users and designers. As they apply the system and gain experience with it, the users recommend to the designers improvements to procedures, computer programs, displays, etc. Eventually, by means of "heuristic" programming, information systems may have a capacity through their computer programs, as distinct from their human operators, to improve their performance by an inherent adaptive or learning capability.[13] A weapons system is not adaptive in this sense.

A given model of an aircraft or a missile pushes the hardware state of the art to the limit. A given stage or phase of an information system does not necessarily reflect a limit of the computer state of the art. It may reflect a variety of other factors, such as the desire to initiate at least a modest capability as soon as possible, limited funding, or the fact that the user's requirements are not clearly known so that the ultimate system cannot be specified in detail immediately. Also, in the case of military command and control systems, the rate of technological change and of changes in mission requirements suggests that freezing the design as final at any given stage is undesirable. Hence, a modest beginning is made by using an initial operational capability with the understanding that later phases of the system will incorporate technological changes and new mission requirements. But the final operational capability for the information system is equivalent to that of the entire increment of models for a given weapons series.

In Figure 2.1 the development process for information systems is shown as a number of iterations in which the entire sequence of phases is repeated. This is of special interest to management in that several phases of development may be occurring simultaneously; that is, as the figure shows, the first development cycle may be in the production phase, while the second is in the design phase and the third in the requirements phase. Hence we begin to see why practices derived from the acquisition of weapons systems, in which research, development, production, deployment, and utilization follow one another in a linear sequence, as shown in Figure 2.1, are not applicable to evolutionary information systems.

This iterative, evolutionary character of development for information systems relies heavily upon the flow of data among the design personnel of the developers working in the various phases of the different development cycles, as shown by the dashed lines in Figure 2.1. The system could not meaningfully evolve without the provision of feedback from, say, the production phase of the first iterative development cycle to the requirements phase of the second iteration. At the same time, unresolved but important problems of design uncovered in the second iteration may be passed to the next design phase for more careful consideration and possible resolution. One of the most common problems of this nature encountered in the development of information systems is the failure of the user to provide the software developer with adequately detailed requirements for the first iteration. A function of the designers during phases subsequent to the initial requirements phase is to forward their requests for additional infor-

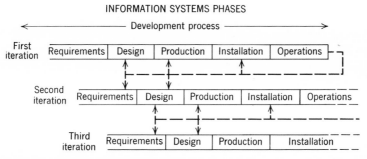

WEAPONS SYSTEMS PHASES

Research	Development	Production	Deployment	Utilization

Exploratory development	Advanced development	Engineering development

INFORMATION SYSTEMS PHASES

Development process

First iteration: | Requirements | Design | Production | Installation | Operations |

Second iteration: | Requirements | Design | Production | Installation | Operations |

Third iteration: | Requirements | Design | Production | Installation |

Figure 2.1 Comparison of the life cycles of weapons and information systems.

mation on requirements to the user, to indicate why the requirements are not adequately documented, and to suggest the areas in which they should be amplified or clarified. This information from the user must be provided in time to meet the schedules for subsequent iterations.

If we examine the overlapping design and production iterations in the evolutionary approach to the development of information systems, and if we bear in mind the flow of information among the software development personnel, we can begin to sense the problems of "configuration management." This term pertains to managerial control over changes to the system design at all levels of design through final production of end items. In the typical development cycle for weapons systems, which proceeds in the traditional linear sequence of phases, configuration management is fraught with difficulties.[14] How much more confidently, therefore, can we anticipate difficulties for configuration management in the development of information systems via the evolutionary process, in which valid suggestions for change may arise in a variety of phases in a number of different iterations or design cycles? Under such circumstances the maintenance of a common system data base (items describing the system) which will be acceptable to all developers, hardware as well as software, is an extraordinarily difficult policing function for management.

The evolution of information systems raises a number of other questions related to recent changes in the approach to systems acquisition by the Department of Defense. The intimate relationship which is necessary between the user and the software developer during the requirements and design phases in the development of information systems raises doubts about the desirability of competitive bidding between different software developers. A frequent complaint of users is that, even when only one developer is involved, they are asked the same question about their operations by different personnel from the same development organization. Obtaining information about the user's daily operations as a basis for designing the new system is a delicate task even under ideal conditions. It is difficult to imagine the chaos if two or more software competitors were simultaneously engaged in obtaining operational information and conducting operations analyses.

The close relationship between the user and the software developer does not terminate with the delivery of the initial system operational capability. In the evolutionary development process this is merely another phase of intensified feedback from the user to the developer as the former tries out his new system in his daily operations. It is at this point in the development process that the most effective test and validation of the system design can be attempted. It is at this point that the user can best determine whether the system does, in fact, satisfy his requirements for information-processing and decision-making assistance. The results of these operational tests should be fed back to the software developer as inputs to the next design cycle. This feedback interaction between the user and the software developer is repeated after the completion of the second design cycle, and so on. (These issues are discussed more fully in Chapter 10.)

The weapons acquisition model draws a clear line between the system design level and the system implementation or production level.

The dichotomy between system design and system production is less sharp for information systems. This has been stressed in the reports sponsored by the Department of Defense, which call for the *increased participation* of the software implementer in the initial system design study.[15] But this cannot be accomplished if the task of the software developer is fragmented in accordance with the traditional hardware acquisition process. The development of information systems should be characterized by the application of what we shall refer to here as the *continuity of personnel* principle.

In the development of weapons and other types of hardware systems a sequence of different personnel with a variety of specialized skills determine the system requirements, conduct design and analysis, carry out the development (exploratory, advanced, and engineering) activities as needed, produce the system, and test and evaluate it. The nature of hardware is such that this type of linear division of labor is effective. It compares favorably to the assembly line of the traditional factory. It is questionable whether this same linear division of labor can be usefully applied in the case of software development to anywhere near the same degree. Much of the energy of the project manager for the software development effort is devoted to ensuring that the requirements as defined by the system designers are actually realized through the process of detailed programming and coding. Ideally, therefore, the same personnel should carry out the entire process of software development from the determination of preliminary system requirements until the acceptance of the operational system by the user.

The dashed lines in Figure 2.1 are meant to suggest the need for interaction among system designers, program designers, and program writers and coders. The program designers must be accessible physically to the program coders in the more detailed design and production process. Similarly, the system designers must be accessible to the computer program designers. It is difficult enough when the designers and programmers are members of the same organization to ensure continuity from initial requirements statements, through the design process, to detailed programming and final coding. But if the personnel who produce the requirements documents, the system designers, and the computer programmers are all members of different and, conceivably, competitive organizations, the discrepancies between the requirements and the ultimate product will increase rather than decrease.

The value of maintaining personnel continuity throughout a software development effort is illustrated by the production of an information system for the Department of Defense Damage Assessment Center, which was built in a very short period of time in spite of many trying difficulties. This achievement was made possible to a large extent because the system requirements, the system design, and the computer programs were prepared by the same people. As each step was completed, the same personnel then undertook the subsequent task. This continuity was reflected in the reorganization of the project as it proceeded. Because the same personnel wrote the programs from their own operational requirements documents, it was possible to maintain quality in the product and, at the same time, avoid the delays which usually occur when the programmers attempt to obtain more detailed but necessary information not included in the program requirements documentation. Documents describing computer program requirements are not easy to understand, and programmers make many decisions in the course of interpreting them which may seriously affect the quality of the programs. If the same people prepare the requirements and write the programs, these problems can be circumvented.

The continuity of personnel principle for software development applies throughout the development effort. It is applicable within any one design-production-installation sequence and also between iterations of this sequence. The concept of planned evolution in the development of information systems cannot be implemented efficiently without continuity of key personnel from one design iteration to the next.

4. Hardware/Software Sciences

Studies made within the defense establishment of military information systems—command and control systems—agree that computer technology exceeds at the present time our ability to put together the most effective systems. Hardware systems not specifically designed for military use, such as satellites and research rockets, all push the hardware state of the art in such areas as propulsion, guidance, miniaturization, and communications. Although information systems could profit from improvements in such areas as core storage capacities, speed of operations, display devices, and input/output devices, the technological limitations in these fields do not, of themselves, constitute insuperable constraints on the design of contemporary information systems.

The incorporation of the computer as the basic component in large-scale information systems to assist in decision making involves the designer of such systems in a host of so-called "soft" sciences—human relations, management science, psychology, social psychology, sociology, and applied anthropology. These sciences and others, such as human engineering, are necessary in the design of information systems since they contribute to the understanding of the behavior of human beings as individuals and as members of groups. Valid performance measures for information systems in which human beings and group dynamics play vital roles cannot be established if the human and group factors are ignored. By contrast, in the design of weapons and other types of hardware systems, human beings and groups play minor or nonexistent roles. In such systems, therefore, the relevant sciences are the more traditional and more advanced "hard" sciences such as physics and chemistry.

The major management problem areas which are the result of the less deterministic nature of software and the contemporary software state of the art may be listed as follows:

1. The identification of all software products to be acquired.
2. The types of specialized skills required to produce software items.
3. The lack of a commonly accepted set of terms to identify software items.
4. The problem of distinguishing between "research," "development," and "production" in the software development process.
5. The difficulty of establishing appropriate relationships and sequencing software items among themselves and with hardware items so that an integrated system can be built.

Each of these problem areas is discussed in some detail in the following sections.

Identifying Software Products. A computer-based information system is a very different kind of system from a weapons system, a communication system, or a transportation system. Consequently the components of these different types of systems are also different. In the acquisition of the first generation of military command and control systems by the Air Force, it has been apparent that those responsible did not always know how to identify *what* was being acquired, nor could they always determine whether the products being acquired were what had been asked for by the users and specified in the contracts.[16] Furthermore, if the products to be acquired cannot be identified adequately, it becomes a difficult matter to estimate needed funds and schedules and to decide with any degree of efficiency *who* should be responsible for designing and producing the items. Thus, lack of clarity with respect to the identification of the product to be acquired leads directly to a number of managerial difficulties.

It was pointed out in Chapter 1 that there is no generally accepted definition of software in the electronic information-processing field. If differences of opinion exist as to what software is, there are bound to be different interpretations as to the types of knowledge and related specialized skills needed to produce software products. If software is conceived by computer equipment manufacturers, for example, as only utility computer programs, the primary specialized training required is in the area of computer programming; but if the broader usage of software is considered, as in the products associated with the "personnel subsystem" concept, then other types of specialized personnel are needed in the development effort in addition to programmers: human factors scientists, training specialists, psychologists, human engineers, handbook writers and editors, etc.[17]

Specialized Skills in the Production of Software. The typical potential user of an information system has been accustomed to buying hardware. As a result, he is familiar with the types of specialists normally involved in the design and production of hardware elements. He knows about systems engineers, system analysts, and operations research, or at least he has heard that such specialists and fields of knowledge make contributions to the development of hardware systems, and he is willing to pay for these skills. But it is not uncommon to find not only that the typical user of an information system does not know what kinds of sciences play a role in the design and production of software, but also that he may have a bias or distinct prejudice against what is commonly called the "soft" sciences. Since the output of the soft or social sciences is less tangible than the hard sciences—it is not a black box—the user tends to be reluctant to pay for it.

The role of experts from the field of group dynamics, a branch of social psychology, may serve to illustrate the participation of non-hardware scientists in a particular information system development. This illustration is taken from the System Training Program (STP) which the RAND Corporation developed as a by-product of investigating the inadequate performance of systems with human beings as components.[18] One of the so-called STP principles emphasized by RAND researchers was the provision of knowledge of results to personnel participating in training exercises. This knowledge of results was presented in a "debriefing" immediately following the exercise. It was not enough merely to solve the technical problems of recording trainee performance, analyzing the results, and summarizing them in some meaningful fashion. There were two other very important issues which the software developer had to resolve: (1) how could the results of the exercises be presented to the trainees, and (2) how should a debriefing be conducted to ensure maximum participation by all trainees?

These issues were investigated by the software developer's staff of experts on group dynamics, working closely with psychologists familiar with learning theory. Experience with the training program had shown that maximum problem-solving activity on the part of trainees did not occur if the exercise results were presented in a manner which the trainees might interpret as blame fixing. Also, since many of the operations in the transmission of data and information during the exercises were invisible both to the observers and to the trainees, it was evident that full understanding of what had occurred during the exercise depended upon creating an atmosphere in the debriefing which would encourage personnel to talk freely about the actions and decisions they had taken.

How do you persuade people to talk freely about their mistakes in front of their peers and superiors? How do you suggest to military officers that maximum participation in a debriefing by *all* personnel can be achieved in a permissive, nonthreatening, non-blame-fixing group atmosphere? How do you get individuals to think of their operational environment with a system perspective? Research on these issues was conducted by the group specialists and psychologists; manuals on the proper conduct of debriefings were published; and training programs for debriefing officers were held.[19]

We can use decision making as another example of an important area of concern to the software developer which has many intangible features. Somewhere in the preliminary requirements documents the developer must present the results of his analysis of the main classes of decisions made by the user's organization. The developer should have on his analysis and design staffs personnel familiar with the theory of decision making in its sociological and social psychological, as well as mathematical, dimensions. Understanding the types of decisions made at all levels in the enterprise and the classes, formats, and content of information needed to support these decisions requires intensive study of the daily operations of the enterprise. A basic type of design issue which the developer's staff must resolve pertains to the form and content of displays in which information will be provided to assist the decision makers. Human engineers and experimental psychologists have important roles to play in determining the type of display (wall, printout, individual console, group, etc.) which will be most helpful for specific classes of decisions. Ideally, research and experimentation on the most effective displays should be completed in time to affect the specifications for the display equipment.

It can be argued that all software activities devoted to decision making should be supported by funds labeled "research" or "exploratory" and "advanced" development. Very little is known at the present time about the nature of decision making by top-level managers and military commanders. Frequently, such people cannot explain how they make a decision. The cognitive processes which underlie decision making are uncharted territory. The relationship between information and decision making also is not well understood. Indeed, much of the current work in this area treats the decision maker as if he were just another machine. But it has been shown that decision making is much more than a straightforward cognitive process since it is invariably embedded in some organizational or institutional context.[20] Such important facets of everyday decision making in large-scale organizations as avoidance of decision making, the postponement of decisions, the failure to make a decision, and the institutional framework of decision making are largely ignored in the typical research in the systems field. Yet these types of decision-making phenomena are also factors in the performance of man-machine systems.

Obviously, research activities in such areas as group dynamics and the relationship between displays and decision making consume scarce resources—personnel, funds, and facilities—and it takes time to conduct research, to publish the results, to develop the specifications for displays, and to develop orientation and training programs on the conduct of debriefings. The professional nonhardware scientists participating in the software development process are well aware that these activities are necessary to maximize system effectiveness, but it is up to the managers—the users, procurement agencies, technical managers, and hardware developers—to understand *why* these things must be done and to provide the necessary resources.

Lack of Common Software Terminology. The distinctive jargons of specialized disciplines, in addition to the lack of a consensus on the identification and content of software products, contribute to confusion with respect to software terminology in current use. Another source of confusion is the fact that many of the terms used to refer to software products are borrowed from the hardware and weapons development fields. One can never be sure, therefore, whether a term such as "system design specification" means the same thing to different people in the software development industry and in the hardware field. What is the difference or similarity between a "system requirement," an "operational requirement," and a "performance requirement"? Sometimes these various terms are deliciously combined as in "system operational performance requirement." Then we have terms such as "logical design," "internal design," and "operational design." In most cases the meaning of such a term can be grasped only after careful study of the document in which it is embedded.

The emergence of any new technology is always accompanied by an associated jargon specific to the processes, activities, and objects of that technology. The software field, no less than any other, has its own needs for a unique language. The facts that there is as yet no common agreement on the terminology used and that the referents of the terms change through time reflect the early stage of information system technology. We can look forward to considerable improvement in this situation in the future. Efforts to standardize terminology are being pushed within the data-processing industry, in the armed services, and also within the Department of Defense.

The problem of identifying and naming appropriate software development products is attacked through systematic and standardized documentation.[21] The documentation system serves many purposes. The documents are the bases of communication—the means for the transmission of vital system information among all the participants in the development effort. The documents reflect an agreement between the user and the software developer with respect to *what* will be produced; they make possible the coordination and integration of software and hardware development activities and products; they attempt to ensure continuity of development among the software development personnel from the requirements level down through the final component output or product; they are used to brief and educate new user and developer personnel or other interested parties such as procurement agencies, technical managers, other potential users, and interfacing organizations; and they also serve to establish design base lines for future activities, changes in the design, and subsequent design iterations.

A major concern of managers responsible for the development of information systems, therefore, is to provide the resources required to establish a documentation system which will serve as an adequate guide for the development process. The design, creation, and maintenance of an adequate documentation system for information systems may seem excessively costly to managers accustomed to the documentation usually provided for weapons and other types of hardware systems. But it must be borne in mind that an information system is embodied in a set of documents—the documents are the product and are worth every penny they cost, assuming that they are good documents.

Distinguishing "Research," "Development," and "Production." How can we characterize the investigations and experiments which are conducted in the course of information system development on such problem areas as group dynamics and the relationship between displays and decision making? In traditional weapons acquisition funding, distinctions are made among "research funds," "development funds," and "production funds." Are such investigations "research"? If the traditional term "development" is applied to these investigations, are they "exploratory," "advanced," or "engineering" development?

Although it may be relatively easy to demonstrate that group dynamics and decision making are aspects of software development which push the state of the art and are, therefore, research or exploratory and advanced development types of activities, *some* computer programming should also be viewed in the same light. Computer programs constitute a continuum from straightforward, routine programs which have been tried out and tested in past applications to *attempts* to write programs for areas of operations which are not only nonroutine but also difficult to describe and define. Long-range planning, policy planning, and the characteristics of input messages are examples of such areas. In the planning for a software development effort, it is essential for managers to differentiate routine programs which can be reliably scheduled and costed from nonroutine types which, since they do push the state of the art, cannot be scheduled and costed on a firm basis. These latter types of programs represent the frontiers of knowledge in the field of computer programming in the same sense that, say, cryogenics is a frontier of knowledge in the hard sciences. The software designers who must design solutions to nonroutine types of operations are, by the nature of the case, involved in research and in exploratory and advanced development.

When the contractual arrangements are being made for the design and production of computer programs, it is necessary for distinctions to be made between the routine and nonroutine types. Preliminary studies must be undertaken early in the development effort to identify these areas of operations which may require research and exploration if they are to be automated. These areas should be listed in the contracts as such, and appropriate scheduling and funds applied to them.

To illustrate the place of experimentation in the design of computer programs to accomplish the most effective use of limited storage capacity and available equipment, we shall review briefly some of the experimentation conducted on the characteristics of input messages for the 465L SAC Control System. The reader is requested to decide whether the illustration may be labeled "research," "exploratory development," "advanced development," "engineering development," or "production."

The effectiveness of an information system depends upon the quality of the data which enter it. Accuracy and timeliness are two important attributes of input data in most systems. It is the responsibility of system designers to ensure that these attributes are accommodated in their design. Although experience with the characteristics of input messages from other systems and analytical techniques is basic in the design of input data, experimentation in the laboratory, which simulates to some degree the system operation, is a vital empirical technique for developing, testing, and verifying design decisions.[22] Figure 2.2 is a hypothetical example of a message which describes a flight plan in the 465L SAC Control System. Such a message would normally be transmitted as an input to a computer by an operator who would type it upon an electronic keyboard device.

There are, of course, many different ways in which such input messages can be constructed. In one study conducted in the course of the design of 465L, for example, at least twenty different methods of composing messages were identified and evaluated. The evaluation criteria included (1) relative frequency of errors in typing messages, (2) legibility, (3) content comprehensiveness, (4) relevancy of message content to tasks, (5) brevity, (6) facility of preparation, and (7) facility of learning by keyboard operators.

Ideally, the constraints imposed on the design of message formats should be design criteria of the type just indicated, *not the equipment*, such as the input device and the computer processing the input. We should note here the interaction of software and hardware design. In an information-processing system the data to be processed are of *primary* importance. Hence, equipment design is dependent upon the

4/C/OI/012/*ADRES/NRS17/*ADRES/TPL32/
*OPER/—HOTSPOT/USCM/40385/WESTOVR/1725/0986/$/$/0010l2/2520/167485/2244/
04023/023110/306241/1115/04/7250/11011250/02/06/1101/*TORAR/030847/
*TORAR/030852/*TORAR/030903/*REFTIM/1011905/*OFFLO/0108/*RECIV/0042T/
*RECSOR/101/*ARA/-REDBULL/*REFTIM/1020158/*OFFLO/0114/*RECIV/0096T/
*RECSOR/102/*ARA/-BLUEBOY/*LOC/4445N06849W/LS/030/01/*LOC/4415N06855W/
CR/300/01/*LOC/4305N06825W/CR/$/$/*LOC/3905N06412W/CR/$/$/*LOC/4201N
05504W/CR/$/$/*LOC/4430N04413W/CR/$/$/*LOC/4615N04214W/CR/$/$/*LOC/4624N
04316W/CR/$/$/*LOC/4515N04043W/CR/$/$/*LOC/4326N03900W/AR/$/$/*ARNR/01/
*TRACK/2/*LOC/4035N03612E/CR/$/$/*LOC/3722N02705E/CR/$/$/*LOC/3412N02600E/
CR/$/$/*LOC/331lN02206E/CR/$/$/*LOC/3147N01916E/CR/$/$/*LOC/4007N02240E/
CR/$/$/*LOC/2800N02225W/AR/$/$/*ARNR/02/*TRACK/5/*LOC/2930N01830E/CR/$/$/*LOC/1925N
l7000E/CR/$/$/*LOC/3100N01819E/OP/$/$/*RADIUS/03/*ORBTM/015/*LOC/2914N
01735W/CR/$/$/*LOC/1450N01924W/CR/$/$/*LOC/2345N01617W/CR/$/$/*LOC/4300N
02700W/CR/$/$/*LOC/4315N03515W/CR/$/$/*LOC/3942N04705W/CR/$/$/*LOC/4318N
05125W/CR/$/$/*LOC/4410N05355W/CR/$/$/*LOC/4445N05948W/LP/$/$/*LAND/
WESTOVR

Figure 2.2   Hypothetical flight plan outline message (solid block form).

54

design criteria for input messages. The design of equipment, therefore, *should follow rather than precede* the determination of the characteristics of the input messages.

One clear need in design is to build into the computer a capability for input message error detection. When this is done, messages containing errors are rejected by the computer and the originator of the message is automatically notified. Basic design questions which must be resolved in the message rejection-correction loop include: (1) Will the computer continue error checking after an initial error is detected? (2) Will it continue error checking after designated types of errors are detected? (3) Will the computer check an entire message for all possible errors before rejecting it? It is apparent, if the third course is not followed, that a single message may be rejected as many times as there are errors in it. This could result in excessive delays in message transmission. Another type of question the designers must resolve is this: should the entire message be returned to the originator when an error is found or only the portion containing the error? In the latter case the designer must also decide how much of the part of the message containing the error should be returned to the originator so that the context of the error can be understood.

We must note here the interdependence of a human factors problem with the data-processing problem of determining the message format. If a requirement is specified by the designers for the originator to retype the entire message when it contains an error, and the message is rejected by the computer after each error is found, how many times can an operator retype a lengthy message without reaching his frustration threshold? It is apparent that we are dealing with psychological questions as well as issues which pertain to data-processing techniques. Experimentation in a laboratory can contribute to the resolution of these problems by suggesting possible tradeoffs among the data-processing state of the art, the requirements imposed upon messages by operational tasks, and the capabilities and limitations of human beings.

If the types of design questions raised in the preceding paragraphs are to be resolved, not by guesswork, but by empirical testing and verification, the management of the development effort has some critical responsibilities. First, the importance and role of experimentation must be recognized, and, regardless of whether it is labeled research, development, or production, appropriate funds and personnel to design and conduct the experiments must be provided. Second, management must organize the flow of design activity so that the results of experimentation can feed into the design in an orderly and timely manner.

Relations and Sequencing of Hardware and Software Products. In contemporary information system development, the hardware and software development efforts frequently occur as parallel or concurrent streams of activity. The development effort for the production of computer programs may also be broken down into concurrent activities —utility programs, operational programs, support programs—while a further breakdown may be made among the operational programs. It should be apparent, therefore, that one of the major problems facing the management of an information system development effort is to ensure that (1) hardware and software activities and outputs are properly related to one another, and (2) within the software development effort, the various activities and outputs are also properly related to one another.

At the contemporary stage in the history of information system development, it is unlikely that the hardware developer is completely familiar with the nature of the software that is also being designed and produced concurrently with his hardware. Nor is it likely that the software developer is well versed in the development process for hardware. Neither party, therefore, may know the needs of the other for information pertaining to the accomplishment of their respective portions of the total system. It is the responsibility of management at the highest levels to facilitate the exchange of vital information between the hardware and software developers. Current contractual arrangements frequently make this exchange impossible.

The issue of interest to management, in addition to the problem of ensuring satisfactory sequencing of all technical activities, is the planning, controlling, and directing of such activities. How can this be done if, as we have tried to show, so much of the work of the software developer is exploratory or experimental in nature?

In the previous sections, in our discussion of group dynamics, the interrelationship of displays and decision making, and the attributes of input data to the computer, we have seen that designers and software developers must deal with many intangible factors. They involve the software developers in a considerable amount of research. It is difficult, if not impossible, therefore, to impose upon this type of work arbitrarily conceived schedules and funding, or to establish schedules based on the estimated completion dates of items of equipment. We have stated that equipment design should ideally be dependent upon the design criteria for input messages; equipment should be designed after the characteristics of input messages have been determined experimentally. The managerial dilemma is evident. How can the sequencing and relationships of experimentation on input messages with respect to the design of equipment be determined in advance if no one can predict with accuracy how long a period of experimentation will be required? There is no simple answer to this question. The establishment of experimental facilities—for example, by the Air Force Systems Command at the Hanscom Complex in the form of the Military Information System Design Laboratory—should make it possible to conduct the types of experiments we have referred to in the previous pages as activities separate from actual system development efforts. The findings in the software state of the art made in these facilities will eventually become the common property of the software development field. But in the years immediately ahead it is unlikely that any number of such experimental facilities will be able to resolve *all* the problems which arise in the course of a typical large-scale development effort. Software developers will be forced to continue to conduct research activities with inadequate funds provided for such purposes, or with production funds, and under the constraints of hardware-oriented schedules.

5. Cost/Effectiveness Ratio

In the allocation of scarce resources, critical management decisions must be made regarding the cost of materials and products needed for a given enterprise, military or nonmilitary, and the cost of a system for controlling and directing the use of those materials and products. Armies in the past, just as those in the present and presumably in the future, have had to allot a limited amount of money for either the weapons of war or the means of controlling and using the weapons. As the cost of weapons increases exponentially with their growing technological complexity and sophistication, each weapon considered for the national inventory must be carefully evaluated on the basis of the effectiveness purchased for each dollar invested. Similarly, an information system must be evaluated in terms of the effectiveness bought for a military command by the investment of limited funds. As the cost of both hardware systems and information systems rises steeply, managerial decisions must be made respecting the allotment of limited funds for more and better weapons or for more and better information systems.

When examined in terms of absolute dollar value, the price of an information system may appear high, particularly those costs accruing during the preproduction phases of development for which we have been arguing. There are two points to be considered here. First, the funds required to design and build a first-generation computer-based information system are amortized over the years in which successor systems are designed and built. The experience, knowledge, and software products gained during the construction of the first system are passed on to subsequent systems. Second, an information system provides the user with a very large amount of effectiveness for the money it costs when this effectiveness is measured over the life-span of the system. With appropriate modifications, given the planned evolutionary approach, the system will last for the life-span of the user. Funds allotted for the design and production of weapons systems, by contrast, are lost as soon as those weapons systems are fired, as in the case of missiles, or become obsolete (in approximately four or five years). It is meaningless, therefore, to compare weapons systems with information systems in terms of absolute dollars.

Interestingly enough, in spite of the financial bargain represented by the cost of an information system, we live in a nation in which, by virtue of tradition and custom, the expenditure of two billion dollars for the Polaris System alone in the fiscal year 1963 is not regarded as excessive, but all sorts of means are sought to reduce the hundreds of millions of dollars to be spent for *all* military command and control systems (this figure includes sensor and intelligence systems), a sum which is only a small fraction of the total amount spent on weapons systems. Weapons systems are needed as instruments of war as long as war is a possibility, but command and control information systems are the instruments of *both war and peace.* All the important decisions leading up to the decision to launch missiles in a thermonuclear war are the prerogative of command and control personnel who must make up their minds, for better or worse, on the basis of information from various types of computer-based systems. More important than the decision to launch a conventional weapon, a 20-megaton weapon, or a 50-megaton weapon is the decision whether or not to launch any weapon at all; and this depends upon the right information getting to the right people, in the right format, at the right time.

As we have noted, this is essentially a problem of the allocation of scarce resources. But the problem cannot be resolved efficiently unless the highest managerial levels understand the cost/effectiveness ratios of weapons systems vis-à-vis information systems. This implies an understanding of the function of information systems in the controlled use and nonuse of weapons as well as the functions of weapons as such. There is no more important system in this country than the National Military Command System. A presidential decision to go to war or not to go to war may depend upon the information which will flow through the system. Yet there is hardly a single major weapons system in the inventory of the United States which does not cost more than the sum allotted for the development of the NMCS.

The design of effective information systems which serve national or industrial purposes calls for efforts in the area of long-range planning which at present do not have a well-established place in the operations of the United States government or in industry. Future long-range planning should include the evaluation of the *relative* effectiveness which a given amount of dollars can purchase in the form of weapons systems (a production system in industry) versus command and control systems (a management control system in industry). It is not rational to invest billions of dollars in the acquisition of weapons or production systems only to submit them to ineffective command and control or management systems.

6. Independent Operation/Operational Integration

In a poll of fifty of the top companies in the command and control business conducted by the publication *Armed Forces Management*, 28% of those questioned agreed that the toughest problem "is and will continue to be for many years the integration of totally incompatible, unstandardized existing systems. . . ."[23] This problem of the integration of existing—and future—information systems in the military and industrial realms reflects another basic difference between weapons systems and information systems.

The typical weapons system is relatively self-contained and self-sufficient. It is this quality of independence of the system from the user which makes it possible for the same weapon to be used by various services within the same nation as well as by different nations, assuming the existence of an adequate technological base. This point was discussed in Section 2.1. By contrast, the information system is not self-sufficient or self-contained. This characteristic interdependence of information systems is referred to in the technical literature as "functional integration" and "technical integration." "Functional integration" refers to the operational interdependence of associated systems. Thus the defensive mission of NORAD is functionally integrated with the deterrent mission of SAC. In industry a "total system" may consist of a production control system functionally integrated with personnel records, inventory control, and management displays. "Technical integration" refers, as the term implies, to the compatible linkages of data and equipment in the mechanical or electronic sense. The technical integration of NORAD and SAC implies that SAC, for example, is capable of receiving digital data automatically from the NORAD information system and displaying it automatically, without human interference, for the SAC Commander-in-Chief.

In the past, the influence of weapons systems and a traditional hardware orientation has tended to emphasize technical integration at the expense of functional integration. There are other reasons, too, why functional integration is likely to be relatively neglected, such as the sensitivities of existing organizations to jurisdictional problems. For understandable reasons the decentralized department manager resists the trend toward "recentralization" made possible by computer-based management systems.[24] In the past few years an important series of technical studies of the problems associated with the development of information systems has stressed the point that the key problem facing the highest levels of management in the defense establishment is not merely technical integration, but functional integration as well.[25]

Since these reports were published, there has been increasing recognition not only that information systems in general within the military and industrial realms are functionally integrated but also that in their totality they represent "a hierarchy of systems" culminating in the National Military Command System or the "integrated information system" providing top-level managerial control in industry.[26]

Many important managerial difficulties stem from the delay in understanding that information systems cannot meet their requirements without appropriate planning for functional and technical integration. In the case of information systems, unlike hardware systems, requirements data essential for system design overlap the boundaries of the subject system; indeed, it may be a difficult design decision to determine precisely where the boundaries of the system are. Since the information needed for one information system, such as the SAC Control System, flows from other systems external to it as well as from internal sources —that is, those units officially recognized as SAC units, securing the operational information needed to establish system requirements for an automated control system involves the developer in contractual and jurisdictional problems. The developer has a contract to build a system for one user, but some of the information he needs to do the job belongs to another organization with which he does not have a contract. As long as missions overflow traditional organizational lines, this problem will plague the developer. It will continue to plague him until such time as the problem is clearly recognized by the highest managerial echelons, and organizational reforms are undertaken to align contractual responsibilities with missions and the information system required to support these missions. In the meantime, management must devote more attention than it has given heretofore to the integrational aspects of system development. The developer is frequently left to resolve jurisdictional arguments as best he can, usually at the price of considerable additional cost and schedule slippage.

The problem of functional integration may not only be found between different service organizations and different military commands; it may also occur within a particular command entity. This is illustrated by the case in which, for a particular command and control information system, the intelligence function was being developed under a separate contract and as an independent system in spite of the fact that it provided almost 50% of the important inputs to the command and control system. Yet the software developers were unable to obtain information, at certain key stages in the design activity, on the characteristics of the intelligence input data to the command and control system. This information was jealously guarded by the intelligence directorate within the command entity, and its dissemination to the software developers was long delayed. Because of the aloofness of the commander from the development activity, it was extremely difficult to resolve the problem and to convince the intelligence personnel of the necessity to provide the data required to build the system.

Although the examples of these types of jurisdictional dilemmas in the writer's experience stem from military information system development, the problem also exists in industrial organizations. Evidence is already accumulating that similar difficulties will plague development efforts for urban planning, medical, educational, and law enforcement information systems.

Functional interdependence of information systems affects the developer in other ways. In the course of system design, for example, the design effort is necessarily constrained by interface considerations. At each point of interface, ideal design decisions may have to give way to compromises in order to establish the necessary linkage with other systems. In such cases the developer may see the need for the coordination of design decisions with other agencies and organizations outside the immediate jurisdiction of his contract, but neither the user nor these agencies and organizations may recognize the need or be willing to devote the time and effort to respond to it.

Since, under present financial and procurement procedures and responsibilities, information systems are procured independently by different users and agencies, the boundaries and interfaces of any given system are always in a state of flux. This flux is, of course, not controllable in any way by the system developer. Thus, changes of all kinds in the external environment—changes in the operations of interfacing systems, in their equipment, in operational missions, in the nature of the threat (in the case of military systems)—may require adaptive modifications to the system under development to ensure compatibility. Such changes, of course, may require the expenditure of additional funds, the assignment of additional man-hours to the task, and delays in the production of lead items with a resulting ripple effect down the entire development effort.

A consequence of the functional and technical interdependence of information systems in the defense establishment is that configuration management is more difficult than it is in the case of weapons systems. A change in the mission of an associated command, the adoption of a new information system by a related command, the introduction of weapons or other equipment, such as communications equipment, with revolutionary capabilities, the adoption of new doctrines or strategies at the national level—all of these kinds of changes, which occur with great frequency, can require accommodating modifications in the information system under development. Hence the design of configuration management is not adequate if it is based on the notion—a hardware-oriented notion—that the boundaries of the system are traditional service or command boundaries. By the same token, the boundary of a department-acquired information system in industry may be a fossilized relic of a passing era.[27]

2.5 SUMMARY

This chapter has described the more salient management problems associated with the development of information systems. It was the objective of the chapter to show that these management problems are derived from three closely related factors: (1) the widespread lack of familiarity of managers and administrators with the development process for information systems; (2) the use of an irrelevant model of hardware system development for the management of the information system development process; and (3) the incompatibility between existing management organization and administrative procedures, and the unique nature of the information system development process.

The basic system development activities which must be accomplished in the creation of a typical information system were listed. One of the primary responsibilities of management is deciding who should perform these activities for a given system development effort. All the activities may be performed in-house by the user, or they may be distributed between the user and any number of external agencies and organizations. The tendency in large-scale development efforts to resort to the latter alternative because of inadequate in-house technical capability gives rise to many managerial difficulties. These difficulties were traced to the three factors noted above.

The major portion of the chapter was devoted to a review of the managerial problems derived from the prevalent use by managers of an irrelevant model of weapons system development for the acquisition of a very different kind of system—the information system. These consequences were systematically explored by comparing the basic differences between weapons systems and information systems. The following differences were considered:

Weapons Systems	*Information Systems*
1. Multiple users	1. Single users
2. Many-of-a-kind	2. One-of-a-kind
3. Model changes	3. Planned evolutionary change
4. Hardware state of the art is critical	4. Software state of the art is critical
5. High cost/effectiveness ratio	5. Low cost/effectiveness ratio
6. Operational independence	6. Functional integration

This systematic comparison of weapons system characteristics with information systems characteristics brings out the extent to which contemporary managers—users, procurement agencies, and technical managers—may be utilizing an irrelevant system model for the acquisition of information systems. The review of the differences between weapons systems and information systems also serves to highlight the extent and seriousness of the incompatibility between existing management organization and administrative procedures and the information system development process.

Some of the preconditions for the alleviation of typical managerial difficulties in the design and production of information systems, as this chapter has tried to show, are (1) overcoming the prevalent lack of familiarity of typical users and administrators with the information system development process (this is, of course, the primary objective of this book); (2) establishing a model which reflects the general characteristics of the information system development process (this, also, we are attempting to do in this book); and (3) designing and establishing a management structure and administrative procedure which will be compatible with the nature of the information system development process. This subject, fortunately, lies outside the scope of this book.

REFERENCES

1. F. E. Kast and J. E. Rosenzweig (eds.), *Science, Technology, and Management.* New York: McGraw-Hill, 1963, p. 2.
2. John Diebold, "ADP—The Still-Sleeping Giant," *Harvard Business Review,* September-October 1964, pp. 62–63.
3. *Ibid.,* p. 63.
4. H. H. Goode and R. E. Machol, *System Engineering: An Introduction to the Design of Large-scale Systems.* New York: McGraw-Hill, 1957, p. 8.
5. For an airing of some of these complaints, see the address by Major-General C. H. Terhune, Jr., to the American Federation of Information Processing Societies, Las Vegas, Nev., November 12, 1963.
6. On the subject of vague management objectives see R. M. Gordon, "The Total Information System and the Levels of Data Processing," *AMA Management Report No. 46,* 1960, pp. 23–33; and on the adaptation of information system requirements to change see "Martin-Marietta Corporation: Centralized Operations Control," in *Total Systems,* A. D. Meacham and V. B. Thompson (eds.). Detroit: American Data Processing, 1962, pp. 148–160; also Gilbert Burck, "Management Will Never Be the Same Again," *Fortune,* August 1964.
7. For examples of the problems that organizations have had in the creation of information systems see G. P. Shultz and T. L. Whisler, *Management Organization and the Computer.* Glencoe, Ill.: The Free Press, 1960; "Advances in EDP and Information Systems," *AMA Management Report No. 62,* 1961; A. D. Meacham and V. B. Thompson, Ref. 6.
8. M. J. Peck and F. M. Scherer, *The Weapons Acquisition Process: An Economic Analysis.* Cambridge, Mass.: Harvard University Press, 1962.
9. This list is adapted from James W. Singleton, *Software Design and Implementation.* Santa Monica, Calif.: System Development Corporation, TM-864, November 30, 1962.
10. See Gilbert Burck's comments on this same point in "Management Will Never Be the Same Again," Ref. 6, p. 202.
11. In "How to Organize Information Systems," *Harvard Business Review,* March-April 1965, pp. 65–73, John Dearden argues that many current fail-

ures to use computers effectively in industry are due to an emphasis on a "total systems" approach and that information system design, to be effective, must be "decentralized to operating management." However, this argument leaves unresolved the issue as stated in Ref. 2, pp. 60–65, that the computer's true potential has not been realized for several reasons, including "inadequate planning, mostly parochial rather than corporate-wide in scope." Mr. Dearden believes that the several types of information systems within a given industry (finance, personnel, logistics, marketing, etc.) should be coordinated, but he does not discuss how or by whom the coordination of department managers will be accomplished.

12. For some indication of the problems encountered by American Airlines in the development of its reservations system, SABRE, see Gilbert Burck's " 'On Line' in 'Real Time,' " *Fortune*, April 1964, p. 144.

13. H. A. Simon and Allen Newell, "Heuristic Problem Solving: The Next Advance in Operations Research," *Operations Research*, **VI** (January-February 1958), 1–10.

14. See, for example, *A Summary of Lessons Learned from Air Force Management Surveys*, Air Force Systems Command, AFSCP 375-2, June 1, 1953, pp. 11–15.

15. *The Challenge of Command and Control*, Winter Study Report, AFCCDD, TR 61-4, March 1961; *Summer Study on Command and Control*, Institute for Defense Analysis, Summary Report, September 15, 1961.

16. See *The Electronic Systems Acquisition Process*. Bedford, Mass.: The MITRE Corporation, TM-69, October 31, 1963, pp. 1–2.

17. *Handbook of Instructions for Aerospace Personnel Subsystem Designers*, Air Force Systems Command, AFSCM 80-3, July 15, 1962.

18. R. L. Chapman et al., "The System Research Laboratory's Air Defense Experiments," *Management Science*, **5**, 250–269.

19. A. Katcher and M. Hunter, *How to Lead a Debriefing*. Santa Monica, Calif.: System Development Corporation, TM-132, November 19, 1957; A. Katcher and J. Jaffe, *A Method for Training Debriefing Leaders*. Santa Monica, Calif.: System Development Corporation, TM-101, January 27, 1958.

20. H. A. Simon, *Administrative Behavior*. New York: Macmillan, 1947; C. I. Barnard, *The Functions of the Executive*. Cambridge, Mass.: Harvard University Press, 1956 ed., particularly Chap. XIII; R. K. Merton, *Social Theory and Social Structure*. Glencoe, Ill.: The Free Press, 1957, pp. 195–206.

21. *Systems Management: System Program Documentation*. Washington, D.C.: Department of the Air Force, Air Force Regulation No. 275-4, February 12, 1962; N. E. Willmorth and C. J. Shaw, *System Documentation*. Santa Monica, Calif.: System Development Corporation, SP-974, October 1, 1962.

22. The material in this section is based upon a study conducted by W. Watson et al., *An Experimental Study of 465L Message Processing*. Santa Monica, Calif.: System Development Corporation, TM-LO-790, December 26, 1962.

23. "Where Defense Should Improve Command/Control Development," *Armed Forces Management*, July 1963, p. 33. For a discussion of a similar problem in industry see M. H. Grosz, "Standard Oil Company (New Jersey): Technical Developments," in *Management Organization and the Computer*, Ref. 7, pp. 179–192.

24. Gilbert Burck, "Management Will Never Be the Same Again," Ref. 6.

25. See Ref. 15.
26. The "integrated information systems" of General Motors and Standard Oil (New Jersey) and their erstwhile decentralized divisions are analogous to the National Military Command System.
27. J. W. Forrester, *Industrial Dynamics*. New York: Wiley, 1961.

Chapter Three

The System Requirements Phase

P. E. Rosove

3.1 INTRODUCTION

The purpose of this chapter is to describe the significant activities, alternatives, products, and problems which are characteristic of the initial phase of system development—the requirements phase.

The development of an information system consists of translating a user's goals and objectives into a design for and, eventually, the creation of a physical configuration of facilities, computers, computer programs, personnel, communications, and equipment. The goals and objectives must be transformed into a set of operational requirements before design work can begin. In this chapter we are concerned with the formulation and establishment of these requirements.

The activities conducted during this phase attempt to answer the following types of questions: Why is the system needed? What is its purpose or purposes? What is it expected to do? What problems is it supposed to solve? Who are the system users? What are their objectives? What preliminary qualitative and quantitative requirements for the system can be inferred from the users' objectives? A "requirement," in this sense, may be defined as a characteristic which a system or one of its elements should possess if the system is to accomplish a given objective.

Requirements statements, in their totality, at all system levels and in all functional areas tell us *what* the system is supposed to do in both qualitative and quantitative terms, rather than *how* it is to do it. It is the function of system design, by contrast, to answer the question: how?

The chapter is divided into two logically related sections. Section 3.2 deals with the variety of ways in which the detection of a need for an information system takes place. The initiation of the requirements phase for the formal acquisition of a system is described and is related to the manner in which the need arises. Section 3.3 then discusses the alternative development strategies from among which the user, in consultation with the developer, must choose.

3.2 INITIATION OF THE REQUIREMENTS PHASE

The initiation of an information system development effort may take many different forms. These various forms should be examined since they have significant consequences for the subsequent nature of the requirements phase in particular and the development effort in general. The problems which give rise to the decision to create an information system or to modify an existing system fall, for the most part, into three main classes: (1) those arising from an existing system's operations; (2) those arising from advancing science and technology; and (3) those detected in the course of long-range planning studies by some sort of planning organization. In the first two types of situations, the problems are literally thrust upon the system users; in the third case the advanced planning organization actively seeks out existing and potential problems.

Problems Arising from Operations of the Current System

Operational problems arising in industry serve to illustrate the detection of need for an information system as a replacement for or a modification to an existing set of methods and procedures prescribing the flow of information (which may or may not be conceived as an "integrated" information system). After World War II, industry in the United States was characterized by growth and geographical expansion. Organizations such as the Monsanto Chemical Company, Martin-Marietta Corporation, International Shoe Company, Standard Oil Company of New Jersey, General Electric, and hundreds of others grew in many dimensions: sales volume, assets, employees, number of markets, new products, number of plants, raw materials used, number of services rendered to customers, and so on. Managerial control problems increased in proportion to organizational growth and the attendant complexity of daily operations. It was found, for example, that as the Allis-Chalmers Manufacturing Company grew in size and complexity of operations, control problems multiplied at the same or an even greater rate.[1] The amount and variety of paper work needed to maintain control increased. This, in turn, required the development of increasingly elaborate control procedures and still more "mountains of paper." The generation of the paper reports and accounts was not in itself a technological problem, but as the sheer volume of paper work increased, the manipulation and use of this information became inadequate.

At General Electric the standard joke was that a factory could not make a shipment until the papers involved weighed as much as the product.[2] In the case of the Standard Oil Company of New Jersey, one of the largest corporations in the world, composed of over 200 affiliates marketing petroleum products in 135 countries and dependencies, the parent company functions exclusively as a management organization.[3] It is primarily concerned with coordinating the operations of its affiliates. The central management organization, therefore, is the hub of a vast network of communications over which flows information which is used in reaching management decisions. Basic data in the flow of information to management are petroleum statistics. Before the use of computers, several different departments and affiliates in the corporation gathered such statistics with considerable overlapping and duplication of effort and, therefore, at unnecessary cost to the corporation. Similarly, personnel data were gathered and stored by many different departments: employee relations, personnel, plans administration, payroll, medical, insurance, and social security.

The magnitude of the problem faced by Standard Oil, particularly the high cost of duplication of records, is brought out by considering the control of stock levels and purchase ordering. Maintenance and operating supplies included approximately 30,000 items, with an additional 5,000 items in a central tool inventory, as well as the prospect of adding 4,000 items of laboratory supplies for research activities.

By 1956 not only the giant corporations but also relatively small companies, such as the Atwood Vacuum Machine Company, which employs about 1,550 people in five plants, found themselves overwhelmed by paper work.[4] The operations of this automotive internal body hardware manufacturing company involved 2,000 finished parts and assemblies, processed from 10,000 different parts made from 500 types of raw materials. By comparison to the Standard Oil Company of New Jersey, the Atwood Company is not large, but the problems associated with keeping records of such numbers of items and materials are large scale by any standards.

Thus, for both small and large companies, increasing organizational growth and complexity of operations inevitably had a profound impact on management. The direct results were inaccurate reports on operations, costly time lags in the dissemination of information, rising costs of maintaining paper work, crucial gaps in the reporting and summarizing of information, and excessively high costs associated with the stretch-out of the production cycle from recording the customer's order to delivery of the finished product.

Creation of a "New" System. The scope and nature of an information problem which the management of an enterprise is compelled to face may be of such dimensions that a system defined as "new" is recognized to be essential. But it is by no means a simple matter to clarify what is meant by a new system. The case of the International Shoe Company may serve to illustrate the dilemma.[5] Information-processing elements of a manual and semiautomatic nature existed in this company, but they had not been designed or created as a system; the various components which provided for the flow of information had been developed independently and at different times to meet a number of uncoordinated needs. These components were finally replaced by a system which was designed as a "totality" to meet all the information needs of management. The general manager, who was in charge of the introduction of a computerized system, regarded the computerization of information processing as one aspect of over-all reorganization of the company.[6] In this system development effort, the new element in the situation was a *viewpoint* in which information processing was conceived as one element of an integrated system—the integration of the organization and the information network.

It is necessary, then, to take note of at least three logical possibilities when a new system is under consideration. There may be (1) no existing relevant information-processing elements of any kind, (2) relevant but unintegrated information-processing elements, and (3) an obsolete or inadequate information system. Situations in which there are no relevant information-processing elements *of any kind* are rare. The most common situation the developer encounters in the contemporary period is one in which an organization possesses, or several organizations dealing with a common problem possess, unintegrated information-processing elements.

We can illustrate a typical contemporary situation by describing the need for "an integrated scientific and engineering information system" which is receiving increasing attention.[7] National concern has been focused upon a new problem—the shortage of scientists and engineers. Studies of scientific and engineering manpower have indicated that the difficulties in this area are caused by the currently inadequate methods for collecting and processing information about scientists and engineers. Plenty of information is available in many sources and forms; but "there is a very serious mismatch between the information available today and the questions decision makers in this area need to have answered if they are to plan for the future intelligently."[8] It is suggested that modern computers could be utilized to process the available data on such people. An "integrated system" modeled after a large-scale military command control system might be a potential solution to the problem.

This concept of an integrated information system for scientific and engineering manpower clearly suggests a "new" system. No such integrated system now exists. Yet there are many unintegrated "systems" which collect, process, and disseminate manpower information about scientists and engineers to various users: the federal government, industry, and universities.

In this case there is no single entity or system which can be used by the system developer as a model or source for the determination of system objectives and requirements. The determination of requirements can begin, nevertheless, by study of the current users of information about scientists and engineers and the kinds of data needed by them. This is essentially what has been done. A requirements analysis was undertaken by first determining who were the users of manpower information. This was followed by consideration of the kinds of questions these various users might want to have answered by an information system. Then the investigators went on to inquire about the types of information needed to contribute answers to the users' questions.[9]

The initiation of the requirements phase is markedly different when there already is an operating information system. Since the system exists, the user will normally attempt to solve operational difficulties as they arise, as an in-house technical activity. Usually a manufacturing company, such as the International Shoe Company, will have a methods and procedures department or some similar organizational unit with the responsibility for the development of information processing. However, if the problems are such that the user recognizes his in-house capabilities to be inadequate for determining what the operational difficulties are or how they should be solved, he may call in an outside agency to serve as a consultant or to assume full responsibility for resolving the problem.[10] There are two different ways in which the user may express his needs to an outside development organization. These alternatives have significant consequences for user-developer relationships and the nature of the development effort. In the first instance the user does not know what his problems are, and in the second case he believes that he does know.

The Current System Has Unidentified Problems. In this situation the user, in effect, says to the developer: "Here is how I am currently conducting my operations. However, I am running into difficulties which result in inefficiencies, but *I do not understand what my problems are.* Will you analyze my operations and tell me what I must do to accomplish my goals?"

This type of situation has advantages from the point of view of the developer. The user's admission that he does not understand the nature of his operational problems gives the developer a relatively free hand for the creation of an information system concept. It provides him with the authority to analyze the difficulties, determine the system requirements, and design the solutions. It may even make possible a re-examination of the user's goals and objectives. This alternative is an invitation to the developer to study the user's current operations in whatever detail necessary. It also suggests that the user is psychologically prepared to rely upon the experience and knowledge of the developer to get the job done.

There are also disadvantages in this situation. First, it is likely that the user lacks the in-house technical capability to conduct his own system analyses. This may make communication between the user and the developer unnecessarily difficult. Furthermore, the user may have the naive notion that by bringing in a specialist from the field of information systems he can simply dump his troubles in the developer's lap and sit back, contributing nothing, while the developer concocts a panacea for all his ills. He may fail to appreciate the extent to which the developer must have his close cooperation throughout all stages of the development effort.

In general, however, a situation in which the user admits that he does not understand the nature of his difficulties is a desirable one as far as the developer is concerned. The disadvantages are less critical than the advantages. The reasons for this will become more evident when we consider the consequences of the alternative way of stating the issue.

The Current System Problems Are Identified by the User. The developer encounters a very different situation when the user initiates a system development effort with this kind of statement: "I have a job to do, and here is how I am doing it now. However, in conducting this operation *I have a number of problems, which are as follows.* What I would like you to do is to solve these problems for me." This situation differs from the previous one in that the user has already conducted some preliminary analyses of his operational difficulties. He believes that he already understands his problems, and the developer is merely being asked to provide the solutions.

There are several advantages to this situation. First, it is apparent that the user has some degree of in-house capability to analyze his own operational difficulties. Thus, communication and cooperation between the user's analysts and the developers can be established at the outset. Since user personnel are involved in the determination of requirements for the new system, they will be more likely to maintain a continuing interest in the activities of the developer and the design and production of the new system. This is a great improvement over situations in which user personnel remain indifferent to the development process. Also, the user is, of course, the expert on his own operations. No outsider, whatever his degree of excellence, can bring to the task the same range of knowledge about the particular enterprise.

However, a situation in which user personnel believe they already know their problems and ask the developer only for solutions is not an unmixed blessing. It is evident that the developer under these conditions is being saddled with constraints. Although it may be an advantage to be given the definition of the problems, it is possible that the difficulties have not been correctly or completely identified. Personnel most closely involved in the operations of an enterprise are sometimes least able to look at it in a detached and objective manner. Traditional ways of operating tend to be accepted without question. In contrast to the previous alternative, the developer is not being invited to study the user's information system as a totality but is being arbitrarily confined to the problems specified. This approach to a definition of the situation possesses the inherent danger that the objectivity and detachment of an outsider will not be used to maximum advantage. The end result is that an a priori statement of the problems by the user may serve to impede, rather than facilitate, the development effort.

If the user presents this alternative to the developer, it suggests that he may not really understand the nature of information systems. An information system, for maximum effectiveness per dollar cost, should be an operational and functional totality. Operational problems cannot be treated as isolated elements, unrelated to the total information flow. It may well be that a study of the total operation of the enterprise will reveal that there is an underlying cause of several apparently isolated operational problems. If the user's statement of the problems is accepted as given, and only solutions for these difficulties are sought, such underlying causes may never be isolated and identified.

Since in this case there is a current system, what may be called "operational solutions" exist to the user's requirements, needs, and objectives.[11] An operational solution may be defined as a way of employing given resources to accomplish a set of objectives under a given set of conditions. Examples of operational solutions from the military realm include the Strategic Air Command's airborne alert posture for strategic bombers and rendezvous refueling techniques. These are operational methods for meeting the needs of SAC. In other words, must the developer accept the airborne alert concept as a user objective, or may he examine the *prior* objective for which the airborne alert is an operational solution, that is, survivability of the force?

The requirements for a given information system may be either derived from an analysis of the user's mission or objectives or deduced from existing operational solutions or new operational solutions that the user may invoke during the lifetime of the system. In the former case the developer would derive very general requirements, which theoretically would accommodate every possible operational solution that might be created. But the difficulty with requirements defined so broadly is that an information system derived from them may be so general as to provide little actual assistance to the users. However, the system must be general enough so that it can accommodate any possible operational solution which the user may want. This will not be accomplished if the user accepts his operational solutions as fixed and defines the problems in advance for the developer. The ideal solution is for the developer to concern himself with *both* general requirements deduced from the user's mission, goals, and objectives and more specific requirements deduced from existing and anticipated operational solutions. *But the requirements deduced from the user's goals should be respected as of higher order.* Thus, although general capability is difficult to create and is not efficient in handling specific tasks, the developer would be wise to provide such a capability and, at the same time, to satisfy the requirements deduced from the existing and anticipated operational solutions. By bearing in mind the requirements for a general capability as the system is being designed, the developer can incorporate such features at relatively little additional cost to the user.

The most effective information system capability cannot be created unless the developer examines not just the problems defined for him by the user, but also the entire operation of the enterprise and all the requirements for information as deduced from the user's needs and objectives.

Problems Arising from Advanced Science and Technology

Scientific and technological advancements generate information at rates of speed which make existing information-processing facilities and methods hopelessly inadequate. Tiros I, the weather satellite, for example, during its three months of operational life produced over 22,000 pictures of the earth's cloud cover. As a result, the problem of the Weather Bureau shifted from simply obtaining weather information to indexing and classifying it. The staggering nature of the problem faced by the Weather Bureau is indicated further by the fact that its National Weather Record Station receives data from 1,200 stations around the world, 600 Air Force and Navy weather sources, 1,000 ocean-going vessels, and some foreign sources. The station is reported to have 400 million weather punch cards and is adding cards at the rate of 35 million per year.[12]

A prominent biologist, Bentley Glass, points out that because of the exponential increase of scientific knowledge in his field the biology textbooks currently used in secondary schools represent knowledge of thirty years ago.[13] According to his estimates, the number of biological serial publications is doubling every fifteen years. There are now 20,000 journals of interest to biologists, and at least 6,000 of these are of "major significance." He estimates that the fund of biological knowledge was four times greater in 1930 than in 1900, and sixteen times greater in 1960 than in 1900; it will most likely be 100 times greater in the year 2000. Glass cites the results of a study conducted in 1959 on the reading habits of fifty scientists which showed that they were experiencing a "growing inability to cope with the literature." He himself expresses an increasing sense of despair in the face of the impossible task of keeping up with the literature in his field. And if the situation of the practicing scientist is grim, the problem of the teacher of biology is far worse. Teachers, Glass writes, suffer "from a horribly rapid obsolescence."

The exponential rate of increase in knowledge in biology raises crucial questions with regard to the publication and dissemination of new findings in this field, the storage and retrieval of such information, and its transmission to the younger generation. It has been suggested by Glass that, unless steps are taken to deal with these problems, modern science "will eventually bury itself under a mountain of paper." He visualizes some sort of electronic retrieval system whereby an investigator can push a button and receive from a computer a digest of all recent or past information on any given subject of biological concern. Unless some such system is developed for biology and the other sciences, he predicts that instead of continuing scientific progress "our growing inability to assimilate the products of the scientific process, the enormously increasing bulk of our scientific literature, our failure to cope with the problem of the storage and retrieval of information, and the lag in the education of the younger generation . . . may well lead to a gradual slowdown in the rate of scientific advancement . . . until finally the stage of ultimate scientific decline sets in."[14] He suggests that to avoid this fate a world-wide, united effort on the part of all scientists and scientific organizations is essential.

M. M. Dubinin, a Russian scientist, echoes the plea of the American biologist cited above.[15] He emphasizes other problems related to scientific literature which stem from the exponential increase in knowledge. The scientific articles published are made so brief, since the volume of publications exceeds the available magazine capacities, that essential information is not being transmitted. There are delays of two years from the completion of an investigation until the publication of results in the scientific journals. Dubinin proposes an international system of scientific information exchange with (1) standardized investigation reports adopted by international agreement, (2) assignment of a code number to each report, (3) transmission of the reports to a regional reference bureau serving several neighboring nations, (4) translation of the reports into the language of the region, (5) transmission of more detailed data related to the investigation under the same code number to the regional reference bureau, and (6) transmission of all data pertaining to investigations under their code number by regional bureaus upon request to scientists in that region.

Note that Dubinin has told us in his six statements some of the requirements for the new scientific information exchange system. He suggests that the system should be able to transmit reports, to translate reports into various languages, to transmit more detailed data from the reports (presumably upon request from the regional reference bureaus), and to transmit all data from the reports upon request. Dubinin also proposes that the system include "standardized investigation reports" and "assignment of a code number to each report." These statements do not tell us how the reports will be standardized or coded, but they do establish requirements for standardization and codes.

The examples of information-processing problems arising from the advance of science and technology illustrate the generation of requirements for "new" information systems. In these situations there is a manual or semiautomatic "system," but it is inadequate for the task at hand. This is illustrated by the problem of the Weather Bureau. In the case of the biological and other sciences, there are techniques for the dissemination of available information, but these techniques, such as the publication of periodicals, do not constitute an *information system* as defined in Chapter 1.

Since the developer is dealing in these cases with problems created by advances in science and technology, the requirements for these systems may have no precedents. Thus the developer is in the position of being a pioneer; he must create his own development technology as he creates the system. This was, in fact, the situation of the developers in the creation of the SAGE system of air defense and the SABRE system for American Airlines seat reservations.

It is important that the user understand that his own role and the task of the developer are different in a pioneering development effort as contrasted to a type of system development effort for which many precedents, if not libraries of routine computer programs, already exist. These differences will become evident in the remaining portions of this chapter and will be touched upon in other chapters of this book.

A Long-Range Planning Activity

Whether a user has a current system or merely some unintegrated information-processing elements, an ideal method for the generation of system requirements is for an enterprise to have an on-going organizational unit with the assigned responsibility for long-range system planning. The basic function of this unit is to look ahead and anticipate, to the extent possible, the need for new or improved information system capabilities. Large-scale industrial corporations have such units, at least nominally, in their "systems and methods" or "methods and procedures" departments. In the military realm, planning staffs of various kinds and at different levels within the Department of Defense have this look-ahead responsibility. Nonprofit organizations, such as the RAND Corporation, also carry out long-range studies of possible future systems for a particular service. It is a responsibility of such staffs and organizations to generate the requirements for new systems, including information systems.

These various long-range planning units differ markedly in their degree of closeness to the user of the potential system. The RAND Corporation personnel are further removed from a military command than is the planning staff of that command. And the long-range planners on the staff of the Director of Defense Research and Engineering in the Department of Defense are still further removed from the possible users of information systems. Units closest to the users are in the best position to generate system requirements that will, if met, satisfy these users.

As we have noted, it is the user who should assume the primary responsibility for long-range planning for his own information system needs. It is understandable, although not desirable, that for problems arising from the advancement of science and technology, there may not be any organizations responsible for the look-ahead function. In the case of industry, usually, although not always, a group with such a function exists. Of course, as John Diebold points out, the wrong group may have this responsibility.[16] In the military realm there are a great number of agencies with long-range planning functions. However, it has frequently happened in the past that a particular military command in the process of acquiring an information system has not assumed the responsibility for long-range planning. There are many reasons for this unfortunate state of affairs. The using command may not possess the in-service technical capability to conduct such planning for information systems. It may be so concerned with immediate problems that, with inadequate resources of manpower, time, and funds, it is in no practical position to perform long-range planning. Be this as it may, the long-range planning function is clearly the responsibility of those closest to the information system and should not be delegated, either by default or design, to the developers or other external agencies.

The long-range planning unit should establish future operational requirements for the enterprise. In industry, for example, this would call for study of management policies and aspects of the external environment, such as changing markets, the activities of competitors, and taxation policies of the government, as well as factors in the internal environment, such as productive processes and equipment, labor conditions, finances, and organization. Once the operational requirements are defined, they must then be analyzed in terms of the feasibility of implementing an information system that will accomplish them. The determination of feasibility includes the investigation of a variety of factors, including cost, schedules, technical state of the art, and availability of technical and operational personnel. On the basis of their studies, the long-range planners may distinguish the requirements which should be implemented on a priority basis; they may identify the operational functions and tasks which may or may not call for improvements via computerization; they may recognize the need for reorganization of the enterprise; or they may decide to delay or postpone the introduction of an automated information system.*

The product of long-range planning is a document or series of documents which contain the guidance necessary to initiate the development effort and to provide the basis for management control over the subsequent development activities. If the enterprise does not have a long-range planning group, these responsibilities must be assumed by the developer or some other external agency. The following list suggests the range of activities which should be carried out:

- Define the problem in as much detail as possible.
- Determine the objective of management.
- Establish the boundaries of the system under consideration.
- Study the relationship of the system to its environment.
- Study the interaction of the system with other associated systems, both existing and contemplated (system interface).
- Develop a basic concept of the new system.
- Define in a preliminary sense the new system's functions and subsystems.
- Conduct constraints analyses and a feasibility study.

---

* Note that the object of information system planning is not automatically the creation of a "total system," but recognition by top management of the need for the planners to study the totality of information system requirements throughout the enterprise.

- Determine the type of development strategy best suited to the particular development activity.

3.3   DEVELOPMENT STRATEGIES

At the inception of an information system development effort, there are a number of possible strategies from which the management of the development activity must choose. The two most important ones are the following:

1. Should the entire system be designed at one time as a total system, or should it be designed in a series of iterations each one of which would result in a more sophisticated and complete operational configuration?

2. Should the new system be designed upon the basis of the old system via an inductive approach, or should a completely new system be built by using a deductive approach?

Development Iterations and System Configurations

The Single Iteration and Configuration. One alternative which the system developer may recommend is the creation of a single operational configuration following a development effort which proceeds sequentially from the establishment of initial requirements through the design and production of the system. This alternative has been called the "one-shot" or "single-shot" approach. It is satisfactory when the following conditions exist:

- The requirements for the system are clearly defined and specified in sufficient detail so that design work can proceed without uncertainties.
- The system to be developed is stable in nature, that is, neither the system itself nor its environment, assuming the system is of a type that is responsive to its environment, is subject to change.
- Money and time are in short supply.

In point of fact, information systems will always have some need for change as the requirements for them change. However, it is apparent that some systems come much closer to the concept of a stable system than others. There is a continuum of potential systems from the most stable to the least stable. In contrast to military command

and control systems, the objectives and requirements of air traffic control systems, medical data-processing systems, law enforcement systems, etc., are relatively stable through time, and the vehicles controlled by the system or data flowing through the system are also relatively unchanging. The environments with which these systems interact are similarly stable in nature. Thus, before the developer is able to select a single development iteration and operational configuration as a desirable strategy, he must be able to place his system along this spectrum from stable to unstable extremes.

An Initial and a Complete System Configuration. The simplest alternative strategy to that of a single development effort and a single configuration of the operational system involves two successive development iterations the output of which is two operational configurations—an initial operational capability and a complete operational capability. This approach was frequently used for military information systems during the 1955-1964 decade. The conditions which make this alternative attractive include:

- The initial requirements for the system are not clearly defined and cannot be specified in detail at the time that development work must begin.
- The system to be developed is unstable in nature, that is, the system itself and the environment with which it is meshed are subject to change.
- Money and time are available for an initial, partial development effort with assurance that additional funds will be forthcoming at a later date.

Within the context of this dual development-configuration approach there are a number of additional alternatives. These pertain to the range of possible relationships between the initial and the complete operational systems. The two configurations may be designed as relatively independent entities or as closely related entities. The initial operational system may be developed without any consideration whatever for the ultimate characteristics of the complete operational system. This may be the only alternative available to the developer when the system being considered is pushing the technological state of the art so closely that the final configuration cannot be conceived. It is also a reasonable alternative when the rate of system change anticipated is unusually high, as in the case of military systems, in which user requirements and operational features change frequently. Since the ultimate system requirements and operations cannot be foreseen, the development effort is restricted to system characteristics which can be specified. Other conditions which favor this approach are a need for an operational capability, however modest, as soon as technically feasible (a situation which is not uncommon in the military realm) and an austere budget which will support only a modest initial development effort. In both military and nonmilitary environments the lack of adequate funds may make an independent approach to the development of the initial configuration a necessity.

There are a number of disadvantages to a strategy of development in which an initial system capability is designed without consideration for the follow-on configuration. First, if no concept of possible future system requirements and operations is created, the initial system configuration may become obsolete before it attains operational status. Second, without some conception of the requirements and operational characteristics of the ultimate configuration, it is unlikely that adequate provision for system flexibility and adaptation can be built into the initial system. As a result, the necessity to alter the initial configuration with the passage of time to meet changing needs will be an excessively costly proposition.

In the event that the developer selects a strategy in which the two configurations are to be designed as closely related entities, further decisions must be made. The alternatives within this strategy are:

- The final system may be conceived as providing additional and possibly more sophisticated capabilities for the initial configuration.
- The initial configuration may be conceived as some subset of the final system capability.

In the former case the initial system configuration is designed as a total entity with design consideration being given to those requirements and operational capabilities which may be built upon this initial foundation. In the second alternative, by contrast, the complete operational configuration is conceived first, and then some significant subset of the system is selected for initial implementation. The selection of either of these options hinges again on the ability of the developer to anticipate the nature of the final system.

It is apparent that, for a development strategy in which the two configurations are conceived as closely related entities, the alternative in which the initial configuration is designed as a subset of the final system is dangerous in that this approach allows relatively little room for error. Where this strategy is chosen, the developer cannot afford to build an initial system utilizing an unreliable interpretation of future needs. For this reason, given a rapidly changing computer technology and an equally rapidly changing work environment, this alternative is less desirable.

The Model Concept in SAGE. The methodological strategy selected for the SAGE system of air defense reflects a further elaboration of iterative development and a plural number of operational configurations. In the case of SAGE, rather than limiting the development strategy to two configurations, the system is conceived to be constantly altering through time as military requirements change. When the SAGE system was in the planning and early development stages, it was apparent to the designers that the operational environment would be consistently unstable in nature. With respect to both the capabilities of potential hostile aircraft and other types of attack vehicles, and the capabilities of defensive vehicles such as interceptor aircraft and missiles, frequent changes could be anticipated. It could also be anticipated that the changing characteristics of both military offense and defense would be reflected in correspondingly frequent modifications in operational tactics and procedures. As a result of these considerations, the SAGE system is periodically updated through the creation of new "program models," each successive model encompassing improved capabilities and reflecting the introduction of new weapons systems, both offensive and defensive, and new operational concepts and tactics.

It should be stressed that a program model in SAGE is a set of interrelated computer programs which are run in the SAGE computers. When a new interceptor or a new missile is introduced into the defense system weapons inventory, the performance parameters of the interceptor or missile system must be reflected in the SAGE computer programs. Thus, periodically, the computer programs must be revised and released for operational use as new models. Each model differs from the previous one by a variety of major or minor modifications.

In the SAGE model approach there is no arbitrary limit to the number of configurations which may be created and replaced during the history of the system. The decision to create a new model, in the case of SAGE, is made by the North American Air Defense/Air Defense Command Headquarters at Colorado Springs, Colorado. The factors which go into the decision to acquire a new model include such considerations as operational desirability, schedules for the introduction of new equipment, funding arrangements, space available in the computer, and the lead time required for the development of a new model.

Although each SAGE model is a unique operational and logical entity, it should be noted that no model is essentially new. Models are produced relatively quickly since each one is an outgrowth of its predecessors. Each model relies heavily on the experience and skills which the development and operational personnel have derived from antecedent models. Also, new computer programs are additions to or modifications of existing models.

Since the SAGE system began its operations in 1958, new system models have been introduced on an average of one every 6 to 9 months. The production of a new model may require from 12 to 28 months, depending upon the extent of the changes required. Ten different SAGE models had seen operational use by 1962. As of 1963, thirteen models had reached the planning stage.

The resort to an unspecified number of successive models or system configurations as exemplified in SAGE illustrates one of the basic themes of this book—that an information system configuration at any one moment of time constitutes a set of design hypotheses which must be continuously subjected to evaluation, testing, and verification against a variety of criteria throughout the life history of the system. It must be emphasized that information systems are still in the infancy of their technological growth. With respect to the software components of such systems in particular, there is still much that is not well understood. In addition, as we have noted in the previous paragraphs, information systems are subjected to frequent and drastic change requirements. In many instances the final system configuration cannot be anticipated in advance, as in the case of SAGE. Thus, in situations where the developer may have an inadequate set of system requirements, where the future requirements for the system cannot be anticipated, where subsystem and component specifications are difficult to describe in detail, and where the system must reflect changing characteristics of both an internal and an external nature, no single design configuration should be regarded as a "final" or "complete" system.

Relationship of the Existing System to Its Replacement

One way to design and implement a new information system is to build upon the foundation provided by the existing manual or semiautomatic system, using an inductive strategy. Basically, this approach consists of developing computer programs which automate existing system functions and operational procedures. The new system in this approach is thus merely an extension of its precursor. By contrast, the deductive method may be used in which the developer begins his effort by an analysis of the new system's requirements and objectives as stated by the customer. In this strategy the current system is not relied upon as a model for the future system. From the analysis and studies of the system requirements and objectives the new operational functions and procedures are logically deduced by the developer through a design process which proceeds from the most general statements of requirements down through expanding levels of detail until the component specifications can be described. Each of these two strategies has both advantages and disadvantages.

The Inductive Strategy. The choice of an inductive strategy offers the development management a number of advantages. Since the inductive method of design builds upon the existing system, it greatly simplifies the task of the software developer. The functions and procedures of the existing system are well established and well understood by operations personnel. They can, therefore, usually be converted with relative ease into a set of software products. This approach does not require intensive and time-consuming analyses of the user's requirements and operations. Since the new system is simply an automated version of the old one, the typical problems of communication, coordination, and review and concurrence procedures between the user and the developer can be reduced in complexity, if not eliminated entirely. The inductive approach simplifies or eliminates a number of problems for the operational personnel. Since the automated system will be merely a modified version of the system with which they are familiar, they will more readily accept and adapt to the operational needs of the new system. It will hold relatively few surprises for them. It can be anticipated, therefore, that they will manifest little anxiety with respect to operating the new system, and hence they will not consciously or subconsciously offer resistance to it. Finally, the absence of an abrupt change in functions and operations derived from an inductive strategy means that the requirements for orientation and training for system personnel will be minimized. The turnover phase in which the automated system assumes responsibility for operations should be limited in duration and relatively trouble free.

The inductive approach to development has some serious disadvantages which must be carefully evaluated before the decision is made to travel this road. To begin with, there can be no assurance that the existing operational functions and procedures are the most effective ones for accomplishing the user's requirements and objectives. The fact that manual or semiautomatic procedures are effective does not, by itself, ensure that the same procedures will function satisfactorily in an automated system. The technological sophistication in automatic information processing, particularly the capability to perform routine types of decision making, may provide the user with maximum effectiveness through the utilization of a set of procedures which are radically different from the current ones. Indeed, we may reasonably inquire why a customer would be willing to invest in a costly electronic digital computer and its peripheral equipment merely to automate functions and procedures conducted in the past by manual or semiautomatic techniques. John Diebold has argued convincingly that a new technology, which includes the computer, should not be constrained arbitrarily by the traditional work processes of a past era.[17]

It is frequently the case that a user entertains the idea of acquiring a new system because he has a problem—for example, his current system supplies him with too much undigested data or with unreliable, inaccurate, or outdated information. In such situations merely automating the existing system means that a lot of money will be spent to make an existing set of problems for management worse than they already are. An intensification of these difficulties over time suggests that what may be called for is a re-examination of the user's information requirements. The accelerating rate of change in the contemporary environment, which plagues many industries as well as the military, suggests the real possibility that automating an existing information system will not provide a means for meeting the user's future requirements and objectives.

The Deductive Strategy. If the design of the new system is not constrained by existing manual and semiautomatic procedures and methods, a more efficient system design and a more effective utilization of the computer and its peripheral equipment will be possible. The new system can be designed, not in terms of old requirements and objectives, but in terms of current ones, and at the same time provision can be made for new and changing requirements and objectives. This approach will ensure that the new system will not be a patchwork of old and new, but will represent a logically consistent relationship between requirements and operational functions and procedures. The logical process of deduction also provides for greater consistency throughout all aspects of the design. A rigorously deductive approach makes it possible to detect any loopholes or gaps in the design. These interstices are relatively more difficult to detect in an inductive approach, which builds upon existing methods of operation.

The deductive approach to design also has its disadvantages. Where this design strategy is followed, the outcome may be a system which is radically different from the old one. In such a case, the users of the system may resist, if not sabotage, it. They will have to undergo a period of adjustment to the new system through programs of orientation and training. Rather than immediately improving the operations of the enterprise, the new system, when it is radically different from the old, may result in a period of operational degradation until personnel become experts at its use. To the extent that the deductive approach suggests the need for new operational procedures and, perhaps, new system tasks and functions, a high proportion of research and exploration into new methods and techniques of information processing may be required. This may result in difficulties in estimating the cost of the new system and also lead to uncertainties in design and production scheduling.

Combined Inductive and Deductive Strategies. There is no justification for asserting the unqualified primacy of either the inductive or the deductive approach. In any given case of system development, either one strategy or the other may be obviously preferable, or the situation may suggest some possible combination of the two. When the needed information system is completely new, as in the case of the Air Force Satellite Control System, the developer has no alternative but to proceed from a set of system requirements and objectives, utilizing the deductive method. In other situations, such as frequently prevail in industry, the financial condition of the company acquiring the new system may be such that the developer has no alternative but to automate existing payroll or inventory procedures via an inductive strategy. But certainly the most common situation is one which falls midway between these two extremes. Usually there is a manual or semiautomatic prototype system. And, typically, the most sensible strategy for development is to take what is useful of the old system and to develop new automated operations and procedures where feasible within given cost, scheduling, manpower, and other constraints.

We cannot leave this subject without mentioning a critical issue which the software developer must invariably face when he undertakes a major development task. Should the developer merely accept the user's definition of his own requirements and give him whatever he asks for even if it is simply the automation of current manual operations and procedures? Or is it the developer's responsibility to design the best system of which he is capable even to the point of disregarding the user's requests? The issue has been a real one in the past decade and will continue to be critical for some time into the future.

This dilemma is an inevitable consequence of a number of factors. One, of course, is the relative technological naiveté of the typical potential user with respect to information systems. Even more critical is the psychological commitment of the user to his existing way of doing things, and his sociological commitment to the status, prestige, and authority of his official position or group in the organization of the enterprise. The developer, by contrast, is not committed to any of these things. Inevitably, the developer approaches the task with a different orientation from that of the user. In addition to his lack of psychological or sociological commitment to the existing operations and organization of the enterprise, the developer's focus of interest is on maximizing the flow and processing of information. He is impatient with people, organizations, and operations which stand in the way of his efforts. Conflict deriving from such contradictory perspectives is inevitable.[18]

The resolution of this dilemma is by no means simple, but the problem is not insoluble. Basically, the developer's primary obligation is to give the user what he asks for. After all, it is the user's money which is being spent. The second obligation of the developer is to make every reasonable effort, within the constraints of available funds, schedules, and manpower, to bring to the user's attention the discrepancies which the developer visualizes between the ideal system which could be built and the system for which the user is asking.

Inductive Strategy and Evolution by Accident. In the industrial sphere the evolution of information systems by accident rather than design has been the rule, not the exception. During the 1955-1964 decade, many industries undertook the development of various types of information-processing systems. For the most part industry has adapted the high-speed digital computer to its requirements in piecemeal fashion and upon the basis of existing procedures and operational methods. Utilizing the computer to carry out payroll production or to maintain inventories has been the most common application during the first half of the decade. As managers acquired experience with computers and information systems, additional functions were added, not as a result of long-range planning, but merely in increments as the capability of the computer to solve managerial problems in other areas was gradually recognized. This is the inductive approach to system design and the evolution of systems by accident. Perhaps it was inevitable that this should happen, considering the pioneering nature of the information-processing field. But evolution by accident is not the way to build the most efficient systems.

Industry has not been alone in the development of systems by a process of accidental evolution. In the absence of experience with computer-based information systems, and out of consideration for the high costs of computers, it is hardly surprising that applications of computers to military operations have tended also to be piecemeal in nature.

Evolution by accident has some inherent limitations and disadvantages. It is relatively costly since the ultimate integration of computerized elements, as in the case of several associated industrial plants with different computers, requires extensive retrofitting of equipment and the abandonment of old, incompatible items. Since the codes and formats used by different computers vary, integration will mean costly reprogramming. The use of a computer in piecemeal fashion is also expensive since the full capabilities of the machine are not being utilized. It is inefficient to use a computer to carry out only inventory control when, with appropriate programming, the computer could be utilized simultaneously to produce reports useful to other managerial functions, such as sales forecasting, production scheduling, management control, and management planning.

In the development of both military and nonmilitary information systems there is a clear trend in which evolution by accident is being replaced by planned evolution.

A Combined Strategy: Planned Evolution. Planned evolution is defined as an approach to system development in which a fully integrated system *concept* is created with a plan whereby the integrated system will be attained in a series of stages through a process of development iteration. In this approach, a study is conducted on an organization-wide or corporate-wide basis to determine which functions should be automated. The implementation of the initial stage of the system is based upon a selection of certain functions which are assigned priority. The first stage of the system, or the "initial operational capability," tends to be regarded as a prototype or experimental model, although it can be used for operations. Through experimentation and operational experience, successive stages of the system are designed and produced, each stage representing an addition to and an improvement upon its predecessors.

If we assume that we are not dealing with a stable system, the approach to system development based upon planned evolution has numerous advantages over the other alternatives. The initial system relies heavily upon the existing system (where there is one) with the result that the transition to an automated, computerized system is gradual. This, as we have noted, simplifies the orientation and training problem and also reduces resistance by the system users to the new and untried. Costs are relatively minimal since the existing facilities are not simply discarded and the initial operational capability is accomplished within a relatively short time with minimal new equipment and computer programming. Since the initial system concept is modest, off-the-shelf hardware may be used. The contributions of the system users to the development are maximized as the system gradually evolves. Participation of the users from the start makes possible the gradual creation of an in-house capability to conduct both system development and its on-going maintenance. Understanding of computerized operations in the early stages facilitates the participation of the users in subsequent development activities. Their informational requirements can be more carefully defined as experience with the system is gained and fed back into the developmental process. In the case of military systems, the evolutionary approach provides more time to develop "interface" or systems interaction requirements where major systems will be functionally interrelated before hardware is frozen. Finally, planned evolution makes it possible to accommodate the system to changing requirements—changes stemming from within the system itself or from the external environment. This is particularly critical in the contemporary situation, where revolutionary changes in technology occur in cycles of only a few years.

A complex system, by definition, is composed of a number of interacting components. It has been pointed out that in the development of guided missiles hardware prototypes must be built in order to demonstrate that the requirements have been met. This is necessary because the interactions of the missile's components and the environment in which it operates are too complex to be analyzed adequately on paper or in a laboratory. To an even greater extent, complexity of interacting components is characteristic of information systems. In such systems the interaction of the components, which include human beings, is considerably less deterministic than in the case of missiles. In effect, planned evolution in the development of information systems provides for the production of prototype systems in which the complex interactions of components can be tested under operational conditions before more expensive commitments have been made.

Although the concept of planned evolution appears to possess obvious advantages over other approaches, it has been by no means easy to apply. Planned evolution tends to blur the customary distinctions between research, production, and operations. Traditional organizational and funding arrangements in industry, government, and the military have been founded upon such distinctions. These distinctions were and are meaningful with respect to the production of hardware items such as weapons and equipment, in which the end item undergoes relatively minor modifications after it enters full-scale production. In planned evolution, where the initial operating system is regarded as a test and experimental instrument, it is difficult to say where research ends and production begins.

The implementation of information systems via a process of planned evolution implies also that there is an over-all plan for the automation of appropriate elements of the given enterprise at selected times, and that some group in the enterprise has the responsibility to ensure that the plan will be followed. Since the life of the system may extend over many years through successive modifications, whereas there is a turnover of personnel on the average of every two years, adhering to long-range evolutionary plans requires discipline and organization. In the last analysis, only the top rung of management can prevent an evolutionary strategy from degenerating into haphazard change.

3.4 SUMMARY

The purpose of this chapter has been to describe the significant activities, alternatives, and problems which are characteristic of the requirements phase in the development of information systems. The purpose of the requirements phase is to determine why the system is needed, to identify the system users, and to define their information needs.

The chapter reviews the variety of ways in which the detection of a need for an information system takes place. An information system development activity may derive from problems in the operations of the current system, from problems brought about by advanced science and technology, or as a result of a long-range planning activity. Within these different contexts, the consequences for the developer were explored, depending upon how the problem of the user is initially defined, that is, whether the system to be built has no prototype, whether or not the current system has unidentified problems, or whether current system's problems are identified by the user.

Alternative development strategies from which the user, in consultation with the developer, must choose were explored. These alternatives include the number of development iterations, the relationship of the existing system to its replacement (the inductive strategy versus the deductive strategy), system evolution by accident, and the strategy of planned evolution. The advantages and disadvantages of each of these alternatives were reviewed.

No one strategy is presented as universally preferable. In general, given the prevalence of change, we have shown a bias for a deductive strategy and planned evolution with the planners focusing upon the operations of the enterprise as a whole. We take the position that, whatever strategy is selected, it should *not* be chosen *unilaterally* by either the user or the developer.

REFERENCES

1. D. P. Chrystal et al., "Allis-Chalmers Manufacturing Company: Applying Control Concepts to an Organization," *Total Systems*, A. D. Meacham and V. B. Thompson (eds.). Detroit: American Data Processing, 1962, p. 110.
2. H. F. Dickie, "Integrated Systems Planning at G.E.," *Management Control Systems*, D. G. Malcolm, A. J. Rowe, and L. F. McConnell (eds.). New York: Wiley, 1960, p. 139.
3. M. H. Grosz, "Standard Oil Company (New Jersey): Technical Development," *Management Organization and the Computer*, G. P. Shultz and T. L. Whisler (eds.). Glencoe, Ill.: The Free Press, 1960, pp. 179–192.
4. S. G. Atwood, "The Atwood Vacuum Machine Company," Ref. 3, pp. 227–241.
5. L. F. Vogt, "The International Shoe Company," Ref. 3, pp. 133–152.
6. *Ibid.*, p. 138.
7. See R. Boguslaw and R. H. Davis, *An Integrated Scientific and Engineering Manpower Information System: Some Problems and Recommendations*. Santa Monica, Calif.: System Development Corporation, SP-1385, October 18, 1963.
8. *Ibid.*, p. 3.
9. *Ibid.*, pp. 7–19.
10. Lockheed Aircraft Corporation, after spending $2,300,000 on its automatic data acquisition system, and with a staff of 600 programmers, 160 system

planners, and 1,350 data processors, has retained the Computer Sciences Corporation "to help it formulate new manufacturing and procurement status programs," according to Gilbert Burck, " 'On Line' in 'Real Time,' " *Fortune,* April 1964, p. 248.

11. I am indebted to James Cerone for the concept of "operational solutions," and for pointing out to me their importance in the definition of system requirements.

12. From a talk by Julius Bosen, Weather Bureau, Washington, D.C., presented at the Fifth Institute on Information Storage and Retrieval, American University, Washington, D.C., February 11-15, 1963.

13. B. Glass, "Information Crisis in Biology," *Bulletin of the Atomic Scientists,* October 1962, pp. 6–12.

14. *Ibid.,* p. 12.

15. M. M. Dubinin, "Exchanging Scientific Information," *Bulletin of the Atomic Scientists,* October 1962, pp. 13–15.

16. J. Diebold, "ADP—The Still-Sleeping Giant," *Harvard Business Review,* October 1964, pp. 60–65.

17. J. Diebold, *Automation: The Advent of the Automatic Factory.* Princeton, N.J.: Van Nostrand, 1952.

18. For a penetrating analysis of this type of "built-in conflict" in army programs, see Major General J. B. Medaris, "The Anatomy of Program Management," *Science, Technology, and Management,* F. E. Kast and J. E. Rosenzweig (eds.). New York: McGraw-Hill, 1963, pp. 112–128.

Chapter Four

The System Design Phase

J. Jaffe

4.1 INTRODUCTION

Scope of Chapter

This chapter assumes that the major objectives of an information system are to bring *relevant data* in *usable form* to the *right user* at the *right time* so that they will help in the solution of the user's problems. The purposes of this chapter are therefore:

- To show that there are system elements with specific attributes which the system designer must specify in order to reach the four objectives emphasized above.
- To show that the relationships among the system's elements are as important as the elements themselves and are amenable to description and analysis.
- To point out that certain recurrent problems require solution when developing a concept of system structure.
- To show how the management of a design project influences the course and actual content of the design.

The system design scheme to be presented has been found to be practical and viable. However, for purposes of clear exposition it has been altered and restricted, as it inevitably will be again if someone should attempt to apply it to a new design project. This is as it should be, particularly in light of what S. Beer (Ref. 34, p. 73) has said about systems:

"What after all is order, or something systematic? I suppose it is a pattern, and a pattern has no objective existence anyway. A pattern is a pattern because someone declares a concatenation of items to be meaningful or cohesive. The onus for detecting systems, and *for deciding how to describe them*, is very much on ourselves. I do not think we can adequately regard a system as a fact of nature, truths about which can be gradually revealed by patient analytical research. A viable system is something we detect and understand when it is mapped into our brains, and I suppose the inevitable result is that our brains themselves actually impose a structure on reality."

Organization of Chapter

This chapter will describe system design by breaking it down into a number of more or less discrete processes, logically related to one another in that the set of design data from one process becomes a prerequisite for the start or successful completion of another. These relationships are shown in Figure 4.1 as a flow diagram of the over-all system design process. The major portion of this chapter will discuss, in turn, each design process, shown as numbered blocks in the diagram.

Each arrow represents the transmission of certain classes of data about the system being designed or *about the design process itself*. These data are transmitted from one process to the next. They must have specific origins, destinations, and content. The design data that are created in one design process and then transmitted to another design process must be in such a form that they can be accepted without any ambiguity or uncertainty about their meaning.

Perhaps it might be well to state two of the things that this design representation is not. For one, it is not a complete representation of the design process; there is more to design than appears here. For another, it is not a complete time sequencing of the design processes. However, one may consider the representation to be roughly time-ordered, the processes starting earliest being at the top and continuing down to the bottom of the figure, where the processes represented are the end of some describable phase of the design effort. The numbering of the blocks also indicates a rough order. There are some processes that

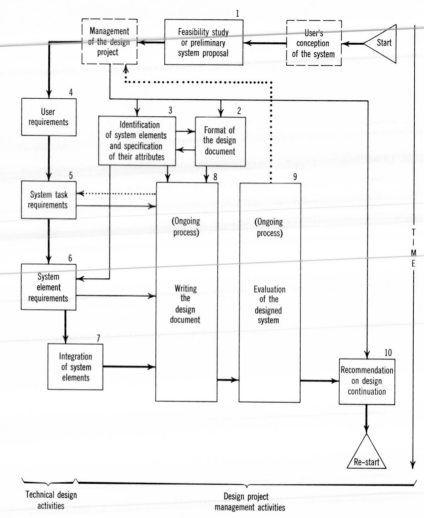

Figure 4.1 A representation of the system design process.

continue throughout a large part of the design effort; duration cannot be shown conveniently.*

---

* Although design is accomplished by people, one should not infer from the diagram that these processes are performed by separate groups of persons simply because they are shown in separate rectangles; they may or may not be, depending upon the nature of the project management, the complexity of the system to be designed, the time available for design, and other factors.

The primary flow of data through the various design processes is indicated by the bold solid lines and arrows. The bold dotted lines show the primary feedback loops. Many other loops probably exist, formally and informally.

The horizontal brackets at the bottom of the figure are intended to show which design processes are concerned primarily with the technical aspects of the system being designed and which are concerned primarily with the management of the design process. It should be noted that there is a difference between the design process itself and the larger "system" of which that process is but a part. In a sense one can say that there is a "system-design system." It consists not only of the management of the design processes and the technical work itself, but also of the entire environment within which the design effort proceeds.

The process blocks in the diagram are numbered for the sake of referencing; in Section 4.3 each topic will refer to one of the blocks. The ascending order of numbers is intended to represent the rough sequence in which these processes should be initiated in the design process. (The time dimension is also established vertically, as mentioned before, but the numbers of the rectangles help to resolve the position of processes represented on the same horizontal.) Unnumbered process blocks shown by broken lines are not discussed in this chapter.

4.2 A REVIEW OF SYSTEM DESIGN

Further Definition of an Information System

Before discussing the various discrete system design processes, it may be helpful to look more closely at what an information system is. By briefly pursuing a more precise definition the reader will be better able to assess the relevance of the material in this chapter.

The means whereby managers receive and transmit information are aggregates of people and equipment that

- are linked at least in part by two-way communications;
- are necessarily interdependent in operation;
- in operation are under the control of an organization of people whose actions are prescribed to some extent;
- characteristically receive, transform, and transmit data which are instrumental in accomplishing the purpose of the managers.

The purpose of the controlling set of people is to maintain or improve its state of being in relationship to some specified environment. This is accomplished by the manipulation of a set of resources capable of effecting changes in, or causing adaptation to, the environment. The data transformations are causally related to the real or contemplated actions taken in controlling the set of resources. The transformed data also convey meaning to the people engaged in controlling those resources within the given frame of reference of purposes and environment. If data are ambiguous a system will try to discover their meaning.

To illustrate this definition let us look at a very simple information system, one that controls a fleet of city taxicabs. The system consists of a number of taxicabs, drivers, a dispatcher, the taxicab company manager, and two communication systems—the public telephone connecting passengers and dispatcher and the two-way radio connecting cabs and dispatcher. (The passengers, the city streets, and the traffic conditions are parts of the task environment, not of the information system.) The dispatcher receives data about the locations and occupancy of the cabs and about the locations and destinations of potential passengers. He correlates these two sets of data, determines which cabs should be assigned to which waiting passengers, and issues orders to particular cabs to pick up passengers at certain places at certain times.

This example of an information system illustrates the definition fairly well:

Two-way communication exists between all elements of the system and between the system and the passengers (the latter being part of the task environment).

The parts of the system, that is, people and equipment, are interdependent in operation. If the dispatcher's tasks are not performed the fleet cannot be controlled. (This is not equivalent to saying that passenger service cannot be accomplished; each taxi can cruise the city streets and pick up passengers. In such a case, however, there is no information system controlling the cabs.)

All parts of the system are under the control of the dispatcher, who in turn is controlled by the system manager or owner. This is a vertically organized enterprise.

The receipt and transmission of data are concerned with the location and status of cabs and passengers. The transformation of data is less evident. The dispatcher has to transform the verbal data about cab and passenger locations into geographical references and plot them on a map. Then, other things being equal, the dispatcher has to obtain from those data the information as to which taxi or taxis are spatially or temporally closest to the waiting passenger(s). Next he has to consider either some explicit criteria for taxi selection or make some implicit judgment in order to assign taxi(s) to passenger(s).

One of the major objectives of the owner of the system is to make money. He may want to do this by increasing the efficiency of the service. Or he may want to make money by expanding the service so as to accommodate more passengers, a measure which, while not necessarily improving efficiency, may increase the dollar volume of the enterprise. Each one of these subobjectives provides a frame of reference for the system designer that will determine the data transformation needed by the dispatcher to assign cabs on a rational rather than on a random basis. Some criteria, derived from one or more of the various objectives of the system owner, may lead the dispatcher to assign cabs so as to minimize passenger waiting time. Some may lead him to reduce the total mileage of the fleet spent on pickup. Other criteria may lead him to doubling-up on passengers. Implementation of each of these courses of action would be dependent not only upon the receipt of certain classes of data by the system but also upon their arithmetic and cartographic manipulation so as to make them more meaningful to the dispatcher. The data and the criteria for their employment assume their meaning in terms of their relevance to the accomplishment of the stated system objectives.

This is not to say that all data and criteria need enter the system with established relevance and meaning. Some data may really be ambiguous, but because of circumstances surrounding their origination they are processed further in order to determine their possible relevance. For instance, the dispatcher may receive a report from one of the drivers concerning an accident on a major traffic artery. While this is not a completely meaningless datum, neither is it immediately relevant. The dispatcher must either passively wait for other reports to associate with the first one, or actively seek additional data, such as whether one of his cabs was involved or how long traffic will be tied up.

At this point the reader may wonder whether this is a good illustration. The report of a traffic accident seems like such an obviously meaningful datum for the system. The point is that the first time, or first few times, an event of this type was reported its relevance was not clear, and yet it was apparently of such a nature as to warrant its retention by the system. If the system designer was experienced enough to anticipate the occurrence and utility of such reports, the system would have been designed to make specific provisions for them. However, such data are always arising in a system, and indeed *the occurrence of ambiguous or new data is one of the major reasons for the employment of responsible and skilled people as operators and users of information systems.*

Hopefully two points of ambiguity about the initial definition of an information system should have become clearer with a critical examination of the example.

First, the central element of the definition would seem to be the interdependence of parts in operation in fulfillment of the objectives of the system. As stated before, although cabs can continue to operate without two-way communications, there would then be no information system. A senior United States Air Force general was reported to have said that without his telephone the only thing he commanded was his desk.

Second, some thought about the role of people in relationship to the operation of the system reveals that there are two types. One role, exemplified by the taxicab dispatcher, is that of an operator. This is a person who, on a routine and workaday basis, is an integral part of the operation of the system. By our earlier criterion, if all of the system operators were absent, there would no longer be a working information system. In their job of reporting their positions and other status data into the dispatcher, the drivers are therefore operators. This definition of the role of people as operators *within* the system comes closest to the common concept of a man-machine system.

The other role is typified by the system owner or manager. In this case the person is not an operator of the system but somebody who uses the total system or a substantial part of it to help him accomplish some stated objectives outside the capability of the system to accomplish by itself. In other terms, the person who fills such a role uses the system as an instrument, whereas the operators are themselves instruments of the system of which they are a part. But the owner or manager on occasion does interact directly with the system. He gives data to it in the form of plans, strategies, criteria, and the like. He also may take data from the system in the form of performance records to be used for evaluation. The system designer and the system owner must keep these two roles conceptually clear because the data and mechanisms needed to support one role usually are not applicable to the other. The taxicab system owner usually does not care about the location of his cabs from moment to moment, nor does he use most of the other data that the system transmits to the dispatcher. In addition to the profit and loss tally sheet, the owner might want data about the percentage of time that cabs are out for their repair or about peak passenger call times. Although one person may, at different times or in rapid sequence, fill the roles of both owner and operator, the two sets of needs are quite different and are determined by the nature of the roles rather than by the coincidence of physical identity.

The major portion of this chapter is intended to show how the various requirements of an information system and the mechanisms that are the parts of the system can be deduced and specified in a fashion that will help the users to achieve their objectives. In the preceding definition of an information system, what we have done is to specify some of the general mechanisms and actions that are always required by a proper design, namely, communications, data transformations, organizational control, and interdependent parts and actions. Furthermore, by becoming aware of the two roles (user and operator) which people may assume in their interactions with other parts of the system, the system designer can begin to sort data and action requirements according to their application (in reaching user objectives) as well as the mechanisms by which data are handled and the routes or channels which they travel.

An Approach to Design: the Mapping of System Tasks

The "mapping" of a system that Beer (Ref. 34) talks about is accomplished by creating a sequence of means-end relationships which link the more abstract objectives of the system user to successively more concrete and specific goals. This takes place by discrete steps (the number of steps may not be the same for all parts of the system). During the development of this sequence of means-end relationships, the design statements begin to sound like descriptions of discrete "tasks" performed by the system elements; an example for the taxi system might be plotting on a map the location of waiting passengers in order to determine which two can be picked up by the same cab without its deviating from a straight line.

A task is composed of a set of actions performed by people (physically or intellectually) and/or by machines in order to reach specified objectives. To control a fleet of taxi cabs is an objective (a means for making money), but to plot the location of waiting passengers on a map is a task that is a step or series of discrete actions in the accomplishment of that objective. Tasks are in large part structured by the nature of the task environment. In the taxicab example, the manner in which the dispatcher plots the location of waiting passengers is in part determined by the quantity of geographical details, the precision required, the location of landmarks, and the scale of the map.

It is characteristic of objectives, on the other hand, that they are structured in large part by the values and judgment of men. A further distinction between objectives and tasks lies in the fact that objectives (of the user) vary, depending upon the nature of the environment, the level of the organization, and the characteristics of the individual user; objectives also are altered during the operation of an information system. The tasks, which are relatively concrete means, are performed in a less changeable fashion.

A major job of the designer, then, is to get the user to recognize the relationship between his objectives and the task mechanisms for accomplishing them. In order to do this system mapping, not only must the means-end sequences be defined but also the reasons for the existence of each step in the sequence and the explanations of how each particular means achieves each end must be stated. We will call this process *rational analysis*.

The first general step in rational analysis is the preliminary analysis of the user's requirements in terms of the objectives he wishes to accomplish. The second step is the decomposition of the objectives into subobjectives, at one or more levels, until the level of tasks has been reached. The third step is the successive refinement of tasks to the point where the designer can infer the data inputs, outputs, and processing the system will require.

When phrased in this way, it should become clear that the early steps in system design are the hard ones and that we do not yet have ready-made analytic tools for the job. There is little practical point in using precision tools when faced with system task requirements that are imprecisely defined. One would not think, for instance, of dissecting a whole elephant with a microtome. Therefore, in the section that follows, emphasis is placed on the process of making system task requirements more and more explicit. On the one hand, the requirements will be related to the ways in which they will attain the system objectives; on the other hand, their relationship to the hardware, software, and people that will perform the actions will be defined.

In the next section, comprising the bulk of this chapter, each design process shown in Figure 4.1 will be discussed in its turn, in accordance with the block number in the figure. The intent will be to identify and define the various design processes that contribute to the progress of system mapping and to the further explication of requirements and system actions.

4.3   THE DESIGN PROCESS

Block 1.   Feasibility Study or Preliminary System Proposal

This is the first numbered block in Figure 4.1 and is the first explicit part of the entire design process. There are other ways of starting the system design process, some better and some poorer. A document that requests the initiation of a study makes a very good start. However, such a document should state the area under consideration and limit it in time, space, function, and structure. Alternatively, it should indicate in what areas no limits are contemplated. Frequently what is called for by this document is a feasibility study from which the system user can extract enough factual information to enable him to decide whether or not to continue with further design.

There is a myth connected with feasibility studies. This myth has very attractive features, for example, that one can specify through a feasibility study (1) a set of alternative design concepts; (2) the approximate length of time required to develop each concept; (3) the cost of executing each concept; and (4) the amount of system growth each concept would allow. Although believers in this myth admit that an almost complete set of alternative designs would have to be produced in order to yield the four specifications above, they reckon without the harsh world of reality that rarely, if ever, allows them more than a fraction of the amount of time and/or resources required for fulfillment.

What then should a feasibility study be? It should be a set of general statements that in effect present the opinion of the investigator about whether anything useful can be accomplished by further work. A good study document can be expected to point to the system under consideration and indicate the incremental utility of the next few steps toward a more definitive statement. It can indicate the general types of services the user expects to obtain from his system: for instance, whether he wants scientific computation, inventory control, large data storage, rapid access to information, sophisticated displays, or various combinations of these and other possible services. Such preliminary statements will do much to indicate the future course and cost of a system.

The situation in which there is no such feasibility document at all to start a major design project hopefully is rare. The reader might ponder for a moment the results of starting a design project without presenting statements of purpose, limitations, and interfaces relating subsystems to the system as a whole.

The results of a feasibility study provide the first statement of technical and managerial guidance to be used in making plans for subsequent design work. Where a previous feasibility study does not exist (produced and hoarded perhaps by a different agency), the design process is started by a preliminary system proposal. Either the proposal presents approximately the same content as the feasibility study and assumes that the accomplishment of a design is feasible, or it must lead to the undertaking of such a feasibility study. Without one or the other further design work cannot proceed rationally.

Block 2. Format of the Design Document

Usually the results of the design effort are presented to the user in the form of a document containing prose, block diagrams, tables, mathematical equations, and other modes of presentation. The format of this document must be specified in advance for the following reasons.

First, as we have already indicated, the substantive content of the design material is likely to be new when it does not deal with equipment specifications. We do not know the names of the design parameters (a characteristic element); this causes errors of omission. There is a tendency to use ambiguous terminology; this causes errors of commission. It is very easy to make such errors when there is no conceptual design schema to which to refer.

Second, when so much of what is designed is conceptual in nature, communication between the designer and the client poses a problem. The designer should show his customer the derivation of the multiple sets of relationships that will comprise his system, in a form that leaves as little room for individual interpretation as possible. From such a form, the reasonably knowledgeable reader should be able to trace the logic which led the designer to specify certain requirements, whether for data, organizations, system procedures, or hardware.

The format of the design itself (which is going to be a document) requires an analysis before it is determined. The first pieces of information needed to select an appropriate format are the uses to which the design is to be put. For instance, if the design is only preliminary, as a feasibility study would be, a rather simple narrative form may be adequate. If the design is to be used as a basis for specifying equipment characteristics, it has to be adequately partitioned so that statements relating to a particular piece of equipment can be associated with one another. Furthermore, the statements that contain the specifications must be couched in terms familiar to the equipment designer. If the design is going to an architect, it might be presented in the form of a floor plan and elevation or a set of numerical requirements, for example, to house a certain number of people, with a certain square footage per person, a specified number of operating areas, and so on. If the design will be used by a personnel manager, it must state the skill levels and specialties of the people needed to man the system.

The two things that all formats should have in common is an agreement on vocabulary between the designer and the receiver of the design, and the rationale whereby the design was worked out. In all cases the designer, before he starts his work, must obtain from his user or users a clear statement of the intended application of the design and an agreement in regard to the format, a common working vocabulary of terms, concepts, measures, or simply standards and conventions.

The design format should be specified precisely and agreed upon by designer and client before continuing. A clear format will significantly reduce the communication problem at all stages, from obtaining design concurrence through implementation to system evaluation. To ignore this step is to risk subsequent misunderstandings among users, managers, and designers.

Block 3. Identification of System Elements and Specification of Their Attributes

What are the system elements to be specified? In designing a new radio, for instance, reference can be made to a number of books that specify standard elements, such as speaker, tuner, and amplifier. Each element is further described by a number of *attributes* (inherent characteristics). The speaker must reproduce a certain range of "frequencies" and output each frequency at a certain sound level. The specification of elements and their attributes lies at the heart of any design process and is perhaps the logical starting point for it.

Attributes are the essential dimensions used to describe the system elements so that, if the attributes were missing, the elements would not accomplish their functions. When the system elements and their attributes are described early in the design phase, the designer and the user have a concrete base from which they can determine whether the services desired from the system are going to be provided.

The elements or subsystems of an information-processing system that are listed below are convenient for analysis; other people may name elements differently, but a particular system concept will not change substantially as a result of nomenclature. The system elements are as follows:

- Data.
- Personnel.
- Display.
- Equipment (that is, input, output, transmission, logical and arithmetic processing, and storage).
- Learning.
- Retrieval.
- Programming.

Each element listed possesses a set of attributes that also have to be described still more concretely. Listed below and discussed briefly are the attributes of each of the seven system elements just mentioned. Although the list may not be complete, it is, hopefully, adequate as a "starter set."

Data Element. In a very real sense a system user's need for information can be satisfied only by acquiring and transforming data. Providing the information is the essential function of an information system. After the acquisition and transformation of data by the system, the data are further transformed into information by the user when he exercises judgment and formulates actions that will help to accomplish his objectives.

Actually, an information system may encompass several parts, people, or machines, each of which acquires and transforms data. Some of these parts function in series and some in parallel. Whatever way they function, and no matter how simple or complex the system may be, data ultimately are always transformed into information about one or more of the following states:

- The environment with which the system and its users are concerned.
- The resources that the user controls.
- The information-processing system itself.

- Commands to the system.
- Commands to the user's resources.*

The attributes of the data elements are as follows.

RELEVANCE. There must be a rationale which makes explicit the relationship between each class of data and the system task that requires it.

NOMENCLATURE. The names of the classes of data, the units used, and the modifiers or qualifiers must all be expressed in a language common to the users and designers of the system. There must be no ambiguity in terms.

GRAIN. Attention must be paid also to the degree of fineness of the data, that is, the denotation of the most specific case in each class and each higher level of aggregation. For example, if the class of data is weapons, one must specify whether this has to be subdivided into manned aircraft and missiles and these in turn broken down into their constituent types, B-52G and so on. In complex systems, different system parts may require different levels of aggregation.

SOURCES. For each class of data the place from which it originates must be specified. Some data, as previously mentioned, result from the cognitive process of the system users; in such a case a person or organization must be designated as the source.

DESTINATIONS. All data must be characterized in a system by destinations: the potential users may be either men or machines. Most often data will have a number of destinations in the form of intermediate processing points or stations.

LOGICAL RELATIONSHIP. Some data in the system may be causally related to other data, some may be covariant, and some may be independent. This state of affairs frequently is seen in data generated by physical events, the status of an aircraft, for instance. The datum that an aircraft is capable of taking off is derived from a whole pyramid of other data reflecting such things as the state of the weather, the condition of the runway, the flight characteristics and physical readiness of

---

* For analytic purposes the distinction between data and instructions must be constantly borne in mind. The data are what the user eventually transforms into information. Instructions are messages to the system or to user resources that initiate or terminate actions in specified ways. This is the same distinction that is applied to computer data, which must always be either data or instructions.

the aircraft itself, and a ready pilot. These relationships must be specified so that when the data are processed the proper sets can be established. This is extremely important in computer programming, where failure to associate proper items can require extensive reprogramming.

PROCESSING. Data entering an information system may

- be examined logically (e.g., sorted or examined for validity);
- be entered into a mathematical calculation (e.g., summed or used as a value in an equation);
- pass through the system essentially unchanged.

It must be determined whether each class of data will be either saved or destroyed, or whether a capability will have to be built into the system to give a person these two options. Each class of data in the system will require one or more of the three types of processing. Perhaps the largest part of the system design job is specifying the data-processing requirements.

The last statement would be true if we took into consideration only the processing of data required by the system user in pursuit of his objectives. When we add the processing of instructions (for example, retrieving data from intermediate storage, without which they could not be processed), the job becomes large indeed.

Processing, then, basically involves the mathematical and/or logical statement of how each class of data will be transformed and used by the next part of the system. In an automated information system, the final processing of some sets of data takes place within a piece of equipment and is never apprehended directly by a person. The final processing for other data produces displays, a part of an information system which will be discussed shortly.

There are other attributes of data, such as their form and timeliness, but these are really more closely related to the attributes of displays. It is necessary to remember the existence of the interaction between data form and timeliness, on the one hand, and displays and communications, on the other; just such interactions require attention in the system elements integration effort. Data form and timeliness partially determine display equipment characteristics and communications load. The reverse is also true.

Personnel Element. Various concepts of a personnel subsystem are prevalent today. Generally they include the attributes of the people who will operate a particular system.

In an information system people not only use the outputs of the system but also are components of the system. It is helpful to distinguish again between these two cases. In one situation people monitor and use information produced by the system but do not serve as an information input source (except very indirectly through policy and procedures) for the rest of the internal system. In the other situation people not only monitor and use the information but *do* inject instructions into the system in the form of computer requests; these are instructions to which the system must respond. The latter case still requires the precise specification of the attributes of the people and their actions that is customary in the former. There is a shift of emphasis, however, from equipment operation to data organization and retrieval. This is characteristic of information systems that require more complex man-machine interactions. These interactions are more flexibly structured than in the situation where men are more passive receivers of data from noncomputing machines that have a relatively limited repertoire of response. In both cases, however, the following are attributes of the personnel subsystem.

DISTRIBUTION OF RESPONSIBILITY. Primarily included in this attribute is the determination of the various "seats" of decision-making prerogatives. This means the specification of the location, skill, and number of people or groups of people who have the responsibility and authority for taking all of the various types of actions available to the system users. *The authority, the responsibility, and the knowledge should reside in the same place.* Furthermore, there must be recognition of the fact that *too high a degree of specification and formalization will decrease the ability of the system users to structure and restructure their organizations and actions* to meet changing conditions. This attribute is closely related to the specific characteristics of the physical communication network, the latter being in part derived from the former. Organizational communication channels include not only who talks to whom but also how the hierarchical and lateral power relationships are structured. It includes who gives orders to whom, who can make requests of whom, and who passes information to whom.

OPERATING PROCEDURES. The human actions (as well as equipment and computer program actions) and the methods for accomplishing them are an inherent part of any information system. The human actions are as follows: monitor, compare, assess, predict, decide, command, inform, request, and comply. These are the things people do in information systems. The particular applications of these actions, plus the ways in which they are accomplished, form the operating procedures. They range from the specification of the format of any communication to the operation of equipment. They also include rules, regulations, situation descriptions, and criteria that guide people in taking actions. Operating procedures play such a major role in information systems that Chapter 7 is devoted to them.

EXTRA-ORGANIZATIONAL ACTIONS. The personnel in a system have two other types of activities in which to engage besides those directly connected with the operation of the system. They have to deal with people and agencies external to the particular system with which they are involved, sometimes on tasks not closely related to system tasks. They also need to be concerned with the maintenance of the human organization; this is particularly true of supervisors. By knowing of these extra-organizational activities, the system designer should be able to keep from overloading the human operator. Too frequently the designer assumes that the only thing people have to do is to operate the system.

Display Element. Although each part of an information system has an output, the term "display," as used here, refers to any presentation of data to people by means of equipment. Displays form the major interface between the user and his system. Because displays are considered to be both data and equipment, they must possess the same attributes that both of these elements possess. In addition, displays possess the following attributes.

DEGREE OF AGGREGATION. An aggregation is defined as a collection of like things. In an information system, the meaning is extended to include collections of data items at the same level of specificity. For instance, in presenting the results of a population census, a tabular display could show just total population (one cell), population by state (fifty cells), or population by congressional district (over 437 cells). This attribute is the one that partly reflects the distinction between command systems and control systems. As we said earlier in the chapter, the level of summarization and specificity of the displayed information is dependent in part upon the nature of the system. A command system for higher echelons generally requires more summary and less specific data than a control system; an executive or commander finds it difficult to deal with a large number of discrete events and items. The data have to be aggregated or summarized in some way even though the final aggregation or summary may in itself be considered a single item in another whole set of related items.

CODING. This attribute of displays is well known to the human engineer. He is concerned with the particular form into which the data are placed to present a signal to a human being. When the visual modality is used, data are frequently coded in graphic or pictorial form (maps). The other end of the dimension is coding which essentially is straight English narrative. Tabular formats probably are somewhere between the two extremes.

A great deal has been written about coding. In information systems, however, no great body of knowledge about it has been built up. System users and designers alike feel that for the performance of certain tasks particular data formats are more suitable than others. On first examination it would seem obvious that more information can be obtained from data coded in one form than in another, but it is very hard to demonstrate this except by using a specific example. For instance, in presenting data about the geographical relationships between two cities, we immediately think of using a political map. If we are interested in the terrain between the two cities, however, we might prefer a topographic map. On the other hand, if the datum needed is the distance between the two cities, a simple numerical format would be more appropriate and potentially more accurate. The presentation of distances between a set of cities could be accomplished by a simple numerical table. Suppose, however, that some data are needed in regard to the relationship among three or more cities. We might wish to know whether, in following a great circle route from city A to city B, we would pass through city C. This bit of information is very easily obtained from a globe or from an appropriate two-dimensional projection. It can also be obtained through mathematical formulations but probably less efficiently unless the data are going to be fed back into a machine computation.

Another example that occurs frequently in information systems is furnished by the need for predicting the status of aggregated events such as inventory items. In some cases it is traditional to present the information in the form of a frequency polygon or smoothed line graph. The latter makes it relatively easy for the user to infer from an extrapolation of the curve what the status will be at some future time. This item of information can likewise be presented quite readily in numerical form derived from an appropriate mathematical equation. If the information needed is the rate of growth or decay, a smoothed line graph gives an immediate indication, particularly in the case of a complex growth such as negative or positive acceleration. If, however, the function is a straight line, one might obtain a more precise indication of the rate by presenting the slope of the line in numerical form.

The examples just presented point out the need for very close examination of the information and decision-making requirements of the system user. This is important not only from the point of view of the people coding the data for most effective decision making, but also from that of the designers of computer programs and display equipment, the characteristics of which will be partly determined by the display requirements.

Let us go back for a moment to the statement, made earlier in the chapter, that command systems usually require more summarized data than do control systems. This statement should not be interpreted to mean that there is a need for highly coded data. In fact, while executives and commanders usually deal with highly aggregated data, there need be neither a high degree of coding nor preliminary interpretation or filtering by other agencies, human or otherwise. As a matter of fact, observational evidence indicates that in many problem situations decision makers should have access to essentially unfiltered, although perhaps aggregated, data.* Insofar as possible these data enable decision makers to draw their own mental picture of the state of their resources and environment. The so-called "big picture" is too frequently interpreted by the system designer to mean that the executive should be supplied with highly coded and/or highly summarized data. From these the decision maker well may find it difficult to infer the nature of the objective state because it has been filtered in such a fashion as to reflect the thoughts of other people through whom the data have passed, these thoughts now forming an indistinguishable part of the data.

TIMELINESS. This is a major attribute of many elements of a system. Timeliness may be set by the nature of the events in the physical world which occur or reoccur at certain times and have certain durations. For instance, if event A takes ten minutes to occur and cycles continuously, data about event A more than ten minutes old are not timely, although they may be useful as history.

Another major consideration, along with timeliness, concerns the degree or kind of significant change. Event A may occur or reoccur every ten minutes but may not result in a change of status, or it may result in a change that is insignificant in terms of some criterion. Some

---

* Aggregating data entails a certain amount of error which can be considered filtering. Rounding errors are one example.

thought will reveal the import of this subject in determining the frequency with which facts about the occurrence of events should be reported into the system and the criteria whereby cues for their reporting are established. "Reporting by exception," for instance, reduces the number of reports; reports are generated only when a criterion range of values is exceeded, or at infrequent periods to ensure the recipient that the reporting apparatus is still working.

The other aspect of timeliness has to do with the needs of the user rather than the nature of real world events. Information needs must be analyzed in terms of the times at which the decision maker wants the data, the time he can afford to wait for them if they are not already present, and the cues whereby the needs for timely data are recognized.

INITIATION OR ACCESS. After we have specified the system task requirements, the data, the methods for inputting data to the system, and the processing of data, we generally tend to forget that the data will not just automatically be displayed. A mechanism must be provided for triggering the action of a part of a system to produce displays. The mechanism may be an executive computer program that governs the preparation of data for display and contains a set of instructions which enable it to recognize the appropriate moment to begin the production. This may be an internal clock, if the display initiation is completely predictable and cyclic, or it may be the recognition of a cueing event.

Another initiation mechanism may be a human operator, who then must be provided with a communication channel for cueing the display-producing part of the system. In a computer-based information system the generic term for this mechanism is a *display request device*, which may be structurally identical to various system input devices.

TRANSDUCTION. We have borrowed an engineering term here to indicate that transduction is an interface between user needs and hardware requirements. The specification of this attribute is done in the naming of the type of mechanism (lantern slide, cathode ray tube, computer line printer, etc.) for converting data contained in a form not recognizable by human beings into one which is. This specification is dependent not only upon the nature of the rest of the structural system but also upon the types of formats needed. For instance, it is very difficult to produce line graphs on a printer. Usually, however, there is a wide choice of alternative transduction mechanisms. The selection is frequently made on the basis of economic and structural engineering factors, such as the degree of optical resolution required, the number of people who have to view the display simultaneously, or the update speed.

CORRECTNESS. This is another highly important attribute from the point of view of the decision maker, whose performance is degraded by the presence of incomplete or incorrect data that are not known to be faulty. Simulation research has shown that major decrements in decision-making effectiveness are due to uncertainty. Uncertainty can mean not being sure of the true nature of the objective situation. It can also mean not knowing the completeness and correctness of the data with which one has to deal. The system designer should be sure to provide mechanisms which indicate whether there are significant variations in either of these two attributes of displayed data.

Equipment Elements. The equipment element is composed of engineered units, the physical devices through which all data flow. When we are dealing with hardware design, it is convenient to regard the element as two major units, the computer unit and the communication unit. The digital computer is perhaps the more complex and, in a very real sense, is a complete system itself, one which inputs, stores, processes, outputs, and transmits data. However, we will not discuss the attributes of a computer as an item of equipment since we expediently claim that the information system customarily would employ a general-purpose one which can do almost any kind of logical and arithmetic processing typical of the class.*

For the analysis in this chapter we will consider only the communication unit. This unit includes all the hardware for sensing, inputting, outputting, and actually transmitting data through the system as a whole. The attributes of the equipment elements are as follows.

ADEQUATE STIMULUS. An adequate stimulus will cause an event to be sensed or an impulse to be initiated and propagated. The hardware has to be capable of detecting the events of interest to the system.

STIMULUS PRODUCTION. Although this attribute may be part of the previous one, special consideration should be given to whether the adequate stimulus is provided by a human being or by an automatic device such as a radar.

---

* One might want to remember, though, that computers do vary significantly in regard to such attributes as speed of basic operations, size of central memory, and parallel input, output, and/or computation processing.

DATA FORM AND TRANSDUCTION AGENT. In this case we are interested in the carrier of the data. It is a series of electrical pulses varying in frequency, amplitude, or other physical form. We are also interested in the mechanisms whereby its form is converted and reconverted throughout the physical system from origination to destination. Displays are a subset of specific transducers. So also are input devices by which the system users introduce data into the system.

CAPACITIES. Here must be specified the rate or rates, under varying environmental conditions, with which data can be transmitted; capacities are expressed in units of data per unit time. Not only are they expressed for various environmental conditions but also for peak and steady situations and for both individual equipment units and aggregates of like units. Capacities are also characterized in terms of *duration* of either peak or steady performances without degradation, and in terms of reaction time from stimulus onset to system response.

COMPATIBILITY. This attribute must be considered in an engineering and human engineering sense and also in terms particularly applicable to information systems.*

RELIABILITY. This is a standard attribute of equipment specified in most engineering plans. Reliability is a measure of the extent to which a piece of equipment or a system will respond to the same set of inputs in the same manner over a number of occurrences of these inputs. Reliability of data is a particular problem for information systems because of the number and complexity of transformations to which they are subjected.

ADAPTABILITY. This attribute is poorly defined at present but deals with such things as increasing capacity by additions of more of the same components or the insertion of new components without seriously interrupting the system operations and without performing a major redesign of any substantial part of the system.

DISCRIMINATION. What is the minimum signal/noise ratio both from a signal transmission point of view and from a human engineering point of view?

---

* In an information system compatibility can be defined as being able to accept the inputs from, and give outputs to, other components at a rate adequate to prevent queues or loss of data. When the output rate of one unit is much faster than the rate at which the next unit can accept the data, buffering is required to keep the data from being lost.

FAITHFULNESS. This is the specification of the ability and characteristics of equipment components, particularly sensing and receiving elements, which enable them to minimize (1) the acceptance of something as a signal when indeed it is not a signal, (2) the rejection of something as not being a signal when in fact it is a signal.

GEOGRAPHICAL DISTRIBUTION AND NUMBER. These attributes are shown by an actual map or schematic drawing of the arrangement of the major equipment units.

Learning Element. This item is included as an element in order to stimulate some thought about the need to design into the system provisions for adaptation in response to experience and new user requirements. Perhaps to call this a system element is not in accordance with the criteria established earlier for such a designation, but certainly various parts of a system can be made to function in such a way as to promote learning. Therefore, this discussion will be limited to a general definition of parts rather than an enumeration of attributes. A learning element can consist of any one or all of the following three parts.

OPERATIONAL EVALUATION AND RECORDING. It is desirable, if not almost inevitable, that the users of a system themselves evaluate its operations. They do this sometimes formally, sometimes informally. Their purpose may be to determine how much they can rely on the system or to institute changes in the system to increase its effectiveness.

When we say that operational evaluation is conducted informally, we mean that it is conducted essentially without the aid of the system itself. The other alternative is to utilize the system to help to conduct the evaluation as well as to act in its usual operational capacity, as it would do in any case. For example, one of the minimum things a system could do to help in its own evaluation would be to record the occurrence of its own internal events.

If the system is going to be used in evaluation, the designer must consider the tasks associated with recording and evaluation on the same level as any other system task and must design the mechanisms for their accomplishment. These include, in computer-based information systems, additional data storage requirements, procedures for conducting both operational and evaluation programs during the same period, the selection of tasks to be observed in action, and eventually the determination of evaluative criteria.

TRAINING. Most of the statements that have been made for operational evaluation apply also to training. In addition, provisions must be made early in the design process for the inclusion of equipment and procedures for processing simulation data and for the observation of system exercises by human beings as well as recording programs.

SYSTEM ADAPTATION. If the system is to be modified as a result of knowledge gained through training and operational evaluation, attributes have to be built into the system which will enable it to be changed. This holds true particularly of computer programs, personnel organization, and equipment capacities.

Retrieval Element. Retrieval is a critical element of an information system, one that is responsible for organizing and obtaining access to sets of data (specified earlier in the design phases) from large and complex files contained in computer storage. Ordinarily the retrieval element would be considered just another part of the programming element.*

Unfortunately, because space is limited, we cannot discuss retrieval here at any length, nor is it clear what all the attributes of this element are. Nevertheless, common sense dictates that at least the following attributes would have to be specified:

- A syntax for man-machine communication.
- An indexing scheme so that a human operator can readily perceive the structure and contents of the system data (or data base).
- All of the attributes of the display element and of the input and output parts of the hardware element.

Programming Element. Chapter 5 deals with the design of computer programs. All that is needed here is a reminder that there are various types of computer programs to be considered in system design: data manipulation programs (that is, aggregating reports of events), input and output programs, utility programs (for example, preparing tapes, punching cards), executive programs—that is, programs which control other programs, and, finally, retrieval programs as distinct from fixed output programs.

---

* However, it is designated as an entity here in order to emphasize an importance derived from the following considerations. First, a retrieval element can be distinguished from the relatively simple computer output process by the complexity of its interactions with a human operator. Second, it can be composed of a discrete set of programs, a unique language for man-machine communication and even special-purpose hardware, for example, to mediate requests from the human operator to the program system.

This section on system elements and their attributes has been long because the importance of the topic warrants emphasis. Good system design requires explicit definition of each element and the identification of its attributes not only in order to determine whether the proposed design will be functional but also to provide a concrete and univocal basis for more precise, subsequent specification.

It may be that all of the attributes listed here are not relevant to a particular system or that still others have been omitted inadvertently. Even so, the major point will not be lost, hopefully, that the system designer is responsible for their complete explication. Rationally he cannot otherwise proceed with his design. Of course, unfortunately in some instances the designer does proceed with the attributes of the various elements only implied, a course that leads the user to various misunderstandings about system capabilities.

In any event, after the attributes are identified, explicitly or implicitly, the designer can then go on to specify the characteristics and values of the mechanisms (in the general sense) that are going to accomplish the functions of each element. As shown in Figure 4.1, these specific mechanisms and values of each element, block 6, are also determined by inputs from block 5, the unique requirements to process the data in satisfaction of the system task requirements. However, we must first discuss how the system task requirements are derived from the general requirements of the user.

Block 4. User Requirements

The design of information systems starts with the specification of the user's requirements and continues with an explanation of how the proposed system will meet them. Since this is initially a question of management's interpretation, this process is shown to stem directly from the management process.* Management must study the user's initial perception of the system and attempt to *forecast* the objectives that the system can help to accomplish when it becomes operational. The reason that this process stems directly from the management process block is that only management has access to the relevant data; once these data have furnished guides and limits to the technical de-

---

* It is difficult to define here the level of management that should be involved; the level will vary partly as a function of the magnitude of the project. Management will have to be involved, however, because such personnel will present and interpret the design to the user.

sign effort, only management can obtain the user's concurrence in the statements of boundaries and limits. Otherwise, as many of us have painfully discovered, the various costs of the end product will exceed the resources of the user.

Statements about the general objectives of the user should be phrased so that the designer can infer the kinds of tasks the system must perform in order to accomplish these objectives. Sometimes, of course, the tasks to be performed are defined as the objectives. This should not be permitted. Objectives are goals, and tasks are ways of reaching goals. Another way of expressing the same idea is to say that objectives are specified by asking "why" and tasks by asking "how." Information systems can have only three general objectives:[*]

- To communicate.
- To process data.
- To control environment and resources.

It may help if we consider that the last objective implies both of the preceding ones. Thus, a control objective implies the need for data processing and communication. Perhaps this sequential relationship is derived on the basis that when the last objective is chosen the others become means to the end.

Frequently some user objectives are so specific that they become a direct part of the system task requirements. Actually, then, these are not objectives in our use of the term; but it is well to remember that, if the user states that one "objective" is to use only a Burroughs adding machine for any data processing, this is a design constraint and had better show up in the specifications. If the designer forgets to include it, he looks foolish for having constrained the design without apparent reason. Although such constraints help to limit the design, they must not be mistaken for objectives.

The user's resources in terms of time, money, and adaptability will also constrain the design. Adaptability is considered in the sense of the degree of radical departures from current systems that the user will allow in the development of novel concepts and the procurement of new items. However, constraints can be very helpful to the designer since they provide limits against which to evaluate the acceptability of the design.

---

[*] Pursuing the "why" of a system ultimately leads to teleology. Since the focus in this book is on design of information systems and not on philosophy, let us stop at the present level.

One can also consider as a part of the user's resources willingness and ability to furnish data about his plans and operations as well as operationally experienced personnel to aid in the design effort. These become important factors because of the designer's needs to understand the user's operational objectives both in and of themselves and within the larger context of the user's general procedures and philosophy.

If the design process is to be iterative, the statement of the user's requirements, that is, objectives and resources, becomes a primary input to the decision on design continuation, which is described in block 10. It may well be that the preliminary iteration of the design indicates the need for a more extensive system than was originally considered. If the user's resources cannot support such enlargement, then the next design iteration will have to reduce system scope or sophistication. Or it may be that the increment in utility that the system would contribute to the user is proportionally small in comparison to the resources allocated. In any event, these problems had best be brought to light before implementation is begun.

Block 5. System Task Requirements

In determining the system task requirements the system designer must ask and answer the following questions:

- What are the tasks?
- Why is each task performed? (Means—end; higher-order means —higher-order end.)
- Where is each task performed, and where are the resources which are manipulated?
- By whom or what is each task performed?
- With what is each task performed? (Data, computational routines, formulas, etc.)
- When is each task performed, that is, under what conditions, at what times? In short, what happens to initiate, continue, terminate, or reiterate the task performance?
- How is each task performed? (This is a fitting together of the previous material.)

Systems are designed rationally when these seven questions are answered. The first four questions must be emphasized at the earlier stages of determining the task requirements. Each system task must be related to the supra-ordinate task. In short, *the relationship between lower-order tasks and the higher-order* ones from which they are derived *must be made explicit.* Many times this is not at all easy to do because of logical complexities, vagueness of statements, or implications potentially undesirable from either the designer's or the user's point of view.

There is also a need for trying to establish conceptually broad statements of system tasks so as to make the job of subsequent analysis easier and comparable across systems or across related work efforts within the same system. A set of such tasks is enumerated below; hopefully, they represent general categories. An information system will usually be required to accomplish a number of these tasks. A system may contain any combination thereof. It is one of the earlier and major jobs of the designer to select the appropriate set from this list for the particular system under consideration.

- Planning to obtain resources.
- Planning use of resources.
- Assessing the environment.
- Assessing one's own resources.
- Manipulating or moving one's own resources.
- Assessing system status.
- Changing system status.
- Interfacing with other systems.
- Surviving (protecting the system's capability to accomplish its mission).

The series of tasks just enumerated is the one by which the user's objectives are accomplished. However, there will be differences in the performance of these tasks, depending upon whether the user desires to emphasize command or control objectives with his system. Command objectives are those in which the user is concerned mainly with planning for and maintaining his administrative and organizational mechanisms in good working order in a slowly changing environment. He is equally concerned with the relatively long-range capability of his resources, whether they are combat aircraft or supermarkets. Control objectives have more the connotation of directing relatively discrete, short-term movements of resources in a rapidly changing environment in order to implement command objectives.

Although the nine general tasks just enumerated apply equally to the satisfaction of both control and command objectives, the distinction can help the designer to determine what kinds of data the user needs to meet each type. A comparison of the data needs for command and control objectives is given below.

Command Objectives	Control Objectives
1. Aggregated and summarized data.	1. Discrete and specific data.
2. Speculative data (e.g., hypothesis and trial solutions).	2. Factual data.
3. Long-range predictions.	3. Short-term extrapolations.
4. Direct communication with other people.	4. Direct access to a data-processing element.

In summary then, the general distinction between the two types is that control objectives usually require a shorter system response time than do command objectives. The trouble with this distinction is not only that the boundary becomes hazy, but also that some so-called command objectives require short response times. Conversely, many so-called control objectives require look-ahead features which seem to satisfy command objectives. The distinction can be useful for initial matching of system capabilities with requirements, but persons interested in information systems should be very careful not to be snared by distinctions which mask the common nature of such objectives and which, if persisted in, can lead them to ignore a solution to a novel system problem simply because the solution mode is not characteristic of the particular system objective.

Nevertheless, a great many problems in system analysis and design have been caused by the failure to distinguish between these two types of system objectives. For a system user concerned with the task of planning to obtain resources, few data are more useless to him than the current status of each item of his total resources. He needs basic data about what the environment may be at a time which is far enough away for him to put into effect a plan for implementing changes in his resources.

The user objectives, then, help to provide a framework within which both the general and the specific nature of the system task requirements can be enumerated. Once the designer selects the appropriate set of tasks, he can derive from them successively more concrete subtasks. He continues to analyze these subtasks until he arrives at some level of description from which he can infer the nature of the mechanisms needed for the implementation of the tasks.

A set of diagrams such as those illustrated in Figures 4.2 and 4.3 should emerge from this analysis of system tasks. These figures present a simplified example of the analysis of a deterrent weapons information system. Figure 4.2 shows the most general level of analysis. It identifies the major tasks and their inputs and outputs. Each connecting line represents the flow of data to or from a task, culminating in the issuance of orders to the deterrent weapons force in the field.

Each numbered block represents a data-processing activity (in

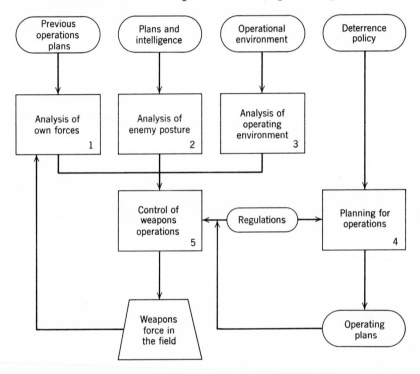

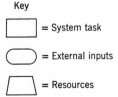

Figure 4.2   Analysis of a deterrent weapons control system (fictitious example).

the general sense of the term) which may be quite complex and involve both computers and people. Roughly the same set of activities
occurs in each block as follows: formulation of the processing problem, data collection, data interpretation, data manipulation, formu-

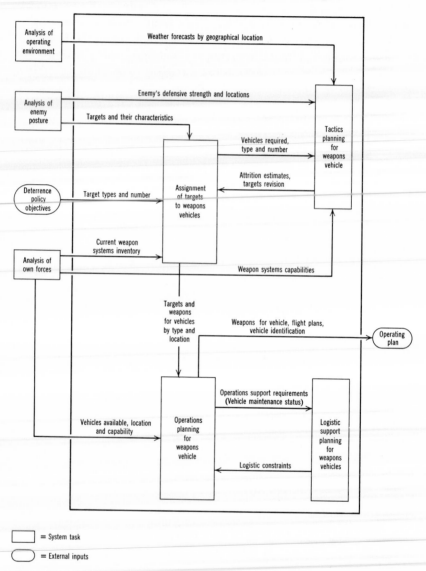

Figure 4.3 An example of subtask specification: expanded view of the system
task, "Planning for operations," from block 4 of Figure 4.2.

lation of decision alternatives or restructuring of the original problem, decision making or problem solution, data output.

Each block also represents a subtask that may require the use of the facilities of the entire system or of only a very small part of the system. The diagrams do not show the temporal order of task performance. This may be developed by a "high traffic" analysis as described by H. H. Goode and R. E. Machol (Ref. 37, pp. 308-312). It would be difficult to show time reference with the subject matter chosen for the illustration because the processing activities seem to be complexly interrelated in terms of recurring feedback.

This process of system task analysis is almost a type of "bootstrap" operation. There is evidence, however, in favor of the point that different groups of people working on the analysis of the same task and possessing comparable background information produce similar designs. The particular arrangement of the blocks in the diagram, the particular sequences, and the particular labels may differ. The essence of the similarity is contained in the specification of the data and their processing to accomplish the task objectives. This is encouraging and leads one to believe that such analytic diagramming may be as much a legitimate process in system analysis as are those processes whose rules are somewhat more formally defined, such as mathematical modeling.

At the risk of being repetitious, it should be pointed out that there are major advantages in employing this technique of task analysis. First, the results of the process, namely, the flow diagrams, furnish a substantial basis for unambiguous communication among the people involved in the design effort. Second, this method allows for the discovery of task relationships that might otherwise remain undetected. Only those who have tried flow diagramming can appreciate the fact that it is hard to close logical gaps. Finally, if such a technique is useful in practice, it takes us closer to the goal of being able to teach others to use it, which of course is one of the aims of this book.

One of the problems with the rational design process, as so far described, is that it tends to make the system look impersonal, as if it might well operate without the intervention of people. However, in successively more concrete levels of analysis, one sees that at various places human judgment would have to intervene to perform the function of data interpretation. Something similar to this process was described by M. S. Meeker, R. J. Rogers, and G. H. Shure (Ref. 15) and employed by them in their analysis of a set of military command staff tasks. Essentially they analyzed and diagrammed a task, indicating the decision points, the decision rules, and other data which enabled them to emerge from each decision point with a yes or no answer. Where the data so mapped, including regulations, were not adequate for determining the decision a priori, they indicated a need for a human decision process. Much more can be said about analysis of the decision processes by means of the block diagrams that define the system tasks, and about allocation of the decision prerogative to a person or computer. It is sufficient here to point out that all the human processing tasks, such as monitoring, comparing, and assessing, eventually lead to decision making. The locus of decision making should be set primarily by user requirements rather than by some academic scheme for comparing and contrasting the strengths and weaknesses of men and computers.

From the analysis of user objectives and system tasks, we emerge with a set of general data requirements and definitions of subtasks of the type indicated in Figures 4.2 and 4.3. These diagrams are fictitious. They show how the task of planning for the use of deterrent weapons is analyzed into subtasks, each with its necessary data types. These data essentially fall into two classes: those generated within a task and those coming into the task from another task or external agency. Figure 4.3 shows system subtasks, still at a fairly general level. In many instances the analysis of system tasks would have to proceed through several more levels before there was enough detail to be able to show all the specific data requirements for task performance. It is not possible to predict how many levels of analysis will be required for each task or for a system as a whole. Furthermore, not all tasks within the same system require the same number of analytic levels.

Let us assume, just for purposes of illustration, that Figure 4.3 represents a final level of analysis; this final level has been reached by answering the questions discussed under "Block 5. System Task Requirements," particularly the first four questions on page 120 of this chapter. The rational design process will then proceed by using the data so obtained to answer the questions indicated as decision hexagons in Figure 4.4.* These questions essentially are the same as those just used to develop task requirements. However, the emphasis here

---

* If one looks carefully at the decision hexagons in Figure 4.4 and then at the attributes of the system elements, a high degree of similarity is perceived. Indeed it is up to the system designer himself to select a set of attributes so that they can be incorporated into questions such as those in Figure 4.4.

is on the last three questions on page 120. Each task is analyzed separately, and the answers are compiled within the numbered rectangles as shown in Figure 4.4.

Once a system task is analyzed in this way, the designer knows what data the system will have to obtain and process for that task. The required data flow can then be incorporated into the design document as follows:

1. By representing the data flow for each system task within the design format previously agreed upon by the user and the designer. This is analogous to "single-thread analysis" as defined by Goode and Machol (Ref. 37, pp. 305-308). Each datum input to or created by the system is traced through the system until it exits or is destroyed or replaced. All intermediate processing and storage are shown and described.

2. By representing the data flow for *all* system tasks and building a composite. This is analogous to the first step in Goode and Machol's "high traffic analysis." This is discussed below under "Block 6. System Element Requirements."

Figure 4.5 shows how the data flow resulting from the task analysis may be incorporated into a structured design document. Part of a system design document actually could be in the format illustrated. Each block in the diagram that contains a number in the lower right corner represents a system element, according to the key provided.*

The number of circles or ovals shows the blocks in the task analysis (of Figure 4.4) from which the data for this mapping are obtained. As a result of the task analysis, each block in the diagram would contain a complete specification of the relevant attributes of that element.

Block 6. System Element Requirements

After all tasks are analyzed, using the single-thread procedure just discussed, the sum of the data within an element represents the total which that element is required to handle. The element must now be constructed so that it can perform its characteristic actions in the way called for by all the tasks. The element has to perform a certain number of its actions within given time and error limits. Also, the ele-

---

* It should be noted that the learning and retrieval elements are not included. At this point in the analysis we are interested only in the operational data flow.

ment is required to "know" when it should start and stop operating and when it needs maintenance. Actually, mechanisms and procedures are required for activating the elements to accomplish the system tasks.

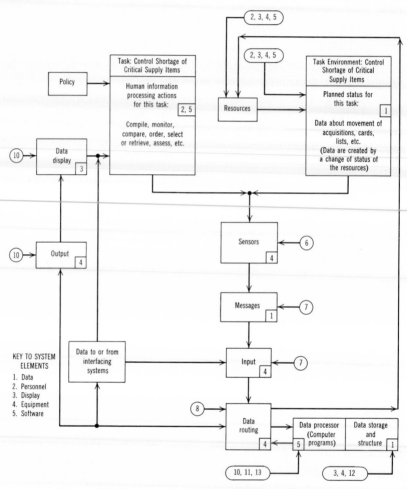

Figure 4.5 Representation of data flow for a system task.

The specification of actual enabling mechanisms (equipment, computer programs, procedures) should not be stated until all the requirements for every element have been obtained and subjected to further analyses, including high traffic analysis.

Block 7. Integration of System Elements

The requirements for system elements initially are stated in fulfillment of the set of ideal requirements that emerges from the analysis of system tasks. In the design process these ideal requirements are usually generated relatively independently of one another. They are also generated before very much work has been done on integrating them. This is probably as it should be, since it is more convenient to start from a situation with few interactions. However, it must be recognized that this interactionless state can only exist as a convenient assumption during the task analysis process. As soon as the designer attempts to integrate such independently derived requirements, he starts around the iterative loop indicated by the feedback from block 8 to block 5 in Figure 4.1.

A good example of the need for an integration process is furnished in the case of specifying the requirements for a display system in a military command post. In this example the following system elements have to be integrated: display, data, personnel, and architecture.

Display. The number of display interfaces or display devices; the size (and other attributes) of the display data.

Data. The number of data to be displayed simultaneously.

Personnel. The number of people requiring access to a set of displays at the same time or over a period of time.

Architecture. The size and configuration of the physical area available; space requirements for passageways and equipment.

All of these elements must be specified. All of them are interrelated. All of them have to be integrated in such a fashion that the designer can make tradeoffs, knowing the ramifications of each trade. For instance, if he wishes to decrease the number of display devices without reducing the number of personnel requiring a fixed amount of simultaneous data, he then has to provide a display device for mass viewing and a room of a certain size and shape.

The extensiveness of the design integration effort is partly a function of the choice of design methodology. A reiterative method makes more provision for this analytic feedback effort. But even where a one-shot method is adopted, a considerable amount of time must be allocated for this process. Obviously, here is an effort which is a major consumer of time. Identification of it, as such, is a must for the adequate performance of the design project management.

Early examination and understanding of the more interactive attributes of the various system elements will help to prevent last-minute integration problems. Also, when these types of problems are recognized early, the design project management can take them into account. This can be done by partitioning the design effort in such a fashion as not to make different groups of people responsible for highly interactive system elements. One would not, for instance, partition off a display project from a data retrieval project.

Block 8. Writing the Design Document

The design is an actual product, a document or set of documents, that is transferred from contractor to subcontractor and from designer to user. Such a document furnishes a legal basis for determining whether or not the contractual commitments of the designer have been fulfilled; it contains the official statement of what the system is going to be. System implementation should not proceed without such a document.*

The job of writing the design document consists mainly of organizing the information generated during the work described in blocks 6 and 7, "System Element Requirements" and "Integration of System Elements," and putting it into the format agreed upon earlier in the design process. The writing process itself, however, is in the area of management activities because management tasks, including presentation to the users, require complete understanding of the design. This understanding is obtained best when management actually writes the design document together with the senior technical designers. If the managers and the designers were the same people, this partition would not exist. Hopefully this is the case in relatively small design efforts.

There are two other reasons for having a separate writing activity. First, where there are several designers on a project, there is a need to make their productions stylistically compatible. This is not as super-

---

* In fact, implementation often does proceed without a design document, usually to be followed by a series of acrimonious recriminations and emergency recoveries. "There is never time to do it right, but always time to do it over" is no less true for being a platitude.

ficial a problem as it might appear at first glance. Frequently, different forms of presentation obscure different design premises. These *must* be detected and reconciled, and experience has indicated that only a centralized and technically oriented management review of the design document is adequate for the job. Second, in a large or complex design effort, it is seemingly impossible to obtain a coherent design without a deliberate effort to integrate the previous design products, even those that, unfortunately, may not be documented.

This whole process of writing the design document requires much more careful description than can be given here. One of the things that is very difficult is checking for errors of omission; generally, it is relatively easy to find errors of commission. For example, there are three things which are frequently omitted from the design specification: the use of design parameters where possible instead of single values, the provision for system adaptation and learning, and prior commitments. The designer must be aware that sometimes commitments are made very early in the design process. They may originate as statements in the feasibility study or preliminary system proposal rather than being developed through the usual analytic process. These early commitments must be repeated in the later design document so that they are not lost.

The design document must be such that the user can retrace the rational derivation of each element. In the case of hardware modules, a schematic diagram is usually called for. But even schematics may not be adequate to explain the choice of a particular logic circuit, or other attributes analogous to circuit logic. The users of system design specifications have an even greater need to trace the rational process because the technology, such as it is, is unfamiliar. Hence the designer is subjected to penetrating questions on the economic justification for the system and its sociocultural implications for the users' organization. This last point is worth elaboration.

Information systems are not like weapon systems and signal-processing systems. They have many implications for the structure and activities of the user's human organization. There almost certainly will be a reshuffling of job responsibilities, organizational communication patterns, and decision prerogatives. This is one reason why an examination of the user's resources must include a review of his willingness and ability to adapt to changes. And certainly it means that he should carefully scrutinize the proposed design from this sociocultural point of view.

A small but typical problem of this nature which frequently confronts the designer of command and control systems arises from trying to determine who should operate a device for entering requests for information into a computer-based system. If the operation of the input device requires a relatively high degree of technical proficiency, such as would be needed if punched cards, computer programs, and machine language were involved, the tendency is to have the designer specify a position for a specially trained and qualified operator; at the same time this man probably would not be the user of the information which he would be instrumental in requesting. The designer is reluctant to specify, and the user to accept, a proposal to train command or executive personnel in the operation of the device. On the other hand, work space may be limited so that the designer is reluctant to have any additional personnel present who are not absolutely required for the operation of the system. If the designer were to remove the device from the premises in which the operations would normally occur, he would have to supply an additional communication link between the information user and the equipment operator. In fact, even if the two were physically adjacent to one another, there would still be an extra communication link; the originator of the request would have to make his needs known to the machine operator. Each additional communication link increases to some uncertain extent the probability of error.

Block 9: Evaluation of the Designed System

At the end of an iteration of the design process, an analysis of the total design may be attempted to determine whether the system as specified can perform all the tasks assigned to it. This analysis can take place in several ways:

- Mathematical modeling and model exercising.
- Functional simulation.
- Nonmathematical analysis; personal judgment.
- Engineering modeling.

Logically there is a fifth category: field testing of the completed system. This is, from two points of view, extremely difficult with large-scale systems. In the first place, a field test of an information system is not really a test at all in the sense that the system will be rejected if it fails; there is too much of an economic investment in it. Second, it requires a very sophisticated and comprehensive technology to exercise, in a controlled fashion, a large information system. Exercising it should also include methods for observing and measuring its performance. There are unique problems with military command and control systems which may be designed to operate primarily under the high-stress conditions of contemporary environments. These can only be simulated through the preparation of a vast complex of synthetic inputs. However, field testing can be accomplished, provided, of course, that the system is capable of being modified as a consequence; that is, certain features of the system will have to have adaptability designed into them (learning element). Chapter 10 is devoted to testing and evaluation.

Block 10. Recommendation on Design Continuation

If management has elected to employ a formal, reiterative design methodology, it will be faced repeatedly with the decision of whether or not it is feasible to continue the design effort. If management is charged with producing a design without regard to such factors as economics, system effectiveness, and incremental effectiveness per unit cost, it need not be confronted with this decision. On the other hand, it is most likely that there are such constraints and that management will have to decide, together with the user, whether the effort should be continued.

In the real world of system design and development efforts, there is small likelihood that a decision to discontinue would be made. This does occur with weapons systems but very rarely with information systems. One of the reasons that design work is not discontinued is that, by the time the question is raised, such a tremendous economic investment has already been made by both the user and the designing agency that neither is willing to waste the effort already expended. A possible result is that the designing agency attempts to make its product appear either better or more advanced than it is. Another alternative is to describe the design in such a way that the listener or reader cannot infer the real capabilities and limitations of the system. Some of this maneuvering, it is hoped, can be avoided by employing a rational design process. Referring to Figure 4.1, we see that, if there is going to be another design iteration, the design should be referred back to the starting point for evaluation by the user. The next reiteration starts with the user's feedback to project management. If there is no more reiteration, then the design is forwarded for implementation (system construction), installation, checkout, operation, evaluation, and modification. An information system is always dynamic.

4.4 SUMMARY

This chapter has tried to show how the design process can be described in such a way as to promote clearer communication about what should be done and about what is or is not being done in any specific case. Experience has shown that misunderstandings frequently develop between user and designer, and almost as often they are not resolved to the satisfaction of either. It is hoped (perhaps in vain) that schematizing the design process will increase the chances of communication and at the same time allow others responsible for design work to benefit from past conceptual mistakes.

In order to describe the design process, the disorder of oversimplification has been risked by showing a temporal sequence of discrete design steps. In fact, it would probably be unusual for a particular system design project to follow the steps shown in Figure 4.1. It would be similarly unlikely for the design steps to be discrete. More probably several steps would be taken either concurrently or with partial overlapping.

Concurrency is a tempting concept, one that is invoked in order to save design and development time and to bring a new system into being sooner. While polemics against uncritical use of concurrency serve little purpose, one must nevertheless try to hold up a proper example (the present scheme perhaps) and not be seduced by the administrative magic that pulls a two-year product out of a one-year hat.

As it is, this chapter has glossed over a number of difficulties and omitted entirely discussions of others. Among the former, the outstanding one is the analysis (literally the decomposition) of system tasks into their constituent subtasks and finally into all their data and processing requirements. Among the undiscussed topics, perhaps the most important are system learning, and information retrieval. Discussions on the latter can be found in the proceedings of almost any professional data-processing organization. Unfortunately the same statement cannot be made in regard to the mechanisms for system learning and adaptation. All that can be done here is to call attention to the need, and to emphasize it by stating that information systems never have enough capacity and are always changing, so that the mechanisms for accommodation had better be available. Too often these problems pass by default to the system operator, who may lack the ingenuity to solve them.

REFERENCES AND BIBLIOGRAPHY

System Development Corporation Technical Reports

1. L. T. Alexander and A. S. Cooperband, *Terminal Air Traffic Control System,* SD-3443, May 1961.*
2. H. M. Case and S. R. Quincey, *A Unified Approach to System Development: An Approach to Wildland Fire Control,* SP-294, May 1961.
3. L. S. Christie, S. E. Fliege, and J. W. Singleton, *System Development of Command and Control Systems,* SP-182, October 1960.
4. V. Darroch, *System Training: A Bibliography,* FN-3541-1, May 1960.
5. R. Gifford, *The Self Organizing Aspects of the Task Oriented Groups,* FN-3794, June 1960.
6. J. B. Heyne, *On the Empirical Design of Management Control Systems,* TM-585, February 1961.
7. R. C. Hopkins, *A Systematic Approach to System Development,* FN-4176, August 1960.
8. J. Jaffe and M. I. Berkowitz, *The Development and Uses of a Functional Model in the Simulation of an Information-Processing System,* SP-584, November 1961.
9. M. O. Kappler, *Automated Information-Processing Assistance for Military Systems,* TR-2, January 1961.
10. W. P. Kent, *Information Flow during System Design and Development,* N-WD-315, November 1961.*
11. I. Nehnevajsa, S. Marks, and E. Vargas, *1958 Systems Literature Abstracts,* FN-LO-185, October 1959.
12. I. Nehnevajsa, *Toward System Mapping,* FN-LO-122, July 1959.
13. P. Peach, *What is System Analysis?* SP-155, March 1960.
14. E. H. Porter, *The System Thinkers: Parable and Paradigm,* SP-285, March 1961.
15. M. S. Rogers, R. J. Meeker, and G. H. Shure, *Command Decision-Making,* N-10911, May 1960.*
16. A. J. Rowe, *Application of Computer Simulation to Production System Design,* SP-85, April 1959.
17. J. Staudhammer, *The System Analysis and Design Program,* SP-506, September 1961.
18. H. Watson, *Command Control Systems: A Selective Bibliography,* FN-6098/000/00, December 1961.
19. B. R. Wolin, *Methodology Note: Design and Redesign of Systems,* FN-2600, December 1959.

---

* This document is an internal, unpublished SDC communication and is not appropriate for release outside the corporation.

RAND Corporation Technical Reports

20. S. I. Firstman and N. Jordan, *Operational and Human Factors in Planning Automated Man-machine Checkout Systems*, RM-2835-PR, April 1962.
21. C. Hitch, *On the Choice of Objectives in Systems Studies*, P-1955, March 1960.
22. M. W. Hoag, *An Introduction to Systems Analysis*, RM-1678, April 1956.
23. N. Jordan, *Some Thinking about "System,"* P-2166, December 1960.
24. H. Kahn and I. Mann, *Techniques of Systems Analysis*, RM-1829-1, December 1956.
25. J. A. Kershaw and R. N. McKean, *Systems Analysis and Education*, RM-2473-FF, October 1959.
26. E. S. Quade, *Pitfalls in Analysis*, P-1694, February 1959.
27. A. J. Wohlstetter, *Systems Analysis versus Systems Design*, P-1530, October 1958.

Other Agency Technical Reports

28. E. P. Buckley and H. W. Sinaiko, *Human Factors in the Design of Systems*, Naval Research Laboratory, NRL Report 4996, August 1957.
29. W. A. Hosier, "Pitfalls and Safeguards in Real-Time Digital Systems with Emphasis on Programming," *IRE Transactions of Engineering Management*, June 1961.
30. J. McGrath, P. Nordlie, and W. Vaughan, Jr., *A Systematic Framework for Comparison of Systems Research Methods*, Human Sciences Research, Inc., HSR-TN-59/7 AM, March 1960.
31. M. W. Raben, *A Survey of Operations and Systems Research Literature*, Institute for Applied Experimental Psychology, Tufts University, January 1960.
32. A. Shapero and C. Bates, Jr., *A Method for Performing Human Engineering Analysis of Weapon Systems*, Aerospace Medical Laboratory, WADC TR 590784, September 1959.
33. G. O. Wright, *A General Procedure for Systems Study*, Aerospace Medical Laboratory, WADD TN 60-18.

Books

34. D. P. Echman (ed.), *Systems: Research and Design.* New York: Wiley, 1961.
35. C. D. Flagle, W. H. Huggins, and R. H. Roy (eds.), *Operations Research and Systems Engineering.* Baltimore: The Johns Hopkins Press, 1960.
36. R. M. Gagné (ed.), *Psychological Principles in System Development.* New York: Holt, Rinehart, and Winston, 1962.
37. H. H. Goode and R. E. Machol, *System Engineering: An Introduction to the Design of Large-Scale Systems.* New York: McGraw-Hill, 1957.

38. R. E. Machol (ed.), *Information and Decision Processes.* New York: McGraw-Hill, 1960.

39. D. G. Malcolm, A. Rowe, and L. F. McConnell (eds.), *Management Control Systems.* New York: Wiley, 1960.

40. J. G. March and H. W. Simon, *Organizations.* New York: Wiley, 1958.

Chapter Five

Design and Production of Computer Programs

J. J. Connelly

5.1 INTRODUCTION

It is the purpose of this chapter to describe the production process for a set of computer programs in an information system development context. There are some basic or generalized phases in this process— for example, design, coding, and testing—which are applicable to virtually any large-scale programming project.[1] However, since each large-scale programming project is unique, in order to present a more meaningful and detailed description we will discuss the specific process which was actually used in the production of a program system, namely, the Strategic Air Command 465L Planning Subsystem. This chapter will give potential users of an information system an insight into how such a system is produced, together with some understanding of the problems and complexities involved. The Planning Subsystem is one of the two operational components that make up the 465L System. The other component is the Control Subsystem. As their names imply, these subsystems perform planning and control functions, respectively, for the Strategic Air Command. Each of these *subsystems* is a large integrated program *system*. The Planning Subsystem is comprised of approximately 100 programs, 320,000 machine instructions, and a data base of over 30,000,000 words. The Planning Subsystem and the Control Subsystem are called *subsystems* only because they are components of the total 465L *System*.

This chapter outlines the general flow of the program production process used for the 465L Planning Subsystem. The five main phases are applicable to virtually any large-scale programming project. Indeed, these five phases specify the way in which the process would appear to be naturally organized.

First, there is the translation of the requirements documents into programming terminology. Here, the programmers study the requirements, identify and resolve any inconsistencies, and arrange the requirements so that they are logically grouped from a programming point of view. This is a necessary first step where the project is large, and especially when the requirements have been written by people other than the programmers. Of course, in a small project, where the programmers themselves have written the requirements, the translation phase would assume less importance.

Second, there is the design phase, in which the detailed design of the programs is worked out and clearly specified. This phase would appear to be always necessary, except perhaps in the smallest of systems. Even then a design phase of some sort is necessary if there is to be any formal written record of how the programs were organized. (In relatively small systems, the design phase might be combined with the translation phase.) In the system described in this chapter, the program was organized in terms of "jobs,"* "tasks,"* and "programs."* This design breakdown was deemed necessary because of the special requirements of the 465L Planning Subsystem. Of course, other projects would not necessarily want to use this design breakdown. However, apart from this feature, the chapter presents the over-all sequence of events by which a large system may be designed.

Third, there is the coding phase. Here, the actual coding is done, usually (in a large system) in a "higher-order" language, which is then translated into machine code by a utility program.

Fourth, there is the verification phase, during which the program is tested for the accuracy of the coding and for adherence to both the design specifications and the original requirements. This chapter points out the great necessity for adequate testing. In a large system, this can be achieved only by having a specific, detailed testing plan. Without such a plan, programmers are likely to oververify some areas and to

---

* See Glossary.

underverify others. This chapter outlines the use of decision point matrices which can be adapted for use with other systems as part of the test plan.

Finally, there is the release phase. This consists of the "packaging" of decks, listings, tapes, and documents, and delivery of them to either the customer or to another group that is to perform over-all system testing of the programs prepared by different groups. This chapter points out the importance of this phase and suggests that it, equally with the other phases, must be carefully planned and specified in advance. A suggested set of contents for this phase is presented.

5.2   THE COMPUTER PROGRAM PRODUCTION PROCESS

Definition of the Process

In order to manage effectively the production process of a large-scale computer program subsystem, one must first have a clear definition of the process. As noted in the introduction, this chapter defines the process used in producing the 465L Planning Subsystem. The total production process, needless to say, requires a manager's attention to a great many functions, for example, processing and controlling system changes, effective utilization of manpower resources, and effective electronic accounting machine (EAM) and electronic data-processing machine (EDPM) utilization. Although these are all integral parts of the total process, in this chapter we are restricting ourselves to a definition of the basic functions of the production process. Furthermore, the production process, as it is defined in this chapter, assumes certain functions that precede the process and thus produce inputs to it, as well as certain functions that follow the production process and thus utilize its outputs.

Inputs to Production Process. This process starts on receipt of (1) system integration* type documents, which specify such things as the formats of the user input messages and output displays; and (2) design requirements* containing the following sections: general statement and description of the requirements; logical designs, including assumptions, in both prose and diagram form; specific requirements

---

* See Glossary.

indicating the areas of human interaction with the program; specific operational program requirements.

The Phases of the Production Process. The production process, as defined in this chapter, is divided into five basic phases—translation, design, coding, verification, and internal release (see Figure 5.1). Each of these phases is essentially a building block; the outputs of one phase are the inputs to the next. Interim documents serve as bench marks to signal the completion of each phase. These documents serve four functions: (*a*) to ensure that programmers perform each step in a rigorous fashion; (*b*) to enable technical supervisors to inspect intermediate steps so as to ensure a high-quality product; (*c*) to enable the managers to judge more accurately where the development of the subsystem stands in relation to where it should be, and consequently to assess better future manpower needs and delivery dates; (*d*) to minimize the impact of manpower turnover, since most of the development is recorded in documentation.

Translation Phase

The translation phase has three purposes: (1) to give programmers a clear understanding of the content of the design requirements; (2) to identify and resolve inconsistencies in the design requirements; (3) to regroup the functions stated in the design requirements so that they are logically grouped from a programming point of view.

Translation of the design requirements is by no means easy when thousands of pages of requirements and seventy or more programmers are involved. Experience has shown that there is a diversity in understanding design requirements because programmers emphasize different things in their reading, and because there is frequently a varying degree of detail in different design requirements.

One of the main problems involved in translating the requirements statements is the lack of a clear, precise, unambiguous, and comprehensive glossary in which all terms are defined. The result is that the same term may be used in different ways from one set of requirements to another, or even within a single requirement. For instance, in one place the word "command" may be used to signify a specific Command as used in Air Force terminology, whereas in another place it may be employed in a very general sense. As a result the programmer is left in doubt as to what the requirement actually is.

Another basic problem is the frequent lack of completeness in

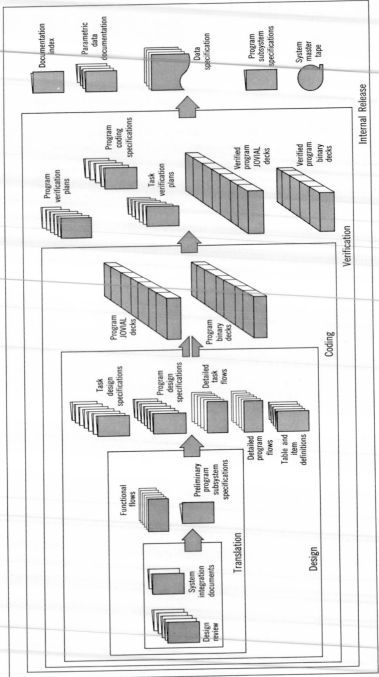

Figure 5.1 Production process overview.

stating requirements. For instance, when speaking of "distance," the requirement may fail to state the type of projection (e.g., Mercator or Conformal) to be used in the program's calculation, or the units of measurement (e.g., land miles or nautical miles), or the degree of precision (e.g., to the nearest nautical mile). Another problem is the prose style of requirement writers. Some writers may be too wordy, thus giving rise to ambiguity, while others may be too terse. Achieving a correct balance and clarity of language is difficult, especially when requirement writers have been given no training in this aspect of the work.

The net result of the above problems is that, in reading the requirements, each programmer is likely to make a somewhat different interpretation of them. This gives rise to difficulties in two distinct ways: (1) the programmer may be interpreting a requirement differently from what the writer intended, so that the program will not fulfill the requirement correctly; (2) interface between the programs may be affected when, for instance, one programmer uses a Mercator projection for a certain calculation, whereas another uses a Conformal projection for a calculation that produces an input to the first calculation.

Many of the problems discussed above are inherent in the writing of the requirements, and we shall not attempt to offer solutions here. An important problem in the *translation* of the requirements, however, is the fact that the programmers themselves often apply little or no method to their interpretation. Naturally, this compounds the problems. Uniformity in the translation by programmers is very important, and we have attempted to achieve this by (1) procedurizing the translation phase into steps with definite objectives at the end of each step, and (2) establishing two documentation points to signify the midpoint and the end of the translation phase.

The translation phase is comprised of both *analysis*, that is, the breaking down of a whole into its component parts to ascertain their nature, and *synthesis*, the combining of parts to form a whole.

Analysis consists of *three* steps which satisfy the first two purposes of the translation phase—to obtain a clear understanding of the design requirements and to identify and resolve their inconsistencies: (1) segmentation of design requirements into functional areas;* (2) identification of design requirement subfunctions;* (3) performance of detailed analysis of each design requirement subfunction. Synthesis

---

* See Glossary.

consists of *two* steps, which satisfy the third purpose of the translation phase—to regroup the functions stated in the design requirements so that they are logically related from a programming point of view: (4) the synthesis of logical tasks* from design requirement subfunctions; and (5) the synthesis of logical jobs* from logical tasks, and the documentation of the preliminary program subsystem specification.* We shall discuss each of these five steps in detail, beginning with step 1.

Step 1. Segmentation of Design Requirements Into Functional Areas. As stated above, the inputs to the translation phase for the Planning Subsystem are the design requirements and system integration documents. The first step, then, involves the analysis of these documents in order to define logical subdivisions of the subsystem. Each subdivision consists of all, or parts of, one or more design requirement and is called a "functional area." The basic criterion employed in defining these logical subdivisions is functional interdependency. For example, in the 465L Planning Subsystem, the flight plan analysis functional area consists of all or parts of the requirements for flight simulation, airborne alert, mating, and routing. The functions defined in these requirements are all involved in the development of flight plans. The intent of this subdivision of the subsystem into functional areas is to distribute the work load logically among the organizational sections comprising the group of programmers who are to produce the subsystem.

A gross estimate of the scope, that is, the number of programming instructions, of each functional area is made, and then one or more of these areas is assigned to each section in the group (a section has about ten to fifteen programmers; a group may have two to five sections).

Step 2. Identification of Design Requirement Subfunctions. The programmers, who will later analyze portions of a design requirement in detail, read all design requirements in their particular functional area in order to obtain a total overview. They then participate in meetings to subdivide further each of the design requirements. Each division of a design requirement is identified as a design requirement subfunction. The purpose of this step is to break down each functional area into manageable parts (subfunctions) so that they can be distributed to programmers for subsequent detailed analysis. Questions

---

* See Glossary.

and/or inconsistencies identified during the preliminary readings are coordinated with the design requirement author.

The design requirement subfunctions are then assigned to programmers for detailed analysis. The assignments are made as a function of the programmer's experience and ability and the complexity and size of the subfunction. Generally, each programmer is assigned one or two subfunctions.

Step 3. Performance of Detailed Analysis of Each Design Requirement Subfunction. The programmers then begin detailed analysis of their assigned subfunctions. Each such analysis consists of a careful reading of the pertinent operational program requirements portion of the design requirement document, to obtain a clearer understanding of the processing therein described and to identify the data required for the performance of the subfunction. Each piece of data is defined in terms of its nature—that is, fixed or variable, form, range, and functional grouping. For example, aircraft total fuel capacity might be defined as fixed, integer, 50,000 to 300,000, and a function of aircraft type and model.

In performing this detailed analysis, each programmer is responsible for coordinating with the design requirement author to validate the analysis. New subfunctions are sometimes created by consolidating, redefining, or splitting up old ones. New assignments of subfunctions are made when necessary.

A form of documentation helps to ensure that the analysis is performed correctly. It signifies completion of analysis, the first part of the translation phase. This form of documentation, the functional flow chart,* is essentially a graphic presentation of the prose statement of requirements. Programmers are required to produce functional flow charts for each subfunction. These charts portray the subfunction processing without explicitly relating it to machine processing. This explicit relationship is made in the design phase. Each chart is reviewed by the technical supervisor for accuracy and uniformity. The corrected chart is then reproduced, and copies are given to each programmer working on the functional area to enable him to review it as it relates to his own subfunction(s).

Step 4. The Synthesis of Logical Tasks from Design Requirement Subfunctions. Synthesis begins with a grouping together and identification of subfunctions as *logical tasks.* A logical task consists of one or more subfunctions which collectively accomplish a specific SAC func-

---

* See Glossary.

tion. An example of a logical task is the flight simulation task. Subfunctions comprising a given logical task might very well have originally been parts of different design requirements. For example, the cruise mode of flight, a flight simulation design requirement subfunction, and the segmentation of sortie routes, a routing design requirement subfunction, both comprise part of the same logical task—flight simulation. In this step, calculations common throughout the subfunctions, such as sine and cosine calculations, are identified for subsequent handling as subsystem routines.

A concurrent activity is the identification of logical groupings of the data required for performance of a given logical task. The data defined during the previous step for each subfunction are collected into sets by their functional groupings; for example, all data which are a function of aircraft type and model are collected into a single set.

Step 5. The Synthesis of Logical Jobs from Logical Tasks, and the Documentation of the Preliminary Program Subsystem Specification. All logical tasks developed within the subsystem are then analyzed and grouped into logical jobs. A logical job is composed of one or more logical tasks which must operate together to fulfill a class of related user input messages.

The basic criterion for establishing logical jobs, then, is man-machine interaction. (The human action requirements portion of the design requirement documents, and the system integration documents, assist in defining this man-machine interaction.) An example of a logical job is the input processor logical task and the flight simulation logical task mentioned previously. For example, the input processor logical task would be identified at this step in the development since analysis of all previously developed logical tasks would indicate that each is performing an input-processing function and that it would be reasonable to centralize and generalize this function.

A parallel effort, closely related to the development of jobs, is the further development of the data base. The data sets previously identified for the logical tasks are now merged to form data sets for the entire subsystem. To illustrate, let us assume that two functional areas require data associated with aircraft units. The first needs the units' locations and types of aircraft; the second, the units' locations and vulnerabilities. At this time, the common data requirement would be recognized, and one data set for units would be established, consisting of locations, types of aircraft, and vulnerabilities.

The results of the translation phase are documented in the "preliminary program subsystem specification." This document identifies the logical tasks and jobs, the data sets, and the input and output requirements of the subsystem. It also contains prose and graphic descriptions of the manner in which the various logical tasks and jobs relate. Publication of this document signals the completion of the translation phase.

Design Phase

Introduction. The design phase, though simple to define, is perhaps the most complex and significant phase of programming. Its purpose is to structure actual jobs,* tasks,* and programs* that comprise the subsystem in order to produce the most efficient and least costly subsystem possible.

The orderly and generally accepted approach to program system design is to work from the general to the specific. In our subsystem, this means first designing jobs, then tasks, then programs. The problem, however, is that, in actual practice, programmers tend to concentrate effort on the design of the most specific components, that is, programs, since these are the easiest to grasp and also seem to affect most directly the progress of subsystem development. As a result the design of jobs and tasks may be left for last and thus be hurried and, consequently, inefficient. Experience has demonstrated that inefficient job and task design results in redundant efforts in design, coding, and verification, extensive rework in coding and verification, and attendant low programmer morale. A solution to this problem is to procedurize the design phase and to establish interim bench marks ensuring that each step of the process is performed adequately.

Methodology of Design (see Figure 5.2). Inputs to the design phase, in addition to the outputs from the translation phase, that is, the preliminary program subsystem specification and functional flow charts, include the system integration document and design requirements that were also inputs to the translation phase.

The following steps comprise the design phase: (1) job design, (2) preliminary task design, (3) detailed task design, (4) preliminary program design, (5) quality review and production of preliminary task and program design specifications, (6) detailed data analysis, and (7) detailed program design.

---

* See Glossary.

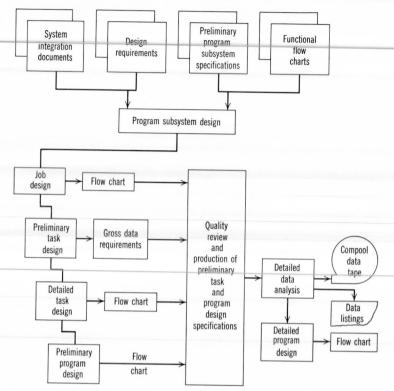

Figure 5.2 Methodology of design.

Step 1. Job Design. Given the logical jobs produced in the translation phase and documented in the preliminary program subsystem specification, the function of job design is to determine whether the logical jobs can be actual jobs. In the translation phase, machine constraints were not explicitly considered since they would have been an additional factor of complexity at that initial phase. It was decided that, for the sake of maximum efficiency, the consideration of these factors should be left to the design phase.

The primary machine constraint considered in job design is the amount and type of auxiliary storage, that is, tapes, disc, drums, available to the subsystem. Since, by definition, no human intervention is permitted during the operation of a job, the required storage configuration cannot exceed that which is available. For example, if a maximum of ten tape drives is available to the subsystem, no desired auxiliary storage configuration can exceed ten tapes.

The first thing, then, that must be done for each logical job is to determine the required auxiliary storage configuration. The data sets defined in the preliminary program subsystem specification are re-analyzed for pertinency to the given job. The maximum size of each pertinent data set, for example, the maximum number of missile units, is used to determine the amount of auxiliary storage required for that data set. The data sets are organized into tape files, drum files, and disc data units. The tape files are grouped so as to form logical tapes.

If the desired auxiliary storage does not exceed that which is available, the logical job can be an actual job. If it does exceed, an attempt is made to change the desired auxiliary storage by reallocating files and thereby forcing a fit. If this attempt fails, the logical job is either redefined or split into two or more logical jobs and the process of job design starts over again. Since the criterion for establishing jobs was man-machine interaction, whenever new jobs are created they must be coordinated with the design requirements authors to ensure feasibility from the point of view of the user.

The completion of job design is marked by the production of job flows which identify the gross auxiliary storage configuration required for each job.

Step 2. Preliminary Task Design. The function of preliminary task design is to design actual tasks from the logical tasks developed in the translation phase. The primary programming constraint is available core memory space, to be distinguished from available auxiliary storage, that is, tapes, disc, drums, which was the constraint in step 1.

A preliminary analysis of the job flow for the actual job and of the associated logical task definitions is performed to determine which of the data now defined on tape, disc, and drum are required for the operation of a given task. The maximum size of the required *data in core* is then determined. This maximum size can differ from the size of files since not all the data contained in the files are necessarily re-quired at the same time in core for calculations. For example, a file might contain data defining all missile units, but the logical task would require, at any given time, only the data defining *one* unit.

The total required amount of core is then computed by adding the amount of core required for the *data* to an estimated amount required for the *instructions* which will accomplish the data functions. If this total required amount does not exceed the amount of core available, the logical task can become an actual task. Otherwise, re-analysis must be made to reduce the number of data and/or of instructions required in core for the task. Factors considered include the task type, that is, whether it is linear, iterative, or a combination of these types, and the complexity and size of each function of the task.

If this reanalysis indicates that the task or data can be redesigned to fit into core, the logical task can become an actual task. Otherwise, the logical task must be split into two or more logical tasks and the process of task design starts again. Next, task designers assess all changes that have been made to the data files. This leads to integration of data and/or redefinition of tasks.

The completion of preliminary task design is marked by the production of the gross task data requirements, in terms of both gross core storage locations and data transfers.

Step 3. Detailed task design. Given actual tasks and gross data requirements, the functions of this step are to associate the computer functions necessary to accomplish the given task functions and to fraction the task into programs.

Computer functions such as reading, writing, sorting, and searching are associated, wherever necessary, with the operational functions identified in the translation phase. This complete set of functions is illustrated in an initial task flow.

The initial task flow is analyzed to determine whether a single program will be sufficient to perform the processing required to satisfy all functions. If the amount of processing is small or is not readily split into logical entities, a single program should suffice. In that case, design proceeds with a determination of the data flow and the preparation of a more specific form of the task flow, the preliminary task input/output flow chart.

If a single program does not suffice, the initial task flow is then further analyzed to determine the concept of task design to be employed. There are two such concepts. The first, the "control program" concept, is to have one program control the operation of all others. The second, the "independence" concept, is to have each program operate relatively independently of the others. Factors which argue for the adoption of the "control program" concept are a nonlinear order of task function operation and a significant amount of common processing.

Once the concept has been determined, the design proceeds with a more detailed analysis of the data flow and a concurrent identification of programs. This process considers various constraints imposed by the physical configuration of the computer and by the system control program, the "Executive"* in the 465L System. The programs will consist of subsets of the functions performed by the task.

Task designers in each functional area identify common functions —and, therefore, programs—and ensure that there is a consistent data base. Throughout the design phase, programmers whose sole responsibility is to ensure a consistent and efficient data base are working with representatives of each functional area toward that end.

The completion of the detailed task design is signaled by the production of the preliminary task input/output flow charts and identification of each program.

Step 4. Preliminary Program Design. The functions of this step are to produce preliminary program design flows from the functional flow charts and added computer functions and to structure the tables* containing the data to be processed. The more important constraints are imposed by the types of table structures and tagging conventions which must be adhered to. (Tagging conventions are the means whereby tables are identified by the use of a specified number of letters and digits, e.g., ABCØ.) Close coordination is mandatory since many programs process the same data. This coordination must take place between the programmers working on the Planning Subsystem, and also between these programmers and those working on the Utility and Support Subsystem.

Completion of this step is indicated by the production of preliminary program design flows and preliminary table structures.

Step 5. Quality Review and Design Specification Production. The preliminary design of all programs and tables and the detailed design of all tasks are reviewed at a series of quality review meetings which are attended by representatives from all functional areas. The purpose of these meetings is threefold: (1) to eliminate future redundant programming efforts; (2) to determine whether computer functions are being accomplished at the most opportune points; (3) to ensure that the quality of the product is high. Upon completion of these meetings, the programs, tasks, and jobs are revised as necessary and are documented in accordance with detailed document format guidance. The preliminary program design specifications include, for each program, a statement of the program's responsibility, a description of its environment, and a program design flow. The preliminary task design

---

* See Glossary.

specification includes a description of the task's responsibility, its environment, its outputs, core storage locations, auxiliary storage locations, and, in detail, its input/output flow. The detailed job flows are prepared for later inclusion in the final program subsystem specification.

Step 6. Detailed Data Analysis. The functions of this step are to fix data definitions and to record the data in the dictionary known as the "Compool"* in the 465L System. Each item in each table is coordinated and fully defined. Data specification request forms are filled out for each item,* table, and file. Data are legality checked (to ensure that values fall between prespecified lower and upper limits), and modifications made where necessary. The data are then placed onto the Compool tape, and listings are produced.

From this point in the production process, the data base is fairly static, and changes are made in a more formal way, that is, by coordinating and submitting written change requests or data specification request forms.

Step 7. Detailed Program Design. The last step in the design phase is the development of detailed program flows. This process involves a further definition of each box of the preliminary program design flows. Logical statements are produced which are at such a level that they can be translated one-for-one into JOVIAL* statements. While developing his flows, the programmer uses the data specifications produced in step 6 above. When the flow is completed, the technical supervisor reviews it for accuracy and consistency, and changes are made as necessary.

Coding Phase

Purpose. The purposes of this phase are to translate programs heretofore defined in terms of design specifications and detailed program flows into sets of higher-order language statements, and to compile sets of machine language instructions from these higher-order language statements.

Problems in Coding and Their Solution. Experience has shown that many problems arise because of the size and complexity of the program subsystem and because of inexperienced programmers. Some

---

* See Glossary.

of these problems are production of inefficient code and consequent lengthening of the verification phase, and improper utilization of electronic accounting machine and electronic data processing machine facilities. A way of minimizing these problems is to procedurize the coding phase.

Methodology of Coding (see Figure 5.3). In general, the inputs to this phase are the detailed program flow charts, the program design specifications, and the complete data definitions.

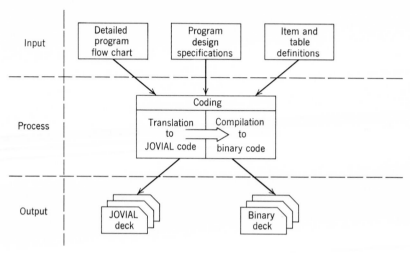

Figure 5.3 Methodology of coding.

Coding starts with the translation of the logical statements, contained on the detailed program flow diagrams, into equivalent JOVIAL statements. These higher-order language statements are punched onto cards. The decks of cards are then submitted for compilation, and errors are corrected until an error-free binary deck is obtained.

Adherence to coding conventions and procedures, *frequent review of the product by the technical supervisor,* and the fact that much of the work usually done in the coding phase has already been accomplished as the last part of the design phase are sufficient to ensure optimum progress.

Verification Phase

Purpose. The purpose of this phase is to purge the program subsystem of errors. The goal of verification is to produce an error-free subsystem. It should be noted, however, that this is a goal which is never totally realized. In striving toward this end, the producer of a large computer program subsystem corrects all the errors that he detects as a result of running a set of preplanned test cases. The realities of life prevent him from verifying the literally millions of possible paths through the subsystem. (See Chapter 10 for a detailed discussion of system test philosophy, objectives, and procedures.)

Problems in Verification and Their Solution. Historically, in this phase, production efforts bog down and schedules slip. Many reasons are presented, by both programmers and managers, to rationalize the occurrence of this problem. Examples are the complexity and size of the program subsystem and the inexperience of the programmers involved. These reasons are valid, as far as they go. Perhaps a more basic cause of the problem is the absence of a defined verification methodology and the consequent inability of management to assess progress accurately and thereby to control production. If there is no organized approach, programmers tend to oververify some areas and neglect others. A solution is a system approach to verification, one in which levels of verification are introduced and for which, within each level, a well-defined procedure is established. The keys to establishing the procedures are the designation of a specific goal for each level of verification and the identification of interim products in the verification process. The interim products provide for managerial inspection and allow the programmer to direct his work toward the stated goal.

Methodology of Verification (see Figure 5.4). The system approach to verification relates directly to the manner in which the program subsystem has thus far been developed and documented. First the system designers generated and published design requirements. Given these design requirements, the programmers designed tasks, then programs. They documented these in task and program design specifications. The "functions which ·are to be tested" are also documented at each level, that is, system performance requirements, task verification matrices, and program verification matrices.

The approach, then, is to verify against each of the three levels of specifications. At these three levels, essentially the same set of instructions is being verified against three different sets of criteria. By starting with the level of greatest detail, and utilizing the program verification matrices, programs are verified against program design specifications. The manipulation of data in core is verified.

By utilizing the task verification matrices, tasks are then verified

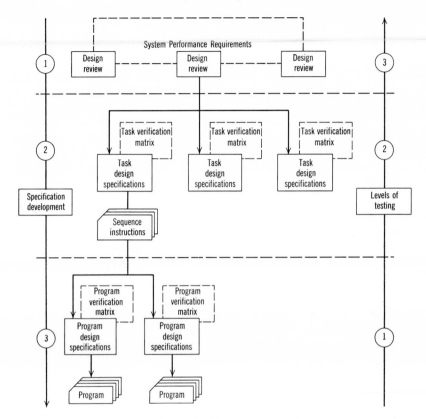

Figure 5.4 Methodology of verification.

against task design specifications. Core-to-input/output device and input/output device-to-core data transfers and program intercommunication are verified.

Finally, by utilizing the system performance requirements, the program subsystem is verified against the design requirements. This is equivalent to Air Force Category I testing.[2] It is performed following the internal release phase and is therefore not covered in this chapter.

PROGRAM VERIFICATION. The specific goal of program verification is to verify each branch of each program decision point. Satisfaction of this goal ensures the code's compatibility with the detailed program flow and verifies that the logic specified in the design phase is actually coded into the program. The inputs to program verification include the detailed program flow, program design specifications, data specifications, subsystem verification model, and, of course, the JOVIAL program deck.

There are two basic steps in program verification, the preparation of a plan and the actual verification on the computer.

Preparation of a Plan. The first step of the procedure is the preparation of a verification plan, which consists of three elements: (1) a decision point matrix, (2) test lists, (3) inputs and expected outputs.

The decision point matrix (see Figure 5.5) is a device for presenting the program decision points in tabular form. Every decision point on the detailed program flow is labeled. If there is a corresponding symbolic region label in the code, the same label will appear on the flow (e.g., AAØ5); otherwise a unique label will appear (e.g., AØ4). The decision point labels are listed vertically on the matrix. Then, for each decision point, each branch is listed horizontally.

Next, determination is made as to which branches of which decision points are to be activated in the first test. These decisions and these branches are indicated on a test list. The same form and method of presentation are used for both the decision point matrix and the test list. The header information on the form allows one to specify the "type" of use along with associated information, such as test number and test weight (see below for explanation of test weight). Next, the number of branches not yet activated is determined, and additional tests and test lists are prepared. The fact that "paths" or combinations of branches have cumulative effects is recognized, and as many paths as time permits are incorporated into the test lists.

In order to prepare these test lists effectively, a great deal of desk checking is performed on the program's logic. Errors found here can greatly minimize the time required for the actual verification on the computer.

Upon completion of the test lists, the inputs necessary to activate the branches specified in the test lists are generated and recorded. Wherever possible, these inputs are taken from the subsystem verification model, which is a collection of representative data describing the subsystem in miniature. In the Planning Subsystem it contains a sample attack force, a sample target system, and the characteristics and capabilities of each. The usage of the verification model data ensures a common basis for verification, as will be explained in the discussion of task verification.

The expected outputs are then manually computed and recorded. The verification plan is reviewed for completeness and accuracy by the technical supervisor, and revisions are made as needed.

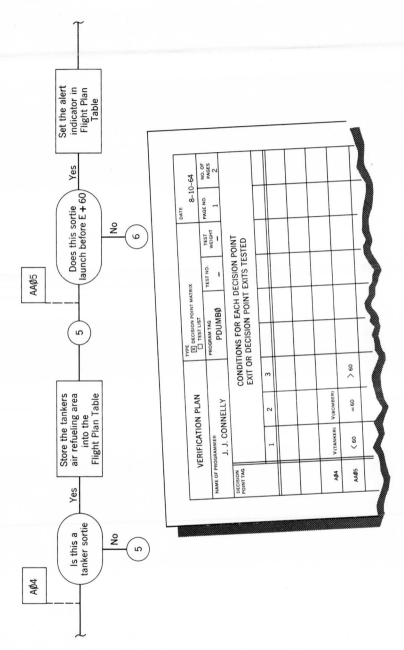

Figure 5.5 The decision point matrix.

157

A test weight is attached to each of the tests as a function of its size and complexity. The application of test weights facilitates a detailed schedule for verification. For example, if three tests are planned, the first weighted at 50, the second at 30, and the third at 20, and if the program is to be tested in ten weeks, then, in order for the schedule to be maintained, the first test should be completed after five weeks, the second after eight, and the third after ten. This detailed schedule permits the manager to assess more closely the progress of program verification.

Verification on the Computer. The second step in program verification is the actual verification of the program. Each test is run on the computer, and expected outputs are compared with actual ones. Variances are noted, and then causes are searched out and corrected. The program is considered to be verified when all expected outputs and actual outputs agree.

TASK VERIFICATION. The specific goal of task verification is to ensure that each program interaction and each input/output operation functions properly. The inputs to task verification include the verified JOVIAL program decks, task design specifications, data specifications, and the subsystem verification model.

In task verification, as in program verification, there are two basic steps: preparation of a plan and actual verification on the machine.

Preparation of a Plan. The first step is the creation of a verification plan. As stated above, a specific goal of task verification is to ensure that each input/output operation functions properly. This is accomplished by ensuring that each sequence parameter is activated. Sequence parameters are higher-order language statements which cause programs to be operated and input/output operations to be performed (see Figure 5.6). These statements, which are the media in which tasks are coded, are prepared from a sequence parameter matrix which graphically portrays each operation and the order in which it is to be accomplished. This sequence parameter matrix is used as the task verification matrix.

Test lists indicating which sequence parameters are to be activated for each test are constructed from the task verification matrix.

In the 465L Planning Subsystem a new concept of task verification evolved because many tasks contained a large number of programs and simultaneous verification of all programs was found not to be feasible. This concept, called component verification, is the verification of a portion of a task at a time. For example, assume that a task

	TAG	OPERATION	OPERAND	EXIT IND.	EXIT
1	PR1	OPER	PROG 1	1	PR2
2				2	PD1
3	PR2	OPER	PROG 2	1	PR1
4	PD1	DO	R1	N	PR1
5				F	END
6	END	END TSK			

Figure 5.6   Sequence parameter matrix. The first column in this diagram is simply the step number. The second column contains the operation tag; the tags in the last column (Exit) refer to this second column. The third column contains the operation to be performed; for instance, OPER indicates that the program listed in the fourth column is to be *operated*. The fourth column contains the identification of the entity we are concerned with; for instance, PROG1 indicates program 1. The fifth column indicates the next step to which to go after this step is completed; for instance, in the first two lines, program 1 has two possible exit points. The sixth column contains the tag of the next step to which to go, depending on the exit point listed in the fifth column.

consists of programs A, B, C, D, and E. One component, then, might consist of programs A and B, another of programs C and D, a third of C, D, and E, and the largest of A, B, C, D, and E. When tasks are verified in this fashion, the task verification matrix developed for verifying components smaller than the total task is based on subsets of the sequence parameters which make up the total task.

Upon completion of the test lists, the inputs needed to activate the specified sequence parameters and operate the tests are devised and recorded. The subsystem verification model data previously employed in program verification are again used. Their usage in both program and task verification minimizes the need for manually calculating expected outputs during task verification, since the outputs calculated during program verification can be used.

Any expected outputs which have not been computed during program verification are now computed. All expected outputs are recorded.

The task verification plan is now complete. It is reviewed for accuracy and completeness by the technical supervisor, and changes are made as needed. As in program verification, test weights are applied to enable the manager to assess progress more closely.

Verification on the Computer. The second step in task verification is actual verification on the computer. This key step in the production process requires many functions to be performed. In the first function, utilizing the JOVIAL program decks, every program is recompiled with the same version of the Compool (data dictionary). This step is very important since the Compool changes fairly often, and all programs must reflect the same data definitions. The results of the compilations are binary program decks. The second function is the completion of the coding of task parameters. There are two kinds of task parameters, the sequence parameters previously mentioned and input/output parameters, which completely define the input/output operations that the task performs. The task parameters are coded, and symbolic decks and listings are produced. These are then submitted for assembly, which results in a task parameter binary deck and listing. At this time the input/output assignment cards are prepared. The system control program, the Executive, when initiating a task, first checks the mounted tapes against the assignments specified on these cards. The third function is the generation or updating of the system master tape with the binary task parameter and program decks. The fourth function is the generation of data environment. In devising the verification plan, the inputs were simply recorded on paper. The function of this step is to generate these same data on tape or disc. The fifth function is the actual operation of the task for the purpose of determining whether the *initial environment* was correctly established by the Executive. The initial environment consists of all programs and data which are to be in core when the task begins to operate.

The last step is the complete operation of each test of the task on the computer. As in program verification, the expected outputs are compared with the actual computer outputs. Causes of variances are determined, changes are made, and the task is rerun until the actual outputs match the expected outputs. When all actual and expected outputs agree, the task is considered to be verified.

Internal Release Phase

Purpose. This phase consists of the "packaging" of the card decks, listings, tapes, and documents that comprise the Planning Subsystem and delivery of all these components to the group that will perform testing of the entire Planning Subsystem as an integrated whole and will install it on the user's computer(s). Equally important is the documentation, including program specifications and computer, operator, and other user handbooks. These documents perform several functions: (1) they give a general overview of the subsystem; (2) they present to operators and programmers the specific methods for actually running the system on the computer; (3) they present the specific methods by which the users will actually operate the system; (4) they specify, via flow diagrams, coding specifications, etc., how the system was produced and thus indicate how it can be corrected, maintained, and modified for future needs. Without documents that are complete, accurate, and clear, users would not know what to do with the decks, listings, and tapes.

Problems in Internal Release and Their Solution. Perhaps the main problem is that, all too often, the internal release phase is not regarded in its true light, that is, the technical persons who produce a good program subsystem feel that they have then done their job and that it is not important to ensure that the components are released in an orderly, organized manner. All of the previous phases may have been done extremely well, resulting in a high-quality subsystem. But if little attention is given to the manner in which decks and tapes are assembled, sequenced, and turned over, a poor first impression may be created on development personnel conducting Category II testing,[3] and subsequently on the users. These impressions can persist so that the subsystem is regarded as being of poorer quality than is really the case. Our solution has been to procedurize this phase, thus ensuring that all necessary steps are followed without exception.

Methodology of Internal Release (see Figure 5.7). This phase consists of producing card decks and tapes, and writing the necessary documentation. Some of the documents will already have been written in previous phases of the production process and need only be updated at the release phase. Other documents, the contents of which depend on the results of the final phases of verification, are considered part of the release package; however, they will not be completed until several weeks after the internal release phase.

The release package consists of card decks, tapes, and documentation. All card decks are accurately identified. They are assigned version numbers which will be updated each time a deck modification is made. The card decks included in the release package are as follows:

Symbolic JOVIAL program decks.
Binary program decks.
Symbolic task parameter decks.
Binary task parameter decks.

Only one tape is a part of the release package. It is the system

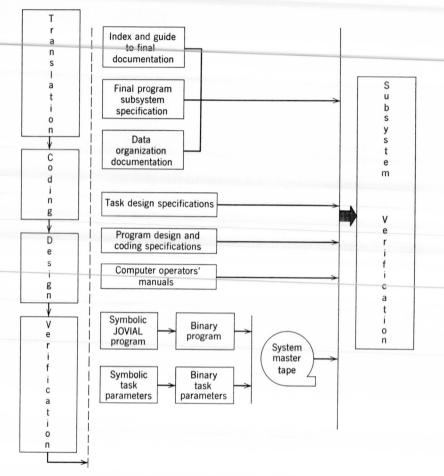

Figure 5.7   Internal release methodology.

master tape and contains the Executive programs, the necessary utility programs and tasks, and all of the 465L Planning Subsystem programs and tasks.

Documentation is the last part of the release package. It consists of the more significant documents produced in the various phases:

An over-all index and guide to final documentation.
Final program subsystem specification.
Data organization documentation.
Task design specifications.

Program design and coding specifications.
Computer operator manuals.

It should be noted, of course, that the group which has produced the subsystem does not divest itself of responsibility after internal release is completed. This group continues with on-going maintenance responsibilities for a specific period.

Maintenance consists of many functions. As noted previously in this chapter, a large-scale program system is so complex that it can never be considered fully checked out. One of the most important aspects of maintenance, therefore, is an on-going search for design and programming errors in the system and correction of these errors. Of course, operational use of the system will also uncover errors which must be corrected. Another aspect of maintenance consists of constant changes which must be made to various parts of the programs, especially those having to do with input/output functions, in order to adjust to varying equipment configurations as items are repaired, modified, or replaced by newer models. Perhaps the most important aspect of maintenance stems from changing user requirements. It has been said that any system produced today, whether it be a purely hardware or a software system, is obsolete even before it is completed. Therefore, to keep the system reasonably up to date with user needs, periodic modifications are necessary. With a program system, these can be made in a "piecemeal" way, changing parts of programs a little at a time to meet a new or altered requirement. Instead, these modifications can be made in sweeping model changes, where large parts of the program system are modified to meet a whole group of new or changed requirements. In either case the costs can be quite high because of the great complexity of the program system.

5.3   TIME PHASING

In this chapter, the actual management methods and controls used to produce the 465L Planning Subsystem have been documented. A question that will inevitably arise is, how much time should this production process take, and, given an estimate of the size of the program system to be produced, how many programmers are needed?

Experience indicates that the total production process for the *initial* development of a large-scale computer program system should take a minimum of twelve months. By "initial" is meant the first time that the system is produced. If the same system is later updated, expanded, or otherwise revised, the time required would probably be less than twelve months. This assumes adequate manpower, computer time, and so forth. The relative weight to be placed on each phase is as follows. Of course, there will necessarily be some overlapping of the phases.

Translation phase	1 month
Design phase	3 months
Coding phase	1 month
Verification phase	6 months
Internal release phase	1 month

Furthermore, experience indicates that a useful working figure is to assume that production will be at the rate of 12 machine instructions per man per day, assuming average level of programming experience, or 240 machine instructions per month, assuming 20 working days per month. These figures take into account vacations and holidays during the year. It should be made clear that this production rate covers the entire period from the start of translation to the conclusion of internal release.

Of course, the figure of 12 machine instructions per man per day will inevitably be increased as the production process becomes better defined and as the programming state of the art advances. Also, it may become possible to reduce the twelve month time span.

Assume that a manager is to produce a computer program system, which it is estimated will contain 72,000 instructions (this estimate must be based upon extensive data-processing experience). Using the rate of 12 machine instructions per man per day, we arrive at a needed manpower figure of 25 programmers for 12 months. By means of the time phasing chart above, the manager can develop detailed work plans and thus keep close check on whether the schedule is being adhered to.

5.4   SUMMARY AND CONCLUSION

The role of this chapter is twofold:

1. To emphasize that, as computer program systems become larger and more complex, it is imperative that managers have a carefully conceived, workable plan for the production process.

2. To make available our experiences in managing the production of a 320,000-instruction computer program system.

The *raison d'être* for computer program systems is that they perform intricate calculations far more rapidly and accurately than human beings can do. A computer program system operates in an orderly fashion, at lightning speed.

But in order to produce a good program system, managers must themselves utilize a system of production, or what has been termed in this chapter a "production process." We might say that managers need a "system for the system" which will help them to produce the best computer program system possible in minimal time and with the lowest costs.

This chapter has delineated such a system, consisting of five primary phases: translation, design, coding, verification, and release. No claims are made that these five phases constitute the "perfect" management system for producing a large-scale computer program system. No doubt, with the passage of time and the achievement of further experience, better "systems for the system" will be evolved.

5.5 GLOSSARY

465L System. The 465L System is the Strategic Air Command Control System. It is a large-scale, computer-based program system that is being designed and programmed by the System Development Corporation, in cooperation with other organizations, for use by the Strategic Air Command.

Compool. Communications tag pool. This is a collection of information relating all item tags, table tags, constants, and parameters to absolute storage locations in core memory or to auxiliary storage. A Compool may take the form of a magnetic tape, a deck of punched cards, or a printout.

Executive. This is a set of support programs which was especially designed to control the operation of the Planning and Control subsystems which comprise the 465L System. The Executive controls input/output operations, sequencing of programs, and so forth.

Functional Area. This consists of each major subdivision of the Planning Subsystem, as derived from the design requirements. The basic criterion employed in defining logical subdivisions is the functional interdependency of individual functions. (Refer to "Translation Phase," step 1.)

Functional Flow Chart. This is a form of documentation which helps ensure that the analysis ("Translation Phase," steps 1, 2, and 3) is performed correctly. It signifies completion of analysis and is essentially a graphic presentation of the prose statement of requirements. Programmers are required to produce functional flow charts for each design requirement subfunction. (Refer to "Translation Phase," step 3.)

Jovial. This is the higher-level programming language that has been developed at the System Development Corporation and is being used in the 465L System.

Logical Task, Logical Job. *Logical task* is the same as the "task" defined below. It is the task in a preliminary stage of development. The primary distinction is that machine constraints have not yet been considered. Similarly, a *logical job* is a "job" as defined below. It is the job in a preliminary stage of development, for which machine constraints have not yet been considered.

Design Requirements. These documents constitute the information base for the computer program production process. They are the primary inputs (along with the system integration documents) to the translation phase. Design requirements contain the following sections: general statement and description of the requirements; logical designs, including assumptions, in both prose and diagram form; specific requirements indicating the areas of human interaction with the machine; specific operational program requirements.

Design Requirement Subfunction. A subfunction is a further breakdown of a functional area.

Functional Area. The purpose of breaking down functional areas into subfunctions is to distribute the workload to programmers on an equitable basis. (Refer to "Translation Phase," Step 2.)

Preliminary Program Subsystem Specification. This document incorporates the results of the translation phase. It identifies the logical tasks and jobs, the data sets, and the input and output requirements of the subsystem. It also contains prose and graphic descriptions of the manner in which the various logical tasks and jobs relate. Publication of this document signals the completion of the translation phase. (Refer to "Translation Phase," step 5.)

Program, Task, Job. The definition of a *program* is equivalent to or the same as that which is standard throughout the programming profession. A *task* is a set of computer programs and associated data environment designed to fulfill specific requirements stated in a part of or in one or more design requirements. Each set (i.e., each task) is discrete in that it has a unique identification and a definite beginning and end, and operates relatively independently of other sets. A *job* (for the Planning Subsystem) is defined as a set of tasks (this "set" may be comprised of one or more tasks) that will perform the functions called for by a "communication request." (A "communication request" is the means by which the 465L Planning Subsystem is utilized by SAC personnel.

They input to the computer, via cards or a keyboard, "communication requests" for specific functions that are to be performed by the Planning Subsystem. The *job* fulfills these requests.)

System Integration Document. This document is produced before the start of the production process as defined in this paper and is thus one of the inputs to the translation phase. It presents what are called "communication procedures" in the 465L Planning Subsystem. These communication procedures include the message formats by which SAC planners request various aspects of the Planning Subsystem to operate, together with the formats of display and hardcopy outputs produced in response to the input requests. The document specifies, for each input request, operational code, permissible entries, format, range of entries or unique values of entries, system response to entries. For outputs, it specifies the format and range of values, together with a sample of the output.

Table, Item. A *table* is a definite allocation of core memory or auxiliary storage registers for the storage of specified information. An *item* consists of one or more bits in a table which are set aside for the storage of specified information.

REFERENCES

1. For a description of the generalized phases for military command and control systems see L. Farr, *A Description of the Computer Program Implementation Process*. Santa Monica, Calif.: System Development Corporation, TM-1021/002/00, February 25, 1963.
2. Air Force concepts of system testing are described in *Testing/Evaluation of Systems, Subsystems, and Equipments*. Washington, D.C.: Department of the Air Force, Air Force Regulation No. 80-14, August 14, 1963. These concepts, however, apply specifically to hardware systems such as missiles and aircraft.
3. *Ibid.*

Chapter Six

Personnel and Organizational Design

P. E. Rosove

6.1 INTRODUCTION

The transformation of a manual information-processing system into an automated system built around the digital computer and its peripheral equipment implies a change in the technological base of the enterprise. Such a change has implications for the human aspects of the enterprise that are closely linked to the technological base—the skills and knowledge of personnel, the content of jobs at all levels, and the organizational characteristics of the enterprise.[1]

The design of an appropriate organizational structure and the selection and acquisition of the necessary personnel must be recognized as long lead-time items in system development. The increasing complexity and sophistication of contemporary technology inevitably results in a lengthening of the time required to select and train personnel. This is particularly true for a new field such as information systems. The development, operations, and maintenance of information systems demand new types of personnel with unique skills and qualifications—computer programmers, systems analysts, human factors scientists, and mathematicians. The typical manual precursor system in both military and nonmilitary enterprises may require very few personnel or none with such backgrounds and training.

168

Personnel and organizational design addresses itself to the task of creating a personnel and an organizational model which is "compatible" with the automated elements of the new system. The organizational structure and the utilization of human resources are viewed as variables which affect system performance in the same sense that system hardware and computer programs affect it.[2] Different selections of personnel and a different organizational arrangement in association with the new computer complex will result in different levels of system performance. The personnel and organizational designer's task, therefore, is to create an organization which will maximize system performance.

For the sake of clarity, it is desirable to define what is meant here by "organization" and to make explicit the relationship of this concept to the term "personnel." "Organization" is defined as a hierarchical structure of positions and groups each of which is assigned specific tasks and responsibilities. Relationships, authority, and the flow of information which link the positions and groups into a patterned structure are formally defined in written rules, procedures, and regulations. Positions are manned by human beings. Personnel and organizational design, then, is concerned with (1) the characteristics of the personnel manning the positions; (2) the characteristics of the positions; (3) the arrangement of the positions to form functionally related units and groups; and (4) the arrangement of units and groups so as to meet most effectively the operational objectives of the system. Organizational design must determine the lateral and vertical relationships of all positions and units. Also, it is concerned with the relationships linking all positions and units to the physical facilities, system hardware, and computer operations.

As a result of the introduction of automated information processing, new jobs may be created and existing ones altered or eliminated. New tasks, duties, and responsibilities may be added to existing jobs, while old tasks, duties, and responsibilities may be abolished. Tasks, duties, and responsibilities may be shifted from one job or position to another with or without modification. The use of a computer to carry out routine types of decision making may alter the existing chain of command. The flow of information into and out of the computer and its auxiliary devices may change the flow of information both laterally and vertically throughout the old organization. The extent of change in the organization may be such that not only will jobs be transformed but departmental lines may also require modification. Thus, the formulation of an organizational structure that will be compatible with an information system built around the electronic digital computer is a key step in the development process.

With respect to the personnel of the new system, the developer must resolve these types of questions:

- What new tasks must be performed to carry out new system functions?
- What behavioral problems are associated with the conduct of the new tasks?
- What kinds of skills, intelligence, and knowledge must the system personnel possess if they are to perform the tasks efficiently?
- What kinds of people possess the required skills, intelligence, and knowledge or could acquire them with the least effort if necessary?
- What is the impact of a computer-based technology upon the job classification system in use in the enterprise?
- To what extent will the content of existing jobs be changed by the introduction of a new, computer-based information system?
- What will be the effect of the new system upon existing career ladders?

Insofar as the organizational characteristics of the new system are concerned, the developer is faced with the following types of questions:

- How shall tasks be grouped into jobs or positions?
- What combination of positions shall comprise work units, groups, or crews?
- What is the most efficient spatial and temporal arrangement of work units for the conduct of system functions?
- How does the introduction of a computer-based information system affect the centralization/decentralization ratio in the enterprise? Does it necessarily imply "recentralization"?
- Will the use of a computer for routine types of decisions eliminate jobs at the level of middle management?
- What effect will the automation of information processing have upon the chain of command in the enterprise?
- Does the use of a computer-based information system imply changes in the relationships between top management and staff personnel? Between staff and line personnel? Between management and line personnel?

Many similar questions must be asked and resolved by the system developer. The developer cannot accept the existing personnel system or organization of the enterprise as fixed; he must examine it in the light of a new technological base.

In the study of the operations of the user's current system which the developer conducts during the initial stage of his effort, an analysis of the organization and personnel manning is also undertaken. This study is an input to the determination of organizational requirements, organizational design, and the production of products relative to the new organizational structure and personnel manning. The organizational study should result in the acquisition of the following types of information:

- The organizational doctrine and philosophy of the enterprise, if any (for example, there may be a preference for decentralized decision making under normal conditions).
- The organization charts, including definitions of tasks and responsibilities for all identified positions and units.
- A description of the chain of command, including the assignment of responsibility for decision making.
- A description of the communication network—the flow of information upward, downward, and laterally through the organizational structure.
- The personnel doctrine or philosophy (for example, job rotation as a means of developing personnel skills, or promotion from within).
- Manning assignments, that is, the types and numbers of personnel assigned to identified positions in the organization.
- A description of the interfaces between the organization under development and associated organizations.

It is important for the system developer to clarify at the outset the user's philosophy and attitude toward his current organization. This attitude may range from a belief that his traditional organization is sacrosanct to, at the opposite end of the spectrum, a conviction that his organization is obsolete and requires a major overhaul. Obviously the developer will be faced with entirely different problems in these two extreme cases. The developer should educate the user, if necessary, to accept the idea that the automation of information processing *may* require extensive changes in his current organization. No one can say in advance, of course, to what extent organizational change may be required.

The developer can also anticipate that the user may undergo some degree of organizational change while the system development effort is under way. Procedures, therefore, must be established from the inception of the development effort whereby the user can keep the developer informed of such changes.

As we have seen, cost analyses are conducted at various stages in the development process. Organizational considerations must also play an important part as variables in such studies. In the most obvious case, if an automated information system is replacing a manual system, a large reduction in the number of personnel in specific skill categories may be achieved. If no reductions in the number of employees are planned, there may still be extensive changes in the types of personnel to be utilized. A reduction or a rise in the level of skill required for many job categories may have an impact on the cost of operating the system. It is evident, then, that the relationship between cost and system effectiveness is dependent, in part at least, upon organizational factors. In a broader sense, organizational change may have profound cost implications. Relatively few research data are available on the extent to which system performance is degraded or improved by major organizational changes.[3] Nevertheless, anyone who has had a close association with a large organization knows what reorganizations can do, over the short term at least, to morale, attitudes, and performance. Developers should bear in mind that organizational changes will have an impact upon performance and that this is an area in which extreme caution must be exercised.

Throughout the process of organizational design, then, tradeoffs must be made among cost, organizational requirements, and system effectiveness. During the early stages of system development, cost analysis and feasibility studies deal with a variety of alternative physical configurations. Throughout these studies, organizational alternatives should be compared also as one aspect of the over-all system configuration. As the organizational design evolves, such comparative studies can acquire a greater degree of precision and quantification.

6.2   PERSONNEL AND ORGANIZATIONAL DEVELOPMENT PROCESS

The development process for personnel utilization and organization follows the logical problem-solving cycle described in Chapter 4. Each step in the logical flow begins with a definition of requirements. These requirements statements are then subjected to analyses from which a set of more detailed requirements is derived. Through this iterative process the most efficient utilization of the user's human resources and the most effective organizational arrangement are defined. However, in order to present a logical picture of the personnel and organizational development, we shall describe the process, as we have done in previous chapters, as if it were a linear sequence of events and activities. Figure 6.1 is a schematic representation of the

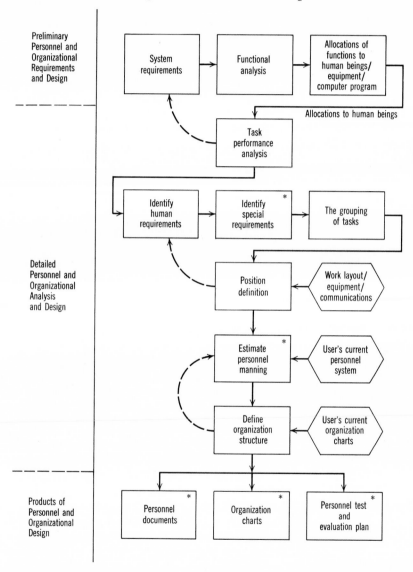

Figure 6.1 The personnel and organizational development process. *Indicates user review and concurrence.

process. The figure shows, in flow diagram form, the inputs, the sequence of activities, and the final products. The subsequent narrative in this chapter follows the boxes indicated on the flow diagram. The reader should bear in mind that the development flow does not proceed in a straight line from box to box but *cycles* back from later to earlier boxes as more detailed analyses make it possible to specify requirements more precisely. This cycling process is suggested by the dashed lines. After each iteration, coordination must be accomplished with respect to the development of facilities, hardware, communications, and computer programs. Design decisions made in these areas affect personnel and organizational factors. Similarly, design decisions made in the personnel and organizational areas *should* affect the design of facilities, hardware, communications, and computer programs.

Preliminary Personnel and Organizational Requirements

Preliminary analysis of the user's needs, objectives, and problems results in the publication of a system requirements document. The specification of preliminary requirements should include statements pertaining to personnel and organization. The requirements document will normally describe in gross terms the organization necessary to operate and maintain the system. These organizational requirements will also include estimates of the personnel needed to man the new system. Many organizational requirements are also implicit in the operational and the physical configuration concepts of the system.

These preliminary concepts describe the major components of the system and the geographic dispersal of equipment, facilities, and operational units. They suggest, if they do not specifically define, the interactions, relationships, and flow of information among the system components. Figure 6.2 is an example of a gross conceptual model for a medical information system. Note that the figure, in addition to showing the types of major components of the system and the flow of data among them, also indicates the relationships of the components to external organizations, that is, interfaces. This type of conceptual model, plus a narrative description, may be regarded as a gross organizational model of the system—a preliminary effort to conceptualize the characteristics of the new organization. Note also that several types of personnel categories are indicated: private physicians, data processors, staff physicians, medical researchers, and librarians.

Gross conceptual and functional models developed during the preliminary analyses are derived through study of the sequence of

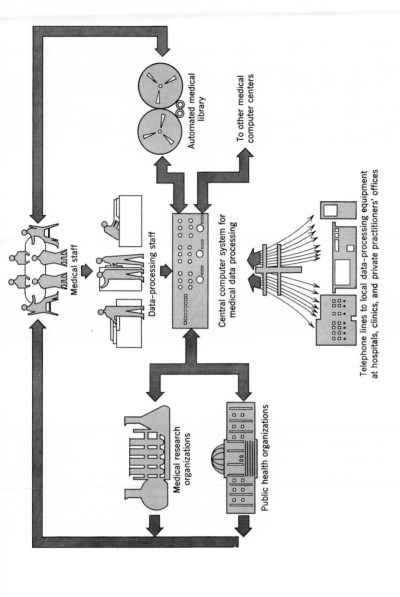

Figure 6.2 Gross conceptual model of a medical information system.

Automated medical library

To other medical computer centers

Medical staff

Data-processing staff

Central computer system for medical data processing

Telephone lines to local data-processing equipment at hospitals, clinics, and private practitioners' offices

Medical research organizations

Public health organizations

functions considered necessary to accomplish the user's objectives. Although these functional analyses stem from the user's current organization, in addition to his objectives, their focus is upon functions, not upon the organization as such. The functional analysis on the basis of which the gross functional model is created is concerned also with the flow of information required to accomplish the user's objectives. Given such data, it is possible for the developer to begin to establish organizational requirements—those which will be carried over from the user's current organization, as well as new ones.

As the development process continues into more detailed design work, analyses are carried out to determine the allocation of functions to the equipment, computer programs, and personnel. These analyses are described in Chapter 4. Once the human action and the organizational requirements are specified, it becomes possible to begin to isolate *task performance requirements*. The following pages describe how these requirements are determined and the subsequent development flow leading to detailed personnel and organizational requirements and end items.

Detailed Personnel and Organizational Design

Task Performance Analysis. The functional flow diagrams prepared in the course of earlier design work play an important part in the determination of task performance requirements. These flow diagrams show the sequences of tasks and the content of each task, at a gross level, which must be carried out if the subfunctions and functions are to be accomplished to meet the user's objectives. The diagrams, it will be recalled, show for each task the inputs, the decision points, the computations and processing, and the outputs going to subsequent tasks. These flow diagrams are the key inputs to the work of task performance analysis. The nature of this analytic work is described below.

TASK DESCRIPTION. A "task" is defined by R. B. Miller as "a group of activities that often occur in temporal proximity (but not necessarily so) with the same displays and controls, and that have a common purpose."[4] A task description may range in degree of specificity from a statement such as "monitors the status of (military) forces" to "loads appropriate magnetic tapes onto assigned tape drives." Task descriptions may emerge at any stage in the development of a system. However, the main source of data for the creation of detailed task descriptions is the functional flow diagrams. Each task description specifies *what* must be done by system personnel if a given function and/or subfunction is to be accomplished. A list of task descriptions, therefore, represents a set of human requirements. The task descriptions are the link in the development process between the functional system requirements, on the one hand, and the human performance requirements, human engineering requirements, organizational requirements, and training requirements, on the other hand. The function of the task description is to make clear in as much detail as possible the relationships between personnel and (1) computer programs, (2) equipment, (3) communications networks, (4) facility work layouts, and (5) other personnel.

Task description statements normally begin with action verbs such as "loads," "transmits," "supervises," "reads." Some examples of task description statements in information systems are as follows:

- "Monitors weather status at airbases."
- "Loads appropriate magnetic tapes onto assigned tape drives."
- "Reads in control cards."
- "Transmits real-time commands on punched data cards."

Since the task description specifies human performance requirements, these data also constitute the performance criteria which serve in the testing and evaluation of system personnel. The human performance requirements are, therefore, basic inputs to the development of the personnel test and evaluation plan. However, the more detailed performance parameters which are essential for personnel testing and evaluation are the products of task analysis.

TASK ANALYSIS: IDENTIFICATION OF HUMAN REQUIREMENTS. The task descriptions specify the kinds of tasks which system personnel must perform. These requirements are then subjected to analyses—task analyses—to determine *how* they can be met and to establish the human performance parameters for each task. For each task description there should be an accompanying task analysis. Task analyses consist of the systematic study of the human behavior patterns and qualities needed to accomplish each task. The degree of task difficulty must be estimated, taking all operational conditions into consideration. Estimates of task difficulty must be related to pertinent personnel requirements, such as educational background, experience, skill level, and physical traits. Each task is analyzed to determine performance parameters, such as the time in which the task must be accomplished, accuracy and reliability tolerances, and security requirements. In its turn, then, task analysis generates a more detailed set of requirements, those which system personnel will have to possess in order to carry out the specified tasks.

The distinction between task description and task analysis and the kind of information generated by task analysis may be brought out by considering the plotter's task in the manual system of air defense. The task description of the plotter's duties would include this sort of statement: "Plots the tracks of aircraft with their assigned track numbers on the plotting board in grease pencil from information supplied by radar surveillance operators via telephone." Task analysis examines the human problems associated with performing the described task. The case of the manual air defense system plotter is of special interest since it involves an unusual physical requirement. Analysis of the task showed that since the plotter would have to write on a transparent board from a position *behind* the board, while other system personnel (radar operators, aircraft identification personnel, and intercept controllers) viewed the plots from positions in front of the board, the plotter would be required to print letters and numbers *backwards*. Analysis of the plotting task revealed, therefore, that performance of the task would require the physical dexterity and mental capability to write backwards, and it also indicated that learning to write backwards would be a training requirement for plotters.

As an example of the type of problem of special interest to the task analyst we can discuss briefly the need to investigate the task stimulus. What kind of input initiates the task? A task may be initiated by a variety of stimuli—voice communications, a light going on, a wall display, or the results of a mathematical computation. Each of these types of stimuli has different implications for human requirements. If a given task is initiated by a coded display on the face of a console located in a darkened room, this has implications for the characteristics of the human beings who must perform the task, such as the ability to remember the meaning of the code, perceptiveness, and attentiveness. When auditory or visual signals initiate tasks at a physiological or reflexive level, the implication for human qualities are entirely different from those for a situation in which the initiation of a task depends upon calculations, logical reasoning, insight, or judgment. Some tasks are initiated by stimuli which are obscured by obstacles or "noise," as in the case of coded messages already noted above, or of static on a radio receiver or "clutter" on a radar receiver. It is apparent that for these various kinds of tasks the nature of the initiating stimuli has important implications for the characteristics of the human beings who must respond to them. Determining the relationship between the initiating stimuli and these human qualities is a significant part of the work of the task analyst.

Many different types of analyses may be conducted to determine the kinds of human characteristics needed to perform the essential system tasks. "Event-sequence," "time-line," "contingency," "task criticality," and "link" analyses are some of the types which may be carried out. Since these types of analyses are described in the technical literature, no attempt will be made here to review them.[5] It suffices for our purposes to say that the developer must decide which among these various techniques or others are the most appropriate for the analysis of his particular design problems.

The data derived from task descriptions and task analyses may result in a decision that a given task is beyond human capabilities. If this conclusion is reached by the designers, alternative methods for accomplishing the task must be studied. For example, tasks which require extreme performance speeds, unusual degrees of accuracy or reliability, or extensive mathematical calculations typically would be assigned to the computer rather than to personnel. In cases where tasks are assigned to personnel or some combination of personnel and equipment or computer programs, task description and task analysis data become inputs to personnel and organizational design, the design of training at both the individual and the system level, the design of operating procedures, the design of operator handbooks, the design of operator performance test and evaluation, and those hardware design aspects referred to as "human engineering."

Identify Special Personnel Requirements. The designer must be particularly concerned with personnel requirements which are unusually critical for successful operation of the new system or which impose unusual hardships or skill requirements upon personnel. In the most obvious case, a user who has had no requirements in the past for computer programmers and hence no experienced programmers on his staff imposes a severe burden upon the skills of his available personnel when he acquires a computer-based information system.

This problem is illustrated by the Backup Interceptor Control (BUIC) System, 416M, for the SAGE system of air defense. A new factor was introduced into the design of BUIC by the requirements for completely Air Force manning at each operational site, as distinct from partly military-partly civilian contractor personnel, which had prevailed in SAGE. This requirement was called for with respect to equipment maintenance personnel for computers, consoles, and input/output equipment; computer programming personnel; and personnel to prepare, conduct, and analyze simulated system exercises run on the computers. Acquiring appropriately trained personnel became a critical factor for the military. The developer must clarify the implications of such a major shift for the user.

In the fulfillment of a contract for the development of personnel requirements, the developer may establish special requirements in addition to the routine variety as a device to call the user's attention to potential problems in this area. If funds are limited, as they were in the case of the BUIC system, development activities may be limited *only* to study of the special personnel requirements.

Two problems about identifying special personnel requirements should be mentioned. First, it is necessary to identify such requirements as early in the development process as possible so that subsequent decisions can be made with respect to funding and allotting responsibility for their detailed development. This can become a complex issue seriously affecting ultimate system performance since special personnel requirements may not become clearly evident until relatively late in the development process—too late for adequate design. Second, if, as a result of an austerity budget, the contract for the development activity restricts the contractor to a concern for special personnel requirements only, the user, with the developer's assistance, should define the area of "special" coverage with great care and be prepared to fill the development gap between the special and the nonspecial personnel.

The Grouping of Tasks. At this point in the development process, design activities have resulted in the allocation of functions to human beings and have been devoted to the identification and description of all the tasks which must be accomplished. Task analysis has been conducted to determine the types of human characteristics required to carry out the tasks. However, the tasks have not yet been assigned to specific system personnel. The next problem is to group tasks in such a way that it will become possible to assign these groups to positions in the organization structure. The design objectives are to conserve available manpower and to make maximum use of existing knowledge, experience, and training.

A variety of criteria is used in the grouping of tasks. These include (1) a common objective or function; (2) the temporal sequence in which tasks must be performed; (3) use of the same equipment; (4) the physical location of the tasks; (5) communications media required to perform the tasks; (6) common human capacities and capabilities; (7) the level of task difficulty; (8) the accuracy and reliability required; (9) the nature of the tasks, that is, routine/nonroutine, frequent/infrequent, critical/noncritical, classified/nonclassified (in military systems); (10) the time required to perform the tasks; and (11) the grouping of tasks in the user's current organization.

Depending upon the characteristics of the particular system involved, any one or any number of these criteria may determine a specific task grouping. Normally, a task grouping will be based upon several closely related criteria. The surveillance tasks in the SAGE system, for example, are grouped with reference to a specific piece of equipment in a particular location; the accomplishment of the surveillance tasks follows a highly routinized and repetitive sequence of events, actions, and decisions; and the surveillance tasks require a limited and consistent level of human ability.

A good example of the grouping of tasks around the criteria of accuracy, reliability, and criticality is provided by the design of a centralized keypunch facility in the augmentation data-processing system of the USAF Satellite Test Center. The Air Force Space Systems Division is responsible for the command and control of orbiting satellites. This activity is performed by a world-wide network of tracking stations which are linked to a central, computer-controlled complex— the Satellite Test Annex at Sunnyvale, California. As the satellites pass over the earth, radar and telemetry data are transmitted from the tracking stations to the Annex, where they are digested by a number of computer programs; in turn, the Annex transmits to the satellites via the tracking stations new instructions relevant to the operations of the satellites in space. The consequences to the mission of a satellite of the introduction of errors through a keypunch input device are very serious. Such missions are, of course, extremely costly operations. The input of a single error via a keypunch can stop a computer during the flight of a satellite or place erroneous parameters into the command instructions. Downtime on a computer during the course of a mission while the operators attempt to track down the error can jeopardize the mission objective, while the introduction of incorrect parameters in a command instruction to the satellite can result in the transmission back to earth of irrelevant or erroneous data or no data at all.

The solution to this problem in the course of design activities was to group all keypunching tasks and to attempt to prevent data errors from entering the system by placing all keypunching operations in one central location under the supervision of a highly qualified person. This solution also called for the associated design of unique quality control procedures.

Position Definition. Position definition is the act of matching human characteristics and qualities to a specific group of tasks. A "position" is composed of a grouping or cluster of related tasks which are assigned to one man in the system on the basis of his defined human qualities.

The developer designs positions in the new system with a number of basic assumptions or objectives: to take maximum advantage of the user's existing personnel and personnel classification schemes; to minimize the need for additional training requirements; to minimize the need for new and more difficult skills, knowledge, and experience; and to minimize disruption to the user's organization and daily operations. In order to accomplish these objectives, development activities for new military information systems rely heavily, as in the case of Air Force systems, on the existing Air Force Specialty Code (AFSC) which identifies standard job classifications. To the degree possible, the developer attempts to match new positions with available Air Force specialties. In the case of nonmilitary systems, the developer should rely on the user's personnel classification scheme.

The grouping of tasks into positions is based upon data derived from several different sources. One major source, as we have described it above, flows logically from the system requirements, functional analysis, allocations of tasks, and task performance analyses. However, other sources constrain the determination of positions. One source of constraint is the user's existing organization, personnel policies, personnel classification system, career fields, career ladders, and available human resources. Other major constraints are the hardware, communications, and facilities. Since the development efforts in these areas are carried out in parallel with the software development effort, many hardware and facility design decisions have been made before the point in the software development flow at which the determination of positions can be made. These decisions operate as constraints upon the ideal grouping of tasks at specific positions on the sole basis of functional flow requirements. The design of displays, consoles, facilities, the physical layout of operations areas, and communications networks, all set limits to the character of positions, the tasks which can be grouped into specific positions, and the relationships of positions to one another. For these reasons it is important to reach this point in the software development as early as possible—before hardware design is frozen. Otherwise a high price may ultimately have to be paid, in terms either of less effective system performance or of redesign of hardware.

The design of operator consoles, of wall displays, and of input and output devices depends upon the tasks which are to be performed by system personnel. Logically, therefore, one would expect that software design would be a lead item over hardware design. However, because of the long lead times required to produce hardware, as well as the traditional emphasis on hardware and the lack of full appreciation of the importance of software design, hardware design and facilities development are usually lead items over software. Both the design of consoles and the constraints imposed upon the alpha-numeric and geographic representations in console displays are aspects of hardware design which should be determined *after* it has been decided what tasks an operator at a position must accomplish if the system performance objectives are to be met. For example, task analysis may suggest that symbolic data should be color-coded, but the equipment design may make no provision for color.

The assignment of tasks to positions involves the weighing and evaluating of a number of alternative solutions to the problems of grouping a particular set of tasks. There is no completely objective technique for making these kinds of design decisions. Usually the making of such decisions can be assisted by extrapolation from the user's current organization. When the SAGE system of air defense replaced the manual system, for example, many of the SAGE positions were modeled after those in the earlier organization. Similarly, BUIC positions in many instances were extrapolated from current SAGE positions.

Table 6.1 is an example of the assignment of tasks to a position, that of the weapons director in the BUIC system. In the example shown, the tasks are grouped under a more general concept called a "duty," while a number of functionally related duties are listed under a still more general concept termed a "responsibility." The manner in which the tasks are grouped and categorized reflects the operational nature of the particular enterprise. In this case two functions, "control" and "coordinate," are distinguished, and within the control function two types of weapon systems are differentiated. The distinction by levels of generality between "responsibility," "duty," and "task" illustrates the different levels of design at which personnel problems may be attacked. By proceeding to a still greater degree of detail, each task can be broken down into its constituent "elements" or "actions." This is precisely what must be done for the design of operating procedures and the production of procedural handbooks. It is also a necessary step in determining the detailed training requirements for the personnel responsible for the tasks, such as the weapons director in this case.

Table 6.1
Responsibilities, Duties, and Tasks of BUIC Weapons Director*

1.0 Control the tactical performance of manned interceptors on air defense missions

    1.1 Commit manned aircraft to interception missions in response to assignments received from BUIC Senior Director (SD)
        1.11 Select weapons sources
        1.12 Specify departure base
        1.13 Utilize Commitment Assistance Display
        1.14 Select weapon tactics

    1.2 Conduct interceptions using manned aircraft
        1.21 Select communications mode (data link or voice)
        1.22 Make commitment/recommitment actions to Combat Air Patrol or interception missions
        1.23 Take airborne actions
        1.24 Return interceptors to base

    1.3 Monitor manned interceptor missions
        1.31 Make periodic checks of fuel and armament
        1.32 Receive and input pilot reports into computer
        1.33 Perform track monitoring functions to assist program
        1.34 Transmit guidance information to voice-controlled interceptors
        1.35 Make manual overrides and options when necessary

2.0 Control the tactical performance of BOMARC A and B missiles on interception missions

    2.1 Commit BOMARC missiles to interception missions as assigned
        2.11 Utilize Commitment Assistance Display if necessary
        2.12 Select weapons source

    2.2 Monitor BOMARC interceptor missions
        2.21 Monitor weapon tracking status
        2.22 Exercise manual options and program overrides as required
        2.23 Assist program in making guidance computations
        2.24 Insert kill information on successful intercepts

Table 6.1 (continued)
*Responsibilities, Duties, and Tasks of BUIC Weapons Director**

3.0 Coordinate functions to ensure continuity of responsibility
    3.1 Coordinate with BUIC Senior Director
        3.11 Assume responsibilities for commitments delegated by SD
        3.12 Request weapons commitment in adjacent sector in cooperating with that sector's SD
    3.2 Coordinate with Air Surveillance Operators
        3.21 Assign responsibility for initiation of airborne manned interceptors
        3.22 Communicate with Air Surveillance Operator concerning lateraltold tracks passed for interception
        3.23 Coordinate with receiving facility concerning tracks lateraltold for tracking purposes
    3.3 Coordinate with external agencies
        3.31 Coordinate with Army Air Defense Command Post for Air Defense Artillery engagements
        3.32 Request adjacent BUIC facility to handle specific tracks
        3.33 Relay information to Airbase Alert Centers
        3.34 Conduct or arrange for emergency rescue operations involving manned interceptors

---

* Source of the table is H. F. Jarrett et al., *Status Report of Position Description Information for the Backup Interceptor Control (BUIC) System.* Santa Monica, Calif.: System Development Corporation, TM-1001, January 29, 1963, pp. 9–10.

The degree of detail in the descriptions of tasks required of the developer by a user may be a function of the budget available. Under an austere budget, the developer might stop his analyses at the task level rather than proceeding further to the element or action level. Another alternative, which was chosen in the design of BUIC, was to provide detailed analyses beyond the task level only for personnel positions recognized to be "special," as described earlier in this chapter. These are decisions the user's management must make in consultation with the developer.

For each position identified, the software designer must specify the physical location, the equipment to be operated, the use of displays and consoles, and the communications with other positions. On the basis of this description, it is then possible to conduct detailed human engineering design of equipment, communications, work areas, and displays.

The design of positions must be integrated with what is already known about equipment characteristics and computer program operations. Where given functions and tasks have been allotted to these elements of the system rather than to personnel, the manner in which these elements will relate to personnel must be analyzed to determine possible consequences. If a position, for example, requires a human being to read a computer printout in order to carry out a given task, the design of such printouts (that is, their rate of printing, format, and legibility) must be compatible with known human capabilities. Similarly, status displays, console switches, electronic "guns," and communications media must be such as to permit effective utilization by system personnel. Where it can be anticipated that the interactions of personnel with equipment and computer programs will challenge human capabilities, such information should be transmitted to the persons in the development process responsible for the production of training plans.

Once the duties and responsibilities of positions have been delineated and integrated with known equipment characteristics and computer programs, it becomes possible to derive preliminary estimates of personnel qualifications for associated levels of the organization.

Estimate Personnel Manning. Design activities up to this point have been focused upon the qualitative aspects of the personnel who must man the system. But once these characteristics have been reliably established, it is necessary to determine, first, how many distinctive positions the system will require (so many surveillance operators, so many computer programmers, etc.) and, second, what the *total* manning requirements will be. The total manning required will depend upon operational characteristics such as workloads under various conditions and the capacity of a position to handle a given workload. The types of equipment, their locations, and the frequency of their use must also be considered. Other factors may also play a part, for example, environmental conditions, limited human resources, and budgetary constraints.

A military air defense system provides examples of the problems associated with determining total system-manning estimates. Air defense must be carried on 24 hours a day, 365 days of the year. Consequently work patterns must be broken down into shifts, such as three shifts of eight hours each or two shifts of twelve hours each. A variety of factors, such as the workload each shift must carry and the availability of human resources to the system user, enters into the determination of which of these two alternatives is preferable. The manning estimates for an air defense operation vary depending upon the mode of operation—peacetime, alert, or wartime. Under different modes of operation the number of personnel on duty for any given work period will range from skeleton crews when workloads are minimal to augmented forces when workloads are maximal. Each of these conditions and associated personnel-manning estimates must be covered in detail by the software developer.

Define Organization Structure. After each individual position in the system has been identified and the personnel manning has been estimated, the next step in the development process is the grouping of functionally related positions into units. The structure of work units (crews, shifts, branches, departments) must be designed. Supervisory positions must be differentiated from operator positions, and the relationships, interactions, and lines of authority between them established. After the structure of each unit is designed, it is then possible to establish the relationships, interactions, and lines of authority and communication flow among the various units. The organizational design which emerges from the flow of development activity—the allocation of functions to personnel, task performance analysis, the design of positions, manning estimates—must be thoroughly checked against the organizational concepts which are explicitly stated or implicitly embedded in the earliest conceptual design activity. If the results of *detailed* organizational design are not compatible with the broadly conceived organizational concepts of *preliminary* design, either the original concepts or the detailed design should be modified until the two are compatible. This illustrates the cyclical nature of the design process which has been stressed so much in this book.

We have entitled this chapter "Personnel and Organizational Design" to focus attention upon organizational design activity, which is the developer's responsibility in addition to the personnel design aspects. Our concern in this chapter is not limited to qualitative and quantitative personnel requirements information—the "QQPRI's" in Air Force procurement and guidance documentation or the so-called "personnel subsystem." Our attention must also be focused upon the arrangement of positions in a structural hierarchy which is compatible with the hardware subsystem, facilities, communications, and the computer program component of the software subsystem. Organizational design may or may not be merely a question of producing unit manning documents and organization charts which are minor variations of the existing ones. In some cases alterations to the user's organization may be minor, but in other instances, depending upon the nature of the enterprise and its objectives, major changes may be called for. Contemporary organizational arrangements in both military and nonmilitary enterprises arose and evolved through time in association with specific operational processes, such as the linear line of battle and the linear productive process of the factory assembly line. There is no assurance that contemporary organizational arrangements are equally suited for the nonlinear operational processes of a computer-based information system. John Diebold,[6] for example, writes as follows:

"New technology provides the means to build information systems which transcend the compartmentalized structure of business organization based upon functional specialties. Much of the difficulty that has been experienced in putting these new tools to work in recent years results from the fact that to do so effectively clashes with the fundamental organization system of today's business. The main shift in organization necessary to utilize the new techniques and systems capabilities will result from the integrated as opposed to the departmentalized conception of the business enterprise."

In the design of a supersonic aircraft, a nuclear submarine, or a manned spacecraft, it is obvious that considerations will have to be given by the system developer to the personnel who will man the system. It will be necessary to determine the types and numbers of persons required to operate and maintain the system. It will be necessary to determine human engineering and life-support requirements. Training plans, training equipment, and technical publications must be designed and produced. However, the degree of organizational change implied by the replacement of, say, the B-52G by the B-70, or a conventional submarine by a nuclear-powered submarine, is relatively minimal. The changes may mean more or less personnel and the modification of existing personnel skills and knowledge to some extent. In some cases, entirely new positions may have to be created, such as nuclear reactor engineers and technicians. Manned spacecraft, despite their uniqueness as systems, have been flown in the past by the traditional test pilot, although he has received additional intensive training to meet the requirements of orbital travel. With respect to this type of system, it is the ground support operation which demands detailed attention to organizational features. The development of an automated information system of the scope of the new electronic command and control systems such as SAGE or the SAC Control System, or of nonmilitary information systems of the type which is described as "total" or "integrated," implies *extensive organizational change*, not merely personnel changes with, possibly, some implications for unit or crew manning.

The subject of organizational design is large and complex. It cannot be done justice in this book. We shall limit our discussion to two illustrations of some of the types of organizational design problems created by the development of computer-based information systems: (1) the manager-staff-line-computer structure, and (2) information flow and the chain of command.

THE MANAGER-STAFF-LINE-COMPUTER STRUCTURE. In the typical large-scale enterprise, of both the military and the nonmilitary variety, top managers and commanders are assisted in their daily decision-making tasks by staff personnel. As the staff is organizationally differentiated from top management, so, too, is the line distinguished from the staff. The structure of manager-staff-line relationships has a long historical tradition, particularly in the military sphere. It is not clear at the present time what the long-range impact of the introduction of automated information-processing equipment upon these traditional organizational relationships will be. Gilbert Burck, however, has noted that one effect of computerization is the increased importance of staff functions.[7] The problem which faces the system developer when he injects the electronic digital computer into the manager-staff-line organization is essentially this: how can the computer with its auxiliary equipment be inserted into the current organizational structure to achieve the objectives and needs of the enterprise with a minimum of disruption and with maximum operational effectiveness?

Other, related questions arise. What relationship shall the automated information-processing equipment have to the top manager, the staff, and the line? Shall the computer be linked only to the staff, while relationships between the staff and the other elements of the organization remain unchanged? Or shall the computer serve both the staff and the line simultaneously, while traditional relationships remain with respect to management? Is it desirable that top management have a direct link to the computer?

There are many ways in which the automated information-processing equipment can be tied into the existing organizational structure. Figure 6.3 suggests four alternative possibilities. It is the developer's responsibility to determine in each specific case which of these, or other possible alternatives, will be the most effective. The measure of effectiveness is the contribution that the alternative makes to the stated objectives of the enterprise.

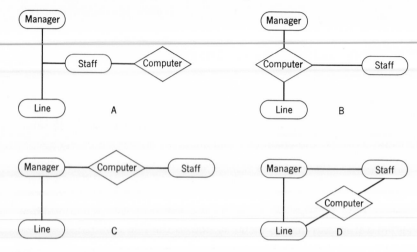

Figure 6.3 Alternative organizational possibilities for the manager-staff-line-computer structure.

Of course Figure 6.3 is a highly simplified version of the real problem. In actual large-scale information systems we are dealing, not with *a* computer, but with *several* different kinds of computers in association with a variety of other equipment: displays, consoles, input/output devices, and memory or storage units. How to design the linkages among all these units as well as those with and among the organizational units of the enterprise involves a host of difficult development problems. In Figure 6.3 we have shown the "line" structure of the enterprise within a single box; yet in the actual large-scale enterprise, of course, the relationships of line departments and divisions to one another, as well as to the computer complex, the staff, and top management, constitute another set of difficult development problems which ideally, at least, it should be the function of organizational design to resolve. This is an area of responsibility for the software developer which is still in the pioneering stage and which is not yet receiving the attention or research funds it warrants.

INFORMATION FLOW AND THE CHAIN OF COMMAND. A second and closely related problem area for the system developer pertains to the traditionally close relationship, if not equivalence, between the flow of information and the organizational chain of command in the typical enterprise. Military organization is used here as an illustration; however, the point being made applies also to nonmilitary enterprises. The differences are of degree, not of kind. In a paper dealing with the relationship between information, authority, and military organization, M. D. Feld writes:[8]

"Channels of military information thus mirror the chain of command. . . . To state it simply: the flow of commands is from superior to subordinate, the flow of information from subordinate to superior. A description of the quantity and the direction of these two items normally corresponds to a literal description of the status structure of the military organization involved."

One result of the traditional transmission of information along the vertical chain of command is that *lateral* communication is not developed to a comparable degree. In the typical large-scale organization, personnel of equal rank, for example, department heads, "are under no formal obligation to communicate with one another."[9] Automated information processing challenges this traditional indifference to lateral information flow. The computer in association with contemporary communications technology makes the flow of lateral information among personnel of equal rank in the organization feasible and economic, while technological and operational conditions (missiles and space vehicles, the need for coordination, rapid product obsolescence, etc.) make it *operationally* essential. In that very perceptive book, *Management Organization and the Computer,* the collapse of departmental walls before the onslaught of computer technology is cited several times as a common experience in a variety of enterprises.[10]

The decision as to whether or not such a collapse of walls will occur after the introduction of a computer-based information system should be based upon rational considerations of experts in organizational design in consultation with the user and in terms of the predetermined objectives of the enterprise.

Personnel Test and Evaluation Plan. In addition to personnel documents and organization charts, a major product of personnel and organizational design is a personnel test and evaluation plan. This eventually becomes one component of the *system* test and evaluation plan. The focus of this component of the system plan is upon the personnel and organizational design. We have maintained that the personnel and the nature of the organization, in addition to the facilities, hardware, and communications, are determinants of system performance. The purpose of the plan, therefore, is to provide the measures and the criteria against which both personnel and organizational effectiveness can be evaluated.

In our discussion of task performance analysis we saw that task descriptions and task analyses generated human qualitative and quantitative performance requirements. The task descriptions stated what human beings in the system must do, and the task analyses set forth how the tasks were to be performed. The task analyses established the quantitative performance parameters—the time required to perform a task, the accuracy and reliability required, the number of messages an operator must be able to input to the system per unit of time, and so on. The task analyses described in detail for each required task the educational background, the experience, and the training and physical characteristics required of system personnel. These statements become the criteria, written into the personnel test and evaluation plan, by means of which the personnel who will ultimately man the system can be tested to ensure that the system performance requirements will be met.

The plan not only specifies the criteria against which personnel and organization will be tested and evaluated but also defines the steps or stages in which the testing will occur. In the United States Air Force, for example, three stages in system testing are formally required: Category I, Category II, and Category III. Category I testing deals with individual system components and is conducted by the developer. Category II is concerned with the testing of subsystems and is a combined effort of the developer and the user. Finally, Category III testing pertains to system tests conducted by the user, with the assistance of developers, under operational conditions. Non-military systems should also approximate this sequence of testing specifically for the personnel and organizational design. The personnel test and evaluation plan should describe the objectives and the methods to be used for each test in sequence.

Table 6.1 listed the tasks assigned to the weapons director in the BUIC system. The personnel test and evaluation plan should indicate for each task the qualitative and quantitative performance criteria. A method for testing and evaluating the performance of each task must be devised. The method may range from simple paper and pencil tests to more sophisticated exercises in which simulated stimuli for each task are generated by the computer. The test methodology should also separate the tasks which can be tested individually from those which can be tested and evaluated only in a working unit or organizational context.

The development of the personnel test and evaluation plan should be closely integrated with the special personnel requirements described earlier. Since these requirements deal with personnel aspects which are unusually critical for satisfactory system performance, it follows that the emphasis for testing and evaluation should also be upon them.

6.3 LABORATORY SIMULATION FOR ORGANIZATIONAL DESIGN

In this section we shall review the role of laboratory simulation and experimentation for organizational design. Mathematical modeling and computer simulation are currently being exploited for organizational *research,* but it is primarily laboratory simulation which has made contributions to organizational design decisions in the course of system development efforts.

In a previous section of this chapter we noted that organizational design represents a pioneering area of software development. As we have remarked, this is partly due to failure on the part of users to appreciate fully the effect of injecting a computer-based information system into a large-scale enterprise. However, a major reason for the relatively slow emergence of organizational design as a legitimate area of concern to software developers is the high cost of the techniques used. This is especially true for the conduct of laboratory simulation. It is a costly proposition to plan and construct a laboratory facility, to maintain the professional and technical staff necessary to operate it, and then to conduct the on-going studies and experiments. It is, therefore, necessary for the developer to justify to the user the need for such a facility, but this is obviously difficult to do before the actual problems which might be solved by the laboratory can be identified.

The use of a laboratory facility in which design decisions can be generated, tested, and evaluated is an adjunct to the logical or rational design process. This is also true of mathematical models and computer simulation. No matter how thoroughly and efficiently the rational process of design is carried out for a large-scale, computer-based information system, there inevitably will be errors, inadequacies, and gaps in the design effort. The larger and more complex the particular system, the more valid this proposition is. It is through the application of such techniques as mathematical modeling, computer simulation, and laboratory simulation that design concepts arrived at logically from statements of system objectives and requirements can be explored, analyzed, tested, and verified. These steps are particularly important in organizational design. Unlike many other aspects of a typical large-scale system, organizational design involves many independent variables which affect organizational performance, and most of these are subjective in character. For organizational design the significant parameters are many in number, inadequately specified, or even unknown. For these reasons the conduct of experiments in a laboratory facility is of critical importance in organizational design.

Although the developer cannot guarantee in advance specific results from using a laboratory facility, he can and should ensure the user that the cost of such a facility will be more than offset by the more efficient system design which will result and by the fact that many costly changes will not be necessary because, thanks to laboratory testing, the faults in the design will be found relatively early in the development process.

Since the pioneering work in 1951-1954 of the Systems Research Laboratory of the RAND Corporation on organizational adaptation through the simulation of an air defense direction center, there has been growing recognition that organizational problems can be successfully studied through laboratory simulation in which the investigator has a high degree of control over the inputs to the system and the conditions of observation.[11] The virtues of studying organizations in the laboratory are to some degree the same as those of other types of laboratory experiments: the complexities of the natural world can be reduced; random factors can be excluded; and the effects of isolated variables can be studied. But, in addition, this technique makes possible the study of *multiple, interacting variables*. The importance of laboratory simulation for the study of military organizations should be evident: the real military organization need not be disturbed; the cost of obtaining essential knowledge can be reduced; and wartime functions and situations can be studied in advance of the real events.

In general, two types of laboratory simulation can be differentiated: functional models and operational models. Functional models do not have the scale properties of the real system but they do duplicate its basic functions. J. Jaffe and M. Berkowitz have pointed out the value of functional models in system design work.[12] M. Zelditch and T. K. Hopkins have used the term "miniature replica" to refer to this type of laboratory simulation and cite the RAND Logistics Laboratory as an example.[13] Operational models, as distinct from functional models, replicate some portion or all of the real organization. There is no need to match reality in all its complexity to test organizational concepts or theory. Indeed, as noted above, the real organization is too complicated to study for the testing of organizational hypotheses. Small temporary groups of subjects are used to simulate complex organizations. This type of simulation is referred to by Zelditch and Hopkins as the "part replica."[14] Some fragment or part of the real organization is duplicated in the laboratory with the missing parts simulated. This was the method used by RAND in the air defense studies referred to earlier and is utilized in Project SOBIG to study organizational problems in business.

In spite of the obvious differences between small groups simulating an organization in a laboratory and the real organization, valid testing of design hypotheses can be carried out. This is possible as long as the hypotheses being tested refer to properties of organizations which can be produced in the laboratory setting. For example, an arrangement of nine people into three three-man units is not an exact equivalent of a large-scale organization, but it does possess some of the basic properties of such an organization, such as division of labor, delegation of authority, coordination, and interaction.

To illustrate the role of laboratory simulation in organizational design we shall review the utilization of the Simulation Facility (SIMFAC) in the design of the Strategic Air Command Control System (465L).[15] SIMFAC was designed along the lines of a functional rather than an operational model. It is best described as a facility in which functions analogous to those being designed for the new system could be simulated at various levels of operational fidelity. But the facility was not a physical replica of the new system. There was no computer, for example, in the facility.

The major objectives of SIMFAC were (1) to aid the design process by providing a capability for testing alternative design concepts; (2) to determine the adequacy of the design specifications to meet system objectives in a simulated environment; and (3) to determine feasible alternative design features when review by the user resulted in a decision to reconsider the original design concept. These objectives fall into three distinct stages in the development process: preliminary design, postdesign/preproduction, and postproduction/postdesign. The studies conducted in SIMFAC concentrated upon the problems associated with the performance of operational tasks such as the information requirements of SAC controllers, the system utilization procedures, and organizational implications, particularly with reference to decision making, information filtering, and task allocation.

Studies in SIMFAC were conducted to determine whether the inputs as designed would meet the requirements for information associated with specific operational tasks at selected system positions, such as duty controller, materiel controller, weather controller, and the battle staff. A variety of system functions was tested, such as monitoring and controlling peacetime force exercises, and monitoring and controlling force status. Some typical organizational problems investigated included a study of the adequacy of the control of system inputs in terms of sequencing, filtering, and communications links among personnel, and the adequacy of the placement of wall displays with reference to the floor locations of operators and their information needs.

One of the virtues of laboratory simulation is that it is heuristic. Important design findings are made in one area during an investigation of another area. This occurred in SIMFAC in studies of the legibility of planned wall displays. It was found that the original plans for displays contained excessive viewing angles and viewing distances, and alpha-numeric characters which were too small. As a result of these findings, design changes were proposed in work space arrangements, operational procedures, and organization. Thus, in this case, organizational design decisions were the by-products of laboratory research conducted for other purposes.

The limitations on the use of laboratory simulation for organizational design should be understood. Such techniques cannot "prove" that one design decision is more valid than another. Since simulation models are generalizations of reality in which some properties of the actual object are left out, the manipulation of models in the course of system development leads to the raising and testing of hypotheses, not to proof. Nevertheless, with this limitation, laboratory simulation has demonstrated its utility in providing designers with objective methods whereby hypotheses (alternative design concepts) can be systematically generated and submitted to a variety of tests.

6.4   SUMMARY

This chapter has described the nature of personnel and organizational design and located its place in the system development process. Personnel and organizational design addresses itself to the task of creating a personnel and organizational model which is compatible with the new, computer-based system and the user's human resources. The types of questions that the developer should ask and attempt to answer with respect to the personnel and organization of the new system were reviewed.

The major steps in the process of detailed personnel and organizational analysis and design were identified and described. These steps included (1) task performance analysis (to determine human requirements); (2) the identification of special personnel requirements; (3) the grouping of tasks; (4) the definition of positions; (5) the estimation of personnel manning; (6) the definition of the organization structure; and (7) the creation of the personnel test and evaluation plan.

In the description of the design process for personnel and organization, the types of analyses conducted by the developer were reviewed and illustrated. The relationship of task performance data, derived from task descriptions and task analyses, to development activities conducted simultaneously with personnel and organizational design was indicated.

The importance of raising questions in the area of organizational design, as distinct from personnel design, was stressed. Some attempt was made to account for the fact that organizational design efforts have tended to be relatively neglected in comparison to personnel design work. Finally, the role and significance of laboratory simulation for the study and resolution of organizational design problems was discussed.

Throughout the description of the major steps in the process of detailed personnel and organizational design an effort was made to indicate some of the major problems, attitudinal, managerial, and technical, which must be resolved by the user and the developer if an effective system is to be produced.

REFERENCES

1. See G. P. Shultz and T. L. Whisler, *Management Organization and the Computer*. Glencoe, Ill.: The Free Press, 1960; also F. C. Mann and F. W. Neff, *Managing Major Change in Organizations*. Ann Arbor, Mich.: Foundation for Research on Human Behavior, 1961, particularly case #4. For a more general treatment of this subject see R. A. Brady, *Organization, Automation, and Society*. Los Angeles: University of California Press, 1961.
2. For a discussion of the relationship between individuals and system performance see N. Jordan, "Motivational Problems in Human-Computer Operations," *Human Factors*, 4, No. 3, 171–175.
3. There are some experimental data on this subject in R. Likert, *New Patterns of Management*. New York: McGraw-Hill, 1961, Chap. 5; also an account of the degradation of operations after the installation of a computer in an electric light and power company in F. C. Mann and F. W. Neff, Ref. 1, pp. 43–52.
4. R. B. Miller, "Task Description and Analysis," *Psychological Principles in System Development*, R. M. Gagné (ed.). New York: Holt, Rinehart, and Winston, 1962, p. 200.

5. *Ibid.; Handbook of Instructions for Aerospace Personnel Subsystem Designers,* Air Force Systems Command Manual 80-3, July 15, 1962; J. D. Folley, Jr., *Guidelines for Task Analysis,* Navy, TDC, Technical Report: NAVTRADEV-CEN 1218-2, June 22, 1964; A. P. Chenzoff, *A Review of the Literature on Task Analysis Methods,* Navy, TDC, Technical Report: NAVTRADEVCEN 1218-3, June 22, 1964.

6. John Diebold, *Beyond Automation: Managerial Problems of an Exploding Technology.* New York: McGraw-Hill, 1964, pp. 121–122.

7. Gilbert Burck, "Management Will Never Be the Same Again," *Fortune,* August 1964.

8. M. D. Feld, "Information, Authority, and Military Organization," *American Sociological Review,* **24**, No. 1 (February 1959), 19.

9. *Ibid.*

10. G. P. Shultz and T. L. Whisler, Ref. 1, pp. 140, 199, 219.

11. R. L. Chapman et al., "The Systems Research Laboratory's Air Defense Experiments," *Management Science,* **5**, No. 3 (April 1959), 250–269; see also a description of Project SOBIG, laboratory studies of organizational problems in business, in J. L. Kennedy, "The System Approach: Organizational Development," *Human Factors,* **4**, No. 1 (February 1962), 25–52.

12. M. Berkowitz and J. Jaffe, *The Development and Uses of a Functional Model in the Simulation of an Information-Processing System.* Santa Monica, Calif.: System Development Corporation, SP-584, November 2, 1961.

13. T. K. Hopkins and M. Zelditch, Jr., "Laboratory Experiments with Organizations," *Complex Organizations,* Amitai Etzioni (ed.). New York: Holt, Rinehart, and Winston, 1961, p. 473.

14. *Ibid.*

15. M. Davidson, *The Use of Simulation in the Development of Man-Machine Systems.* Santa Monica, Calif.: System Development Corporation, SP-1137, September 16, 1963.

Chapter Seven

Design and Production of System Procedures

L. A. Friedman

7.1 INTRODUCTION

Objectives of the Chapter

Before the marriage between a man and a machine can be effectively consummated, a charter must be produced which will link the two in a satisfactory relationship. This charter—a set of system procedures—enables a human being to become thoroughly acquainted with his complex, mechanical mate and to achieve proficient mastery of it. Without the charter, or with one which contains an incomplete set of operating rules, man is ill suited for this marriage.

To illustrate, there is the great contemporary love-match between man and his automobile, a relationship which is not always a happy one, possibly because the charter relating the new driver to his vehicle is not thorough or exhaustive. The transition period from naive learner to experienced driver is hazardous and unpredictable because, among other things, the novice is not supplied with a complete set of procedures to guide his behavior for all driving tasks and situations. Usually the procedures he receives are supplied in a piecemeal fashion and do not cover all contingencies. In addition, the average driver must practice his skills and attempt to become proficient in them in the actual environment of streets, roads, and freeways.

There is only one way to ensure that the new automobile driver will perform safely, efficiently, and as expected by others: we must relate in a systematized manner, under realistic or simulated conditions, the capabilities of the driver, the vehicle, and a set of procedures for operating and mastering an automotive passenger-transport system.

The best and most complete set of procedures for a driver-vehicle charter would consist of instructions for operating the vehicle, information on how automobile components function, the laws and codes of the road, the techniques for driving—including those for such tasks as passing on a curve under a variety of weather conditions and on different forms of roads—and the types of actions and decisions involved in defensive driving.

The central purpose of this chapter is to describe the functions and the unique characteristics of information system procedures, that is, their use for directing and prescribing the operation of the wedded components of large systems, and their value as a system design technique. The automotive transport system example was provided in order to focus attention on the fact that system procedures, although necessary for system operations, are frequently the unplanned products of design. In some respects the situation is analogous to the difference between the haphazard (and often emotional) instruction provided by a husband teaching his wife to drive, and the systematized program offered in high school driver training courses.

The author's prime intent, then, is to emphasize the importance and necessity of having system procedures, first, as a product to guide the "driver" who has to master the components of a computer-based information system and, second, as a system design method. To this end, the chapter will describe the underlying principles and requirements which guide the development and production of system procedures, and it will indicate the significant contributions of written procedures for the development of computer programs and other aspects of a computer-based system.

Scope of the Chapter

The first part of our discussion will be centered around the definition, purposes, and importance of system procedures; then we will proceed to a discussion of their development and production. In the sections devoted to the developmental process, there will be a review of the various sources of information upon the basis of which system procedures can be designed.

Section 7.3 contains a discussion of the interdependence of procedures design with other design activities, such as computer program design and personnel and organization design, which must be developed concurrently with the procedures. Included in this section is a discussion of the relationship of human engineering to computer program design. The final section of the chapter reviews the production of system procedures and provides some examples of them for a computer-based system. In addition, there is a short discussion of the task of validating system procedures.

Definition of System Procedures

The term "procedures" refers to a predetermined sequence of actions which should be taken to carry out some task or job, specifying what shall be done, how it shall be done, who shall do it and when. All organizations develop sets of procedures to assist in the achievement of tasks assigned to various component units. These procedures may be used by personnel to make out reports, control inventories, operate equipment, or direct other people.

With the advent of large-scale, computer-based information systems whereby various organizational functions (management decision making, inventory control, transportation, research, production, sales, etc.) interact with one another, there has arisen a requirement for what is best described as *system* procedures. In the context of the large-scale computer system, the term "system," as a modifier to "procedures," refers to the *interrelationships* of components which receive, generate, process, and display information to support organizational goals and operations. The term "component" in this context refers to the men, machines, and computer programs which comprise the information system. Component procedures, then, are specific to the operation of a component.

System procedures *describe* and *prescribe* the operating interconnections of each system component, that is, the standardized interrelationships among man-machine-computer program operations, actions, and decisions in a time-sequenced flow. Such interrelationships are necessary to *operate, control, utilize,* and *prepare* an information system. These four functions are crucial for the successful operation of a computer-based information system.

System procedures, in order to specify the employment of a computer-based system to receive, generate, process, and display information, must then describe and prescribe the following functions.

1. The *operation* of computers and computer-related equipments, whether it is the operation of a computer console, card reader, paper tape punch, display or information retrieval device, or console typewriter. The procedures for operating computer-related equipment contain the decisions and actions for generating displays and running computer programs for each user task.

2. The *control* or regulation of information processing, transmission, generation, and display. The procedures for information control contain the decisions and actions which specify how information is to be obtained, processed, and displayed for each user task; what computer programs are to be run, in what sequence, to obtain required information; how and when data are to be input, in what sequence; and how displays are to be retrieved for each user task. Thus, as data are input by the user for some purpose, their paths through the computer-based system must be controlled or regulated to ensure that the user's needs are met.

3. The *utilization* of the computer-based system for providing information to achieve the tasks and objectives of the user's organization. The utilization procedures contain the decisions and actions that indicate those data to be input and retrieved which are needed as a base for decision making by the user. The procedures specify what information is available or which displays are required for making each type of decision. The procedures indicate also the various capabilities of the computer-based system, thereby providing the user with knowledge of the extent to which he can depend upon the system to process, display, or transmit his information requirements.

4. The *preparation* of data inputs, information output formats and displays, computer program contents, punched cards formats, tape and disc contents. The concept of information system preparation pertains to the development and determination of information requirements, display contents, information storage requirements and accessibility, computer program functions, and equipment utilization for all system tasks. The preparation function is concerned therefore with "setting up" the computer-based system for operation and use. Another facet of this function is related to the diagnosis of computer-based software difficulties. Thus, if computer programs are not performing as required or displays are not supplying the necessary information, the preparation procedures will prescribe the diagnostic and maintenance activities necessary for ensuring normal operations.

In information system operations, these four functions may be assigned to four separate organizations or to four separate positions within one organization. In some organizations, the three major functions—operation, control, and use—may be allocated to a single position. This means that the user also controls his own information processing (builds his own programs) and operates the computer equipment. In any case, the scope and contents of any set of system procedures are determined by the organizational arrangement or allocation of these functions. Whatever allocation decisions are made, system procedures must be produced for *each* function. More will be said about this subject in Section 7.4, "The Production of System Procedures."

In a complex, semiautomated information system, the system procedures are a "feedforward-control" mechanism. They assist in the attainment of a specific user goal by providing statements of sequenced activities which must be followed; they tell what is going to happen and the steps which must be taken to ensure that it does happen. In other words, operators or users can maintain system stability by following the map laid out in their procedures; they know before they start which road to follow to their destination.

Why System Procedures Are Important to the User

When the power is turned on, the new information system will not operate as smoothly and efficiently as the one it is replacing. The computer-based system should not be expected to perform at maximum proficiency on the day when the last piece of hardware and the last computer program are checked out and installed, and the human beings who are part of the system are assigned to their positions.

If there is no smooth transition from old to new, one possible reason may be that the agent which links the men, machines, and computer programs within an institutional environment may not have been provided. It is imperative that the people who will interact with or use the system be provided with links which can serve to orient and educate them before the system is installed and operated, and to guide them when it is operational. And it behooves the system designer to achieve a smoother and swifter transition, without compromising or degrading organizational goals, by providing the links which will ensure efficient system operations the day the power is turned on. *The procedures are these links.*

During the early stages of system design, the potential user receives documentation on the design of the various system components (hardware and computer programs). The user eventually receives a set of instructions with each component. But he has also a need to learn how these components will be related as a system, what the requirements are for operating the system, and how system utilization fits or does not fit into his current organization and operations. A preliminary set of system procedures (before program coding is performed) provides the potential user with a description of system operations, constraints, and capabilities, thereby enabling him, if necessary, to feed back required modifications to the designers.

In practice, the development of procedures for the operation of components is not new. They have been provided for the operation of every product from children's toys to typewriters and aircraft. Within computer-based systems each piece of hardware comes normally with a manufacturer's instructional handbook, and each computer program or display console is accompanied by a set of simplified instructions. Yet the practical value of such component-oriented procedures during system operations is questionable. An accumulated stack of instructions for equipment and computer programs is no more useful for prescribing how to operate and use a system than a set of automobile operating instructions prepares an inexperienced driver to handle a car on a high-speed freeway. The result is a critical hiatus in system operations, a hiatus known as an "open loop." There is no control element to correct deviations. The computer program halts, but no rules are available for recovering according to organizational requirements. We need, then, to differentiate carefully between component procedures and system procedures.

In the system procedures approach, man and machines and computer programs are viewed as being in series, as they would normally be expected to operate, with a major emphasis on man as the control element. This means that human beings are required to make crucial or complex decisions. The human element is vitally important for the success of operations in a semiautomatic information system because it is the operator who closes the loop. Human control is a necessary feature for a semiautomatic information system such as SAGE, for example. On the other hand, little or no human control is necessary for an automatic system such as a single-thread, closed-loop system (e.g., a radar tracking system). The differences which determine the degree of human versus automated control are as follows. In an ideal single-thread system it is possible to state exactly what will happen to every input at every stage of its passage through the system. Control over inputs, operations, deviations, and outputs is automatic. However, in a semiautomatic system there are time lags which delay information output, and numerous other constraints and contingencies which preclude ideal automatic operating conditions. In general, the more disturbances which enter the system, the greater the need for external control by human beings over these perturbations, and the greater the need for system procedures to "program" the human being, enabling him to exercise this control (thereby closing the loop).

From the system user's point of view, one of the values of written procedures is that they can serve as a document which interprets the operating potential of a set of computer programs and displays. Most potential information system users do not understand computer program jargon, and to submit to them computer program design specifications without some type of understandable guide will only lead to misunderstanding and perhaps rejection of the system.

System procedures, then, can contribute to a successful operation in a variety of ways—they may be used as a means for specifying the role of each position and/or function within the framework of the new system, as a tool for system orientation, and, most important, as a guide for daily operations.

7.2   INPUTS TO SYSTEM PROCEDURES DEVELOPMENT

System procedures must be developed in accordance with the same design specifications which guide the development of other system products, such as computer programs. (See Chapters 4 and 5.) System procedures must be developed during all phases of design specifications because they are needed to assist in the determination of the final operating requirements for each system product. Therefore the system procedures designer must maintain an intimate knowledge of appropriate design specifications in order to develop procedures requirements concurrently. If he accomplishes this, he can then wed the hardware and the software effectively into a total operating system. It must be emphasized here that each of the components—equipment, computer programs, etc.,—represents only a single subsystem. Consequently, the design specifications for each component contribute only to the operating requirements and capabilities of the subsystem involved. Thus, computer program requirements divulge data only on program logic, program exits, and program error checks. From this information it is necessary for the procedures designer to extrapolate the necessary interactions between the computer program and human beings and between the computer programs and equipment.

The remaining part of this section describes which component design specifications become the inputs to system procedures design.

Human Interface* Requirements

The most useful inputs to procedures design are the human interface requirements (which are developed in many cases by the procedures designer). These requirements graphically illustrate, in flow diagram format, decision-action sequences which must be performed by the various system components. The human interface requirements are valuable in that they can be used by designers for determining the allocation of man-computer program functions (that is, which decisions and other processes should be allocated to man and which to the computer program) and also for determining sequences of operations, equipment allocation, and work loads. These inputs have been derived also from a technique called "decision/action diagrams" and "operational sequence diagrams." M. I. Kurke[1] has provided a useful description of the techniques for operational sequence diagramming and its uses.

Figure 7.1 is an example, in flow diagram form, of some human actions and decisions necessary for computer program operations which are developed concurrently with computer program design. The difference between the information contained in this flow diagram and that found in computer program documentation is that in program documentation the interactions with human beings are not specified in great detail. The interactions which are indicated are not put into their proper sequence, and most of the decisions which must be made by human beings are not included.

Computer Program Requirements

Information on the logic and functions of computer programs and especially on expected program interactions with human beings is also derived from computer program requirements. The information needed from program requirements documentation may not be obtainable from

---

* Human interface in this context refers to those points during the operation of computer programs which require human actions and decisions (inputs, outputs, control and monitoring activities) to ensure successful operations.

a single source. In the development of a large-scale information system, there may be a variety of program requirements documents which include varying levels of design detail; for example, earlier documents may state only that certain types of data will be output, whereas later documents may specify the format and contents of the data which are being output. The human interface requirements designer may utilize the earlier documents, while the procedures designer may find the latter ones useful. In any event, the following is the type of information derived from program requirements documents which designers need in order to develop procedures:

1. The program's function, its limitations and capabilities.
2. The data which are to be input and output by human beings, the data input and output by programs, and the formats of these data.
3. The program operating descriptions, that is, program halts which require human actions and decisions; program options and limitations; error checks by the program which result in task termination; the way to start, stop, or recycle programs; the method for recovering errors; display contents and their meaning; the consequences to operations if critical steps are not taken.
4. The computer programs which constitute a system task.
5. The required sequences for these programs and tasks.

Equipment Requirements

The type of information in this design area with which the procedures designer is concerned involves the operational characteristics and capabilities of each piece of equipment vis-à-vis computer program requirements and human interface requirements. It is not necessary for the procedures designer to describe for an operator how to type on a computer console typewriter, but the procedures should contain the requirements for starting and stopping the computer which is controlled by the typewriter (e.g., "type START"). More essential, however, is the need of the designer to know the operational capabilities of such equipment. Can the typewriter be used as an input device? Should all inputs be made via the typewriter, or can another method of input be used? What are the equipment operating characteristics which impose constraints on computer program design and human interfaces? Although a single kind of equipment may be used in many systems, its function may be altered in each system; consequently, its operation and associated procedures will be modified.

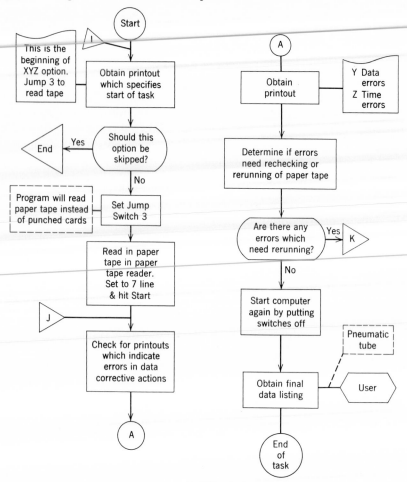

Figure 7.1   Example of human interface flow diagrams.

User Requirements

The scope and contents of any set of system procedures will be limited or expanded, depending upon the needs of the potential user. If a system which is being designed merely modifies a user's current operations, system procedures will be utilized only to modify, and to be incorporated into, the existing procedures. If, on the other hand, the new system changes considerably or replaces old methods, the specification of system procedures will encompass more areas and will require more detail.

The extent of the procedures designer's task will also vary in accordance with the user's attitudes toward automatic operations. The

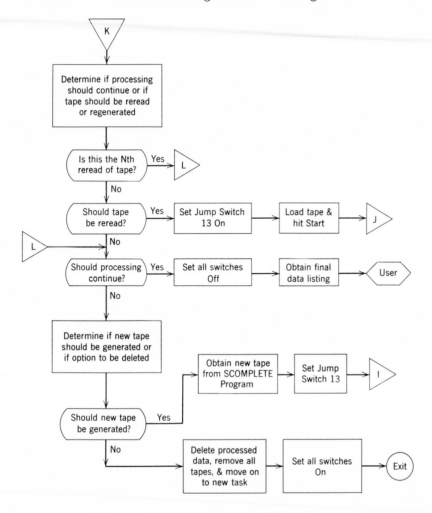

Figure 7.1 (*Continued*)

user may require, for example, that control of the system's operations always be retained by human beings. This will call for the design of more procedures than would be needed if potential users had more confidence in the reliability of automated operations.

7.3 PROCEDURES DESIGN AND OTHER DESIGN ACTIVITIES

The procedures designers perform an important function during the preliminary or early stages of system design, namely, as sources of information and guidance for other designers, such as computer program designers, and for the potential system user. Similarly, other system designers provide information for the development of system procedures. It is most important to emphasize the need for concurrent product design and the contributions different types of designers make to each other's work. The most significant areas for which procedures designers perform contributory functions are computer program design, training program design, and personnel and organization design.

Computer Program Design and Human Engineering

To ensure that the new system will operate in accordance with system missions and goals, it is necessary that procedures designers work with computer program designers. The documented procedures, particularly during the early phases of design work, serve as a source of feedback to computer program designers on the efficiency and applicability of computer program operations in relation to over-all system operations. The feedback can be provided during the development of the preliminary procedures (human interface requirements) and at times during validation testing of procedures. This is necessary because computer programs are not always designed with human requirements or capabilities in mind. The demands on the human operators may result in excessive error rates or in lengthy operations which are inconsistent with operating time constraints. These potential malfunctions can be caught by the procedures designer before computer program design specifications have been frozen.

The design specifications for a set of computer programs may satisfactorily fulfill all of the functions prescribed by a potential user. The set of computer programs may very well survive all tests of reliability and always produce Y outputs from Y inputs. Yet the level of reliability and validity attained in the operational environment may be grossly degraded because the programs cannot be operated within the limits of human capabilities, or the information displayed may not be timely or appropriate for the user's task. Program design cannot afford to omit human factors considerations if there are human interfaces.

In most respects the allocation of system functions is already an accomplished fact when computer programs are designed, although this should not preclude further reconsideration of man-computer program, decision-action allocation as the procedures are being designed. The task of allocation (and this task must be frequently re-examined during the development process) is to determine which actions, decisions, and operations can be assigned more effectively to a computer program and which to human beings so as to ensure in the end a smooth, efficient, and troublefree operation.

Procedures designers must always perform some human engineering analysis of computer programs simply because it is difficult to develop efficient and usable procedures for poorly designed programs. In too many instances, procedures have been used as a stopgap for overcoming some computer program deficiency. The result is usually an added work load for human operators. What follows are some generalized, but not exhaustive, human engineering design factors which can be used to assess the efficiency of computer program operations during the early stages of design. Consideration of these factors should contribute to the development of practical and efficient system procedures. We will review the rationale underlying each of these factors and present several examples of what may happen (or has happened) if human engineering requirements are ignored. The first part of the discussion deals with the general human engineering factors: standardization, automation, control, and tradeoffs. After this there is a discussion of their application to computer program operating requirements: data processing, decision making, actions, inputs and outputs.

Standardization. Groups of computer programs which are designed to accomplish a particular system function, such as reporting a specific type of deviation or generating production plans, should have standardized input media and standardized output formats. Too often input formats and the operations for generating these inputs are designed differently for data-processing tasks within a system function. Such a situation will cause the system users to shunt back and forth from one set of operations to another during the performance of the same task. If outputs (alarms, plans, schedules, or status messages) for a single task are to be recorded on printers, wall displays, typewriters, punched cards, and magnetic tapes, the system users will have to depend upon detailed procedures in order to discover when and where they can expect to find various items of information for the same task.

Automation. It is wiser in most cases to automate operations which the computer programs can perform faster and more efficiently than a human being. This will simplify and minimize the contents and details of the system procedures and lower the chances for human errors. If certain simple and tedious tasks are allocated to human operators, the probability of errors will rise. For example, it is easier for a computer program to sequence a large deck of punched cards (or at least to check the sequence) than it is to require the operator to perform this task. The larger the deck of input cards and the more complex the data being input, the higher the rate of human errors which can be expected. Too often, the system procedures are required to prescribe the sequence. From a human engineering point of view, this is only a stopgap measure for coping with a computer program inadequacy.

Control. Computer program control over data processing means that simple program control decisions have been allocated to the program subsystem rather than to human controllers. If the decision parameters can be determined, they should be allocated to the computer program. Thus, the program subsystem will have control over computer programs, over data processing, and over data display. In this way only the critical decisions will be delegated to human controllers. Human operators and controllers can very easily make the mistake of cycling the wrong sequence of programs, of inputting the wrong information, or of requesting the wrong display. The computer programs should be designed so that they can generate all the information necessary for control decision making rather than designing them to wait for human beings to interrogate the programs repeatedly. When system users stipulate a specific situation or problem, computer programs should automatically control other programs which will process and output all the necessary information to assist the users in making decisions. This will minimize interactions between system users and computer programs.

Tradeoffs. Computer program and procedures designers will have to assess the advantages and disadvantages of program processing and human processing for the purpose of deciding the most efficacious method of computer program operation. Processing recommendations made from a human engineering perspective may require additional programmed instructions and the use of more core storage in the computer. However, such recommendations may result in a more efficient system and more effective human operations. Some automated control functions may place too much of a burden on computer capabilities or extend computer program development costs beyond established limits. In such cases, it may be necessary to allocate some of these functions to human beings.

Some Human Engineering Requirements. Human engineering for computer programs involves the assessment of potential human interactions with a computer program in terms of the system's operational requirements and the capabilities of the human beings who will utilize, control, prepare, and operate the computer programs. There are at least five major computer programming elements which have human engineering implications and from which design requirements can be derived: (1) data processing, (2) program decisions, (3) program actions, (4) program inputs, and (5) program outputs.

DATA PROCESSING. *Calculation, Data Reduction, Sampling, etc.* There are not many computations or manipulations of data that a computer program cannot do faster and more reliably than a human being. Calculations which might take a person days or weeks can be accomplished by a computer in fractions of a second. Programs can process data via complex mathematical equations, algorithms, sampling and averaging techniques, etc., and provide exhaustive lists of information in any form faster than human beings can read or utilize them. If tests of program validity have demonstrated program logic, the probability of processing errors are a hundredfold less than if a man performed the task himself. If a man were assigned complex mathematical tasks, the job of developing system procedures for them would be as complex as designing the computer program itself and many times more difficult for an operator to follow.

Error Checks. There are three major types of computer error checks on human inputs. The first type deals with a program recoverable error, which the program itself corrects. The second type of error involved is program nonrecoverable but human recoverable; the program notifies the user that the data which were input are not acceptable. In this case the computer program allows the user to correct the error. The third type involves human-initiated, nonrecoverable errors, in which persons input incorrect but comprehensible data which are within the limits of program acceptance criteria. The program in this case will process the incorrect inputs, but the results will be invalid. A fourth type of error check, to be discussed later under program decisions, refers to data deviation indications, that is, built-in logic which indicates when input data deviate from a criterion.

The program recoverable error check is an ideal design feature. If enough determinable criteria and standards are designed into the program, human input errors can be minimized since the program will check and correct them. This, of course, is costly in terms of program running time and use of core space in the computer. The tradeoff here would be the utilization of the program recoverable error logic for critical operational processes. In essence, the greater the number of program recoverable error checks which are provided, the fewer and simpler the system procedures which will be necessary to prescribe error recovery techniques.

The nonrecoverable errors can be troublesome. When each such error occurs, the program will probably halt to allow for user intervention. This halt, including correction time, wastes valuable computer time. Again, the criticality of the operation must be evaluated to ascertain if it would not be best to allocate this error check to a recoverable error category. In some systems, one or two such nonrecoverable errors may not hinder smooth operations. But picture a system in which a dozen punched data cards are required to be input for a particular task, and the computer program makes ten error checks on each card. Cumbersome system procedures would then have to be written for correcting each error on each card. Indeed, in the event of a bad day, users may be doing nothing else but running back and forth checking their procedures and correcting cards.

The procedures designer could suggest several solutions to the program designer, for example, to allow the program to cycle through, reject the errors, list them as they occur, and then allow for corrections at the end of processing. Where errors are considered trivial—those which have little or no adverse effect on operations or which can easily be interpreted by users—no reinitiation of the job is necessary. If the frequency of error checks is small but the significance of the errors is large, the program should be interrupted or should automatically halt to allow for corrective action. In these cases, system procedures will have to be developed only when users will interact with the program. Certain nonrecoverable errors can be easily redesigned to become recoverable errors. In this case the procedures designer will have to develop procedures to specify recovery. For example, if the program will accept only fifty punched data cards, it can be designed to drop any excess cards which it perceives. Of course, the procedures will have to specify the program limitations so that the user will not exceed them, but at least program halts and error messages are minimized. In this situation the program can be designed to include built-in criteria for rejecting excess data, and human beings can be informed via procedures that the important data cards should be input first.

Some potentially program recoverable errors are designed as nonrecoverable, thereby increasing the probabilities of human error. This is done by program designers to minimize the number of instructions in a program. The computer program outputs information on the error to allow for human correction. The major problem here is that, if the error occurred in one instance, it will and can happen again. If the potential errors are critical for system operations, the program should be modified to reject and correct them.

The human-initiated, nonrecoverable error is the most difficult to discern and the most perplexing for program design. In most cases the error check has to be included in the system procedures in an attempt to prevent the user from making the mistake. But, again, if he makes it once, he may make it again. Unfortunately, computer program error checks do not take into account all potential human errors, nor should they. Yet system procedures are used as a stopgap in an attempt to prevent certain critical errors which human beings can and do initiate. Here the procedures specify the caveat, but this never ensures that the error will not occur. For example, a procedure might say, "Do not read in punched card number 75 at time X if columns 11 and 12 have a BT entry. RT entries are to be made at time X and BT entries are to be made at time Y. Thus RT at time Y or BT at time X will wipe (erase) all data off the recording tape on tape unit 3." And lo! The data are wiped off the tape at least once a day. Program designs of this type lead to compromises of system objectives. To solve this problem, a tradeoff must occur, and a program error check should be provided to prevent such errors. Computer program designers tend to rely on the system procedures to provide the necessary error checks.

DECISION/ACTIONS. Two major types of control decisions are involved in a data-processing system. The first type consists of the operating decisions necessary to ensure the operating continuity of computer programs and associated computer equipment. Operating decisions determine which computer programs are to be operated, in what sequence, and whether data being input or output are valid. The second type consists of the *system control* decisions necessary to ensure that organizational goals are attained. System control decisions in this context relate to the decisions which are based on information derived from the data system.

Operating decisions in most cases should be left to the computer programs and not to human controllers via complex control procedures. If, for example, some data fail to meet a program requirement, the computer program should have the capability and the logic to decide on the next course of action. If a computer program can be designed to ascertain deviations, it is conceivable that the logic for their correction can also be included. If a computer program performs a single processing function, the program start can be allocated to a human being, allowing this controller a choice of either operating or not operating the program. If the computer program has a single processing function but is operated in most cases with a sequence of other programs (it interfaces at both ends with other programs), it is desirable to have the preceding computer programs call the subsequent ones. Under these circumstances programmed instructions should define the situations under which subsequent programs are to be called. This, in effect, will minimize human interfaces and potential human errors, increase computer program automation, and decrease operating time. If system procedures are developed for the nonautomated sequencing of programs, the procedures will have to include all the information on the definition of the situation and the decisions and actions necessary to call each program. These procedures can be avoided by automating program start activities whenever possible.

System control decisions are allocated to those positions among the system users which have the responsibility to ensure that organizational objectives are attained and that standards are maintained. The role of the computer programs is to provide the necessary information on system status, deviations, and problem solutions. The human engineering requirements for computer programs with this function must ensure that information retrieval and display (on wall displays or printed on display consoles) are timely and automatic to allow controllers to make their decisions. Display format and contents must be understandable (standardized, for example) to noncomputer programmers. Many constraints to real-time (immediate) information retrieval can be minimized by automating program operating decisions so that the data requests of controllers can be serviced as needed.

INPUTS AND OUTPUTS. Two of the more important program operating characteristics which require concentrated human interactions with the programs are data inputs and outputs. In this discussion we are concerned with the types, formats, and contents of such inputs and outputs (rather than the actions or decisions which produce the inputs and outputs) which will affect the structure and contents of the system procedures.

Inputs. One of the basic design requirements should be the standardization of data input formats and contents for system tasks. The need for entering data into an information system can be fulfilled via several avenues, namely, punched cards, paper tapes, magnetic tapes, typewriter, discs, drums, etc. The input vehicle chosen should be based on operational requirements, whether there is a need to make real-time decisions or to update stored data periodically. Not only should operational requirements be considered, but also the information system user's capabilities. If the operating requirement for a computer program specifies that data entry will be made via two or more of the methods noted above, we can expect that individual work loads will be expanded, training requirements will increase, and error rates will be intensified. Information users will have to prepare several types of inputs with different formats for the same task, and operators will be required to move from one input device to the next for a relatively simple task. Similar data being input should be in the same format. Although this may seem to be self-evident, there have been instances where one program required inputs of distance in feet and the very next program specified inputs in meters. This inconsistency is easier to understand when we recall that the program design task is normally fractioned into a number of subtasks as described in Chapter 5.

Outputs. The content, format, and timing of data being output (or retrieved) are some of the most significant man-computer program elements in system design. They are significant because, without correct information presented in a usable and understandable format and output at a certain time, system goals will be compromised. In addition, if there is inadequate information feedback on the results of human interactions with the computer programs, or if there is no feedback on the correctness or appropriateness of an input task, data-processing control will be lost. Procedures designers can make human engineering recommendations on the following aspects: (1) the timeliness of the output: is it presented in time to be of any use, or must procedures be developed to ensure that data can be obtained when needed? (2) the amount of information: does the output contain enough information on which to make a decision or perform an action, or will the procedures have to specify additional outputs? (3) the format of the information: is the content of the output understandable to the user, or will procedures have to be written to explain the format and contents?

Data listings, system status messages, and informational outputs associated with operational requirements are extremely important to the system users in that such information is used to make control decisions, to report system status to management, etc. If the content and format of the listings, status reports, and other outputs are not understandable or are not available to the users at the time needed, the data can lose their major function. The outputs may not be understandable either because they do not contain enough information or because they are presented in a language incomprehensible to the user (in one case, names of geographic locations were output in programming language, in octal, rather than in intelligible mnemonics such as NYC for New York City). If the system user is not a programmer, the data are almost useless until they are translated, usually via the procedures.

Personnel and Organizational Design Requirements

The amount of preliminary task analysis work (analysis of tasks into decisions, actions, information required, etc.) which is accomplished before the commencement of procedures design and organization design determines the degree of interface between these two latter design areas. If there is only a minimal task analysis effort, resulting in a small amount of task information, designers of organizational structures will become more dependent on the preliminary system procedures as a data base. If satisfactory task analyses are produced, the degree of interface is reduced. The scope of the interface will remain the same in either case. Between personnel and organizational design and procedures design there are at least three areas of interface: position definition, work team assignments, and manning estimates.

Position Definition. The personnel and organizational designer provides for the procedures designer data on the spans of control, responsibility, and authority for each position and each organizational unit. Without this information, it would indeed be difficult to allocate procedures to organizational positions or units. With such data, the procedures designer can view the levels of responsibility, authority, and training required for each position specified in the personnel requirements and then allocate procedures or sets of procedures appropriately. The procedures designer must develop a set of criteria which will aid in this allocation. Thus, for example, he would not normally allocate a critical program control or program preparation decision to a computer operator, especially one who has had only on-the-job training and little or no instruction in and knowledge of computer programming.

In turn, the procedures designer provides to the personnel designer recommendations for changes in details of position duties. Since task descriptions and analyses do not always provide adequately detailed data on the priority or sequence of task actions and decisions, it behooves procedures designers to provide this information to the personnel and organizational designers. Information exchanges such as these depend on the degree to which personnel and organizational designers wish to develop duty statements and on how detailed the task analyses were.

Work Teams. Personnel and organizational designers provide general information on work team requirements (positions working together to accomplish a job) and position interface specifications. In turn, procedures designers provide feedback to personnel and organizational designers which may modify these interactions and consequently change organizational alignments. For example, a computer-related position may be required to transmit certain data outputs via pneumatic tubes to a user. The data user may need these outputs to make a real-time evaluation of them. During procedures design, because of operational requirements, the peculiarities of the program system, and the configuration of work areas, it may be necessary to create a permanent user position (to be manned by someone who understands information-processing techniques) to monitor computer outputs during the operation of computer programs which are related to this area of responsibility. This new requirement may thus affect the structure of computer area work teams, their concomitant duty statements, their manning interaction requirements, and their training requirements.

Manning Estimates. The data bases for estimating the number of positions required and the number of persons needed to fill these positions for a specified duty period are derived from several sources. Along with such analyses as work-load studies and traffic analyses, system procedures provide information on the number of positions needed. For example, if a position is found to be required to perform a large number of simultaneous procedures or sequences of actions, an additional position may be called for. In another case, the number of procedures that a single position is required to perform within a specified time period may suggest the need for additional personnel. Thus, by studying the number and complexity of the procedures for a system task or computer function within the times allotted, an estimate can be made by the designers of the number of people required to perform the task.

System Training Requirements

Since the system procedures can be written in such a way as to provide a detailed description of the system as well as of the methods for performing individual tasks, the procedures can be useful as part of the methodology for determining the degree of system training needed.

1. The procedures provide the means by which the training designer can locate specifications of operational requirements for system functions (old and new), system tasks, and position tasks.

2. They can offer another set of training performance standards.

3. They can be used to determine task criticality levels via discernment of critical procedures.

4. They can provide information on data system positions which may require special or unique training.

5. They can aid the training designer to ascertain the complexity or difficulty of a system task so that levels of effort for learning may be developed.

6. They can help the training designer to ascertain the similarities of new tasks to tasks in the system being replaced so that training requirements can be identified.

7.4   THE PRODUCTION OF SYSTEM PROCEDURES

The scope and contents of system procedures depend upon information obtained from potential customers. The purposes for which the procedures will be used inform the procedures designer of the level of detail required. The user's organizational units supported by the data system or responsible for operating it inform him of the scope of procedures. The characteristics of operating units, or the way in which the organization interfaces with the information system, inform him of the content of procedures.

Purposes of Procedures

There are three major types of purposes for which procedures may be used. In any given case of information system development, the procedures may serve any one or all of these purposes:

1. To provide a system description for the purpose of orienting all organizational personnel who must interface with the computer-based information system.

2. To provide material for the dual purposes of training com-

puter-related personnel and for serving as a detailed reference document.

3. To provide instructions for the dual purposes of supporting system operations, control, use, and preparation and for serving as a summary reference document.

In case 1 procedures will be spelled out in broad terms. For the purpose of orientation it is not necessary to detail specific actions and decisions, but it is important to cover general information flow, input and output requirements, and system processes. These procedures will aid in defining a user's place in the information system and will describe system capabilities in a general way.

In case 2 the procedural materials must be relatively detailed, thereby providing to students the amount of information which will enable them to transfer from classroom training to on-the-job operations with a minimum of retraining and supervision. If not enough information is provided, training objectives as well as operating requirements will be compromised.

In case 3 the procedures should contain the required amount of information both for supporting daily operations and for supplying summary reference materials. If too much information is provided, procedures users will have to grope through large quantities of nonessential (for the moment) information to find the required action or decision; if an insufficient amount is provided, they will have to hunt for the required actions and decisions from other sources.

The following sections will describe some of the major requirements for determining the scope and contents of system procedures. Figure 7.2 illustrates graphically the contrasting scope of the three levels of procedures production noted above. The system overview level supplies procedural statements describing, in a general way, the various tasks that must be accomplished for a particular goal. At the system task level, procedures are detailed for each of the tasks within the system overview, for all organizations and personnel concerned with that task. At the position level, procedures are written for every position which has a responsibility for accomplishing part of that task.

The Scope of Procedures

System Overview Procedures. The scope of any set of system overview procedures is based upon the range of responsibilities and operating requirements of any organizational unit which interfaces with

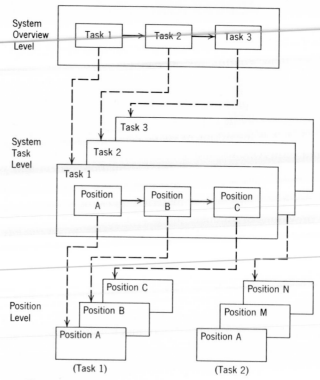

Figure 7.2 Scope and level of procedures compared.

the computer-based information system. Since, by definition, such organizational units either are supported by the computer system or operate that system, they must include in their over-all operations one or more of the four functions defined in the first section of this chapter, which constitute the computer system, namely, operation, control, utilization, and preparation. The areas of responsibility demanded by these four functions become the foundation for determining the scope of the system overview procedures. Figure 7.3 illustrates this scope. The flow diagram indicates the general responsibilities for "users" as well as for computer operators and controllers within the specified "computer complexes."

For example, to determine scope we need to ascertain what the number or types of user organizations are and whether these organizations interface with each other via the computer-based system. The degree to which such interface occurs will contribute to the definition of scope. We need then to ascertain how user tasks are allocated,

Examples of System Procedures

The hypothetical computer-based information system from which the examples are drawn in Figures 7.3 and 7.4 supports the daily production operations of a world-wide network of manufacturing plants. The "users" in this system are management personnel who are responsible for planning and regulating the manufacture, distribution, inventory, and sales of a specific commodity.

The users provide data on current and projected sales to a central computer organization which uses these data to predict the production quota for each branch plant. The central computer organization (which operates the computer equipment and displays, controls the information flow to all points, and prepares the information requirements) controls the "prediction computer programs" for the purpose of determining when a specific product should be manufactured, how many of the items should be produced, over what time period production should take place, and how the products should be distributed. When data processing is completed, this information is transmitted to a branch plant so that responsible personnel there can begin (or cease) production efforts. In turn, branch personnel transmit information back to the central computer organization on current stock, status of manufacturing equipment, availability of personnel, transportation, etc. This information is compressed into suitable formats for the use of management personnel.

Figure 7.3 illustrates, in flow diagram form, the system procedures for readying the system to transmit information to a branch site before daily operations. Figure 7.4 illustrates the system procedures for starting (initializing) the central computer system before information transmission.

Figure 7.3 is a flow diagram sequence depicting the general information flow and functional interfaces for what is considered to be a "job." (A job is composed of a number of related tasks.) Included in the diagram are the general responsibilities, actions, and decisions of three system functions. There are no position-related procedures in this figure. The top row indicates the actions and decisions prescribed for operating and controlling the data system at a central computer complex. The second row indicates the data user decisions and actions and user interfaces with the computer complex organization. The bottom row indicates the decisions and actions required of an interfacing branch site-computer complex.

Within the flow diagram, certain conventions are used to represent

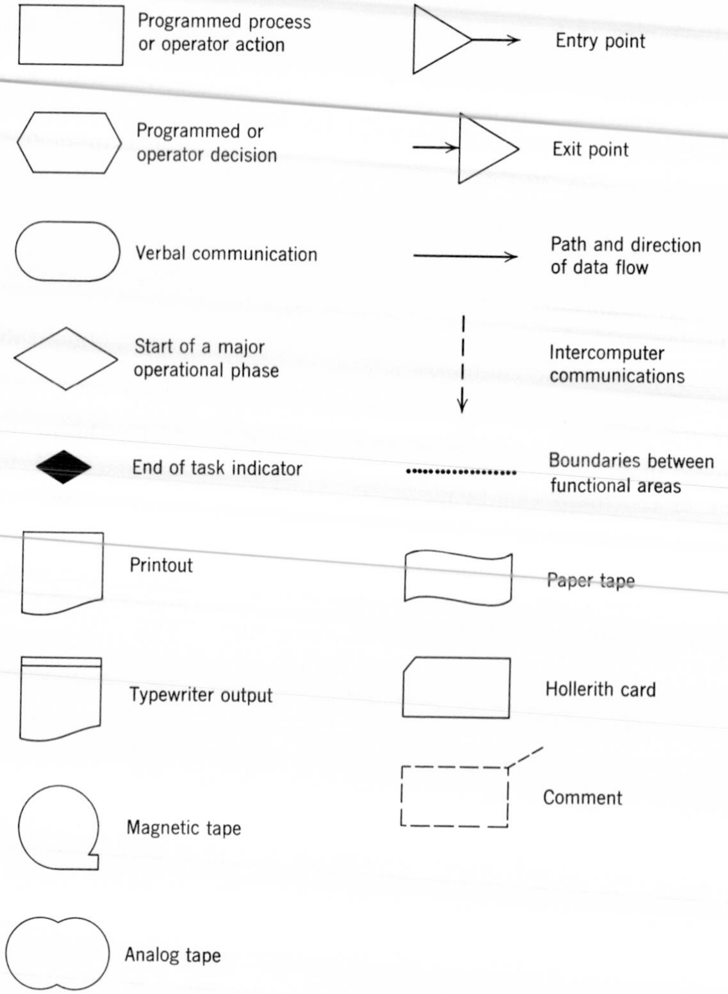

Programmed process or operator action	Entry point
Programmed or operator decision	Exit point
Verbal communication	Path and direction of data flow
Start of a major operational phase	Intercomputer communications
End of task indicator	Boundaries between functional areas
Printout	Paper tape
Typewriter output	Hollerith card
Magnetic tape	Comment
Analog tape	

Figure 7.5 Flow diagram symbols.

various human activities and program actions. These conventions and their concomitant activities are defined in Figure 7.5. The tasks that are part of this sequence can be identified by alpha-numeric characters in the lower right-hand corner of a task block. This identifier informs the procedures user of the task that should be accomplished under various conditions, thereby providing him with the proper cue he needs to initiate detailed task procedures (see Figure 7.4). The correct sequence of operations moves along the abscissa from left to right.

The major advantage of this type of format is that the information in the diagram informs any procedures user of actions and decisions which must be made at any given time in the sequence, plus the actions and decisions concurrently being made by other personnel or organizations (along any ordinate axis). Information in this form makes possible better management control over all operations.

Figure 7.4 is a set of more detailed procedures necessary for accomplishing one of the tasks noted in the sequence in Figure 7.3: "Initialize computer, CC-1-2." In this sandwich flow diagram, the extreme left and right columns include indicators for positions, as well as for concurrent program decisions, actions, processes, inputs, and outputs. In other words, the system task flow diagram depicts all the man-machine-computer program activities which occur at a given time (along any ordinate axis). Although the only two positions indicated are "user" and "computer operator," the entire flow diagram (as a single entity) is utilized by data control (management) to ensure that all steps are completed by all personnel and programs and that the task is accomplished. The following narrative is an example of operating instructions which contain a more detailed explanation where necessary of each action or decision block in Figure 7.4.

SECTION A.   TASK DESCRIPTION

Central Computer Task CC-1-2

INIT II (Initialize Computer)

1. *Purpose*

The purpose of INIT II is to enter into the central computer program the number, date, time of day, and whether or not the program should generate a new Prep and/or recording tape.

2. *Equipment Interfaces*

None.

3. *Options*

An option is provided for making a new Prep tape, making a new recording tape, and later processing of branch data from storage sources at the central computer.

4. *Limitations*

An Initialize function (punched) card must be entered before any other function card will be accepted by the program (Except TERM and TAPE).

Entering the Initialization card (INIT) does not reset the Prep or recording tape unit numbers to their initial values. These will be reset to their initial values only when the central computer program is loaded from the master tape.

The month, day, year, and AM/PM indicator must correspond with the data being processed by the central computer program. Particular attention must be paid to this required correspondence if data are being transmitted from the branch computer.

When reinitializing (because of computer halt due to an error) the operator must put a double end-of-file (DEOF) on the recording tape and reinitialize. In order to write on the same tape, omit the RT option on the Initialize card. If the recording tape is to be replaced by a blank tape, then the RT option must be included on the Initialize card. In order to write a DEOF on the recording tape enter the following instructions in Bank 1, location (0000): 7502, 7500, 114X, 7700, where X is the logical unit number containing the tape on which the DEOF is to be written. Clear, set the Relative Bank to 1, and run. This area of core was specified to inform the operator of an area that may be destroyed without any useful data.

Note: If the core-to-tape dump routine is to be operated before reinitializing, a DEOF will be written, thus eliminating the need for the previous method.

5. Alternative Task Exits

If INIT II is executed immediately after INIT I, the INIT II exit would normally be to PREP I or PREP II sequence.

6. Outputs

Log of the function (on the printer). (See flow diagram CC-1-2, page INIT II-19, for details of task INIT II.)

SECTION B. TABULAR OPERATING INSTRUCTIONS
Central Computer Task CC-1-2
INIT II (Initialize Computer)

Tape Drive 1 Master Tape
2 Prep Tape or Blank
3 Blank
4 Recording Tape or Blank

Normal Operator Actions	Computer-Program Actions and Responses	Error Conditions and Recoveries
1. At the beginning of a new operation, or when the error message CC NOT INITIALIZED occurs, determine whether to input the initialize function via card reader or typewriter.		
2. a. If the function card is to be input by card reader, read-in the function card, and set JS 4.	a. If a card read error occurs due to a mutilated card or to a reader failure, the message CARD READ ERROR occurs.	a. If the card is mutilated in any way, repunch card. Restack card in reader and continue.
b. If the function is to be input via typewriter, type in the initialize card format and hit the carriage return. If a typing mistake is made, type a "/" immediately. A carriage return will be executed automatically. Retype the function. (Once a manual carriage		

Normal Operator Actions	Computer-Program Actions and Responses	Error Conditions and Recoveries
return is made, there is no error recovery before the program processes the input).		
	3. If the CC printer is not ready, the typewriter outputs PNT NOT READY. Program does not halt.	3. PNT NOT READY Turn on printer or set the Select Code to 7400.
	4. If the initialize function is not accepted, an error message is output. (Output will always appear on the CC printer. If input was by typewriter, output will also simultaneously be typed out on typewriter.)	
	a. If the job is illegal or there are too many characters in the field, printer outputs ERR-JOB.	a. ERR-JOB Repunch or retype function correctly; return to Operator Action 2a.

Testing the System Procedures

Unless system procedures are tested after their production, the designer and the potential customer will never be certain that the procedures as written will provide an efficient prescription for operating, controlling, or using the information system. Testing is a critical step in the procedures development cycle for the following reasons:

1. It ensures operational reliability and validity; that is, the user is able to obtain the information he needs every time that he follows the procedures.

2. It ensures quality control of procedural contents; that is, the statements are clear and understandable so that there is no question as to their meaning.

Operational Reliability and Validity. Before any procedures can be put to practical use for operating and controlling the computer-based information system, they must be tested in either a simulated or an actual operational environment. One of the important reasons for this testing is that procedures which are developed from design documents are only nominal (that is, they specify what should be). Experience shows that what is actually done in an operational environment does not always resemble what should be done. Thus, delivering untested procedures to a potential user can result in unsatisfactory operations. A test must be designed to check the validity of the prescribed system procedures; that is, whether they in fact operate and control the computer-based system for which they are written. Can the user obtain the information he requires by following the procedures?

The checkout and validity testing of procedures documents should not be confused in theory and practice with computer program checkout testing. The purpose of a program test (before delivery of the programs to the user) is to ensure that the program can actually do what it was designed to do, that is, to process X inputs to obtain X outputs (see Chapter 5). But these tests do not and cannot check the associated system procedures because they cannot always take into consideration all of the procedures, operational requirements, errors, constraints, human factors, and outputs for a specific task. Thus, a perfect data listing can be output by the program in a test bed. But can the same program print this output in the time required under operational conditions? This is the more critical question.

The amount of procedural testing and the concomitant amount of test planning depend on the extent of new or modified computer programs. If the system is relatively new, the procedures should undergo extensive testing, preferably with potential users as subjects. (This could also function as a training course for the users, if necessary.) Plans for procedural testing can become quite elaborate and complex. For example, these tests may be designed to be used in conjunction with other types of human engineering tests, such as those involving lighting adequacy, noise levels, workspace allocations, and display utilization, or with personnel subsystem test and evaluation.

Quality Control of Contents. Quality control of the contents of statements is a widely neglected area in the development of procedures, but some form of quality control is required in order to make sure that when a user reads his procedural statements there can be no misunderstandings as to their meaning. Unfortunately misunderstanding is not uncommon. From the designer's desk, it is sometimes impossible to foresee the user's difficulty in understanding procedural statements.

Chapanis relates an incident in which a statement of procedures confused many readers.[3] The statement, although very concise and simple, did not convey the writer's meaning. It was placed on a sign between two elevators in a public building to guide elevator users. The sign read:

PLEASE

WALK UP ONE FLOOR

WALK DOWN TWO FLOORS

FOR IMPROVED ELEVATOR

SERVICE

The procedures were intended to direct elevator users to walk if they wanted to go up one floor or down two floors. But what did they actually do? Chapanis relates, "In a small study I did on this sign, I discovered that most people think along these lines: 'This must be one of those fancy new elevators that has something automatic. The elevator doesn't stop at this floor very often. If I want to get the elevator I'd better go up one floor or go down two floors.' And this, in actual fact, is what many people did. When they had trudged either up or down, however, they found exactly the same sign at their destination." One solution Chapanis suggested read like this:

TO GO UP ONE FLOOR

OR

DOWN TWO FLOORS

PLEASE WALK

Procedures testing must take place before the information system is finally turned over to the customer. There is, of course, an adjustment period for all the people who will use the new system. Learning to follow the new procedures takes time, but if the product upon which the users must depend is unreliable, they will probably not be able to operate their new system effectively, and the procedures documents will be relegated to the wastebasket.

7.5 SUMMARY

The major intent of this chapter was to describe the functions, design, and production of those procedures which are peculiar to computer-based information-processing systems. The underlying intent was to argue for the necessity of the development and utilization of procedures as an integral part of general system design. The salient point developed was that information-processing systems, because of the unique and complex requirements they impose upon human beings, require different kinds of procedures from those provided in the past with the delivery of hardware systems. The system procedures philosophy provides recognition of the important part played by each system component *and* emphasizes the role each one (man, machine, program) plays interdependently with other components. Without adherence to this philosophy, the system will fail to operate at maximum, or near maximum, efficiency. In the introduction to this chapter, we discussed this point by asserting that system procedures provide a link among the men, machine, and computer programs within the system, a link which can be used to orient and educate the users before the system is installed and operated, and which will guide them when it is put into use.

The second part of the chapter described the development process for the system procedures. The task of this section was to inform the reader of the importance of the procedures not only as a "cookbook" document to guide system operations but also as an integral part of system design. In terms of the latter, there were discussions on the types of data which procedures designers derive from other system design products and, conversely, the types of data needed by other design areas (personnel and organization design, training, etc.) which are derived from the system procedures. In addition to a review of design requirements for procedures, there was a discussion of how human errors associated with computer program operation and control degrade information system operations. It was suggested that potential human errors can be reduced in number by proper system procedures development and by the human engineering of computer programs. One of the more important contributions of procedures design is a concern for human engineering. This responsibility is applied to the design of man-computer program interfaces.

The final section described the scope and content requirements for the production of the system procedures and the development of test plans. The major justification for requiring procedures testing is that the system procedures can only be considered as nominal (what should be) mainly because their data inputs are derived from other design documents which are also nominal descriptions. Thus, in order to ensure the potential user that he has acquired a valid set of usable procedures, all procedures must undergo stringent testing.

The cost of system procedures development for a computer-based information system is offset a hundredfold by the usefulness of the procedures to system designers and users. If the potential user does not contract for procedures development along with other system products, he will eventually increase the cost of system installation and operation. He will have to develop his own procedures after the system is installed, and system objectives will be compromised as a result of this lack of foresight.

REFERENCES

1. M. I. Kurke, "Operational Sequence Diagrams in System Design," *Human Factors,* March 1961, pp. 66–73.
2. A. Chapanis, "Words, Words, Words," *Human Factors,* February 1965, pp. 1–17.
3. *Ibid.,* pp. 5–6.

Chapter Eight

Design and Production of the Training Program

P. E. Rosove

8.1 INTRODUCTION

Purpose of the Chapter

This chapter is concerned with the development of the training program which may be required when an enterprise acquires a "new," large-scale, computer-based information system. The process for the creation of the program is described. The assumption made throughout this chapter is that the replacement system differs radically from its manual or semiautomated predecessor.

The scope of the chapter has been arbitrarily delimited. It is impossible to cover in one chapter all the varied aspects of training which might be essential to ensure that a newly acquired information system will meet efficiently the needs of the user. In any given case, training needs may require classroom academics, orientation lectures, on-the-job training, group rehearsals of specific operations, and the study of handbooks and manuals. We have chosen to confine ourselves primarily to a relatively new type of training which is a by-product of the computer age—it is training that relies heavily on new techniques of computer-based simulation and has as its goal organizational learning and organizational adaptation to change. By "organizational" in this context we mean entities larger than the face-to-face group.

The process of development described, and indeed the entire orientation of the chapter, are derived from experience with training programs developed for military command and control systems. The precise manner in which this material can be applied to the training of information system users in nonmilitary enterprises cannot be specified here. However, we shall cite the work of knowledgeable people who believe that the relevance of the concepts for nonmilitary enterprises can be demonstrated and who are applying them in specific nonmilitary cases. We believe that with the passage of time, as large-scale enterprises take on more and more of the characteristics of adaptive organisms, the experience gained in the development of training programs for military command and control systems will become increasingly relevant and applicable to their nonmilitary counterparts. The rapid growth of management games based upon computer simulation of the business environment, which owes its origins to developments in military games, is a case in point.

The requirement to design a training capability as one aspect of the system design activity is based on the assumption that, when a large-scale information system is being established for the first time or is replacing a manual predecessor, there will be a need for training. The typical user at all organizational levels is not familiar with the newer, automated information system technology and the operations associated with computerized systems. He will, therefore, normally require a period of training in order to acquire such familiarity. Also, by definition, an information system is composed of a complex network of interrelated and interdependent elements—personnel, computers, auxiliary equipment, computer programs, operating procedures, communication networks, and facilities. Before such systems can achieve an operational capability, they must undergo a period of "shakedown," in which the interrelated and interdependent elements "learn" how to accomplish the objectives of the enterprise smoothly and efficiently.

In the professional training and learning literature three levels of subjects are usually differentiated—the individual, the team or group, and the system as a whole. An efficiently designed training program for a large-scale computer-based information system should provide training at each of these levels. Considerable financial savings can be achieved if the training program designers can develop multiple-purpose exercises: exercises which can be utilized, as needed, to train individuals in basic skills, to train groups to function as smoothly coordinated teams, and to train the entire system as an integrated entity. We shall discuss the design of training for individuals and teams where appropriate, but within the context of a system perspective. In the last analysis it is the system designer's job to maximize the performance of the system, not merely to provide training for individuals or teams. It is perfectly possible to have superbly trained components but still fail to maximize system performance. Our primary focus in this chapter, therefore, is upon the design of a training program for the system as a whole. We shall refer to this type of training as "system training."

There is, of course, nothing new about the concept of training systems involving both men and machines as wholes. The military have been doing something of this sort for centuries in their field maneuvers, task force exercises, and command post exercises. What has varied as a function of time is the size of the total system involved in a given exercise, the extent to which all functionally related elements in the system participate in the exercise, the degree of realism in the efforts to simulate hostile actions and the operational environment, the capability to evaluate or measure the system's performance, and the capability to provide all system personnel with adequate and timely knowledge of the results of their performance. These capabilities do provide something new—a potentiality for the application of scientific method to system design and system evolution.

In recent years new dimensions have been added to the problem of training large-scale man-machine systems as a result of two factors: the increasing scope and complexity of such systems, and the introduction of digital computer technology. To highlight some of these dimensions and the pregnant scientific findings with respect to them, we shall review briefly, by way of introduction to this chapter on training program design, several of the empirical studies conducted for the United States Air Force by the RAND Corporation.

The Empirical Origins of System Training

The RAND Corporation was formed in 1948 as a nonprofit organization to conduct basic research for the United States Air Force. In 1950, John Kennedy, a psychologist who was a RAND consultant, suggested the need for the study of human factors affecting the performance of man-machine systems.[1] The impetus for such a study grew out of the fact that the designers of man-machine systems had to resort to a "degradation factor" in their designs since the operational performance of a weapons system differed from its designed capability. It was recognized that insights had to be gained into the relationship between the human factor and system degradation. To carry out investigations in this area a Systems Research Laboratory was established in May 1951. A basic problem was developing a methodology for studying the human factor in a man-machine system environment. Several methods were examined: gaming, group dynamics, three-man communication networks, model building, and single-variable controlled experiments. The approach finally selected was that of duplicating the organization to be studied. A fairly complete physical model of an Air Defense Direction Center (ADDC) was constructed.[2]

It was recognized that the machine aspects of a man-machine system were determined and fixed by the designer. The human components, on the other hand, were flexible in nature, possessing a capability for adaptation and learning as well as varying in motivational level. The RAND psychologists were interested in the problem of increasing the performance level of a man-machine system by maximizing the capabilities of the human factor. Their problem was conceived in terms of the psychology of learning. The question to which their investigations were directed was this: given a particular system equipment configuration, could the human operators be taught to modify their procedures or learn new ones so as to improve system performance? By physically duplicating an Air Defense Direction Center and by observing its personnel carry out realistic operations, the investigators assumed that they could expose some of the crucial factors in organizational learning.

To understand the nature of the experiments which were conducted, a brief review of the functions and organizational environment of an ADDC is necessary. This description will also provide us with a basis for understanding the examples used throughout this chapter to illustrate various aspects of the design of system-oriented training programs.

An ADDC is essentially a radar site charged with protecting a portion of the United States against enemy air attack. It maintains surveillance of the air traffic in its area by means of radar. It identifies air traffic through the use of flight plans which it receives from the Civil Aeronautics Authority (CAA). If an aircraft is not shown on these flight plans, it may be identified by an interceptor aircraft, which, if it should commit a hostile act, would attempt to shoot it down.

In 1951, an ADDC was a basic component of the Air Defense

Command (ADC), which is responsible for the air defense of the United States. At that time ADC was composed of three regional forces—the Eastern, the Central, and the Western Air Defense Force. Each force was composed of several Air Defense Divisions. These divisions, in turn, were composed of several ADDC's, early warning radar sites, a Division Control Center, and interceptor bases, all linked via communications networks. The entire system constituted a large-scale, man-machine organization. This "manual" system of air defense has since been replaced by the semiautomatic ground environment system known as SAGE.

To carry out their study of organization learning, the RAND experimenters built an ADDC with simulated radar scopes and controlled radar inputs. Communications with the CAA, adjacent Direction Centers in the division, and the Control Center at division headquarters were also simulated by the use of scripts. By controlling the simulated radar inputs and communications, any number of unknown aircraft and a variety of problem situations could be presented to the ADDC crews and their reactions could be recorded and studied. Figure 8.1 shows the basic simulation network as it was later adapted for use in the operational environment.

Four investigations, nicknamed CASEY, COWBOY, COBRA, and COGWHEEL, were conducted by the RAND personnel. A group of 28 college students comprised the CASEY ADDC crew. This group proved to be surprisingly effective in conducting air defense exercises in which normal variations of air traffic were simulated. Within a few days, the students were able to carry out their tasks while amusing themselves with other activities. The simulated amount of air traffic was doubled and then tripled. The students successfully coped with a double load but could not handle a triple load. The Air Force was sufficiently impressed with the results to supply Air Force personnel for the subsequent experiments. In the COWBOY and COBRA experiments the difficulty of the problems was periodically increased. The Air Force crews also successfully handled air defense problems of unusual complexity and difficulty. In these experiments air traffic four times heavier than normal was successfully handled by the military personnel. It should also be noted that the simulation in the COWBOY experiment was enlarged to include more elements of the air defense system (an adjacent ADDC and the Division Control center).

COGWHEEL was essentially a field trial in ADC's 27th Air Division of the techniques of system training which had been developed in the RAND laboratory. The results of the field test satisfied ADC

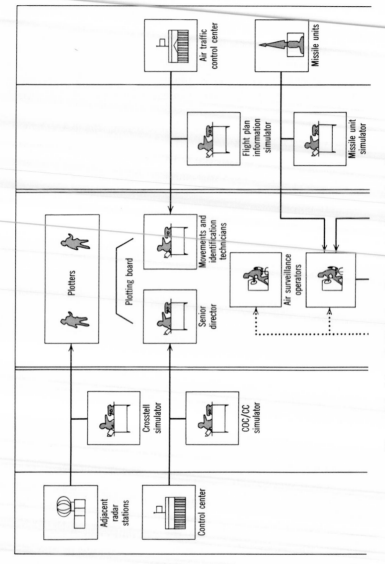

Figure 8.1 Manual Direction Center, simulation data flow.

240

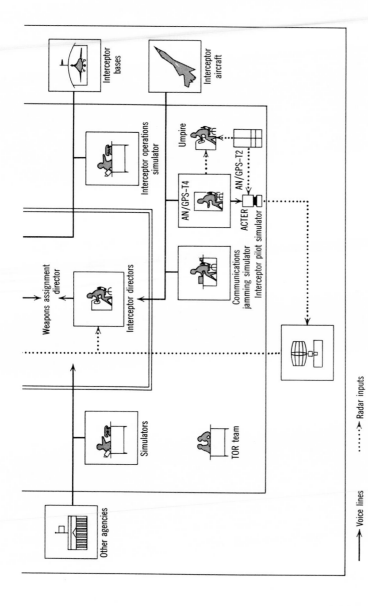

Figure 8.1 (*Continued*)

representatives, and as a result in 1954 that organization submitted a request to the United States Air Force to install the program in 152 of its radar sites. Another result of COGWHEEL was the finding that training could be enhanced by including additional elements of the system. The scope of training exercises was then enlarged to include all the radar sites in an Air Defense Division. The division-wide exercise was adopted as the standard training unit.

The basic training principles which emerged from the RAND experiments can be summarized as follows:[3]

- Exercise at one time as large a part of the system as possible.
- Provide a simulated environment which is as realistic as possible.
- Observe and record selected aspects of system performance.
- Provide system personnel with knowledge of results.
- Exercise the system at a frequency which is consistent with high learning motivation.

Since each of these training principles has been elaborated upon in the published literature, the subsequent pages of this chapter will focus, not upon these principles as such, but upon the development process for a training program. The objective of the development process is to provide adequately for the realization of each of these principles.

In the SAGE Air Defense System, which replaced the manual system, the basic functions of air defense remained unchanged. The novelty of the SAGE system lies in the fact that the functions of detection, identification, interception, and destruction are carried out or assisted by the use of high-speed digital computers, the IBM AN/FSQ-7. The first SAGE sector became operational in 1958, and the system was fully installed by 1962. Figure 8.2 shows SAGE sectors in dashed lines and SAGE divisions (later known as NORAD regions) in heavily darkened, unbroken lines. The main source of information for the system's computers is the inputs from the radar network. On the basis of these and other data, the computers process special programs which handle air surveillance, identification, weapons assignment, interception, and tactics. The routine data-processing functions which in the manual system were performed by men are handled by the computer in SAGE. The system provides more accurate and timely displays than were possible in the manual system, thereby allowing system personnel more time and opportunity for the human functions of monitoring and decision making.

The SAGE training program has a variety of purposes.[4] Exercises are used to diagnose operational problems, to test the effectiveness of operations, to train the personnel who conduct air defense, to test the computer programs for compatibility between the SAGE sectors and regions, and to test new computer program features as they are in-

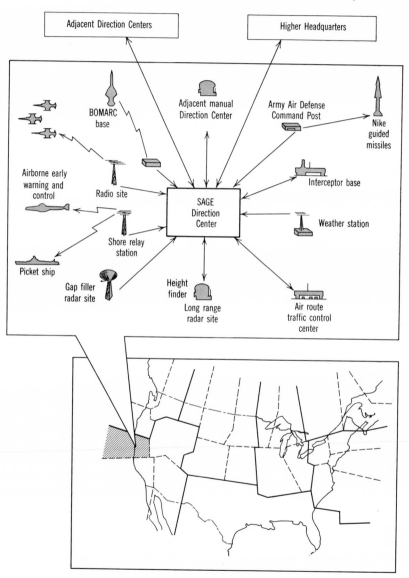

Figure 8.2 A typical SAGE Direction Center.

stalled. The training program includes exercises which vary in their level of complexity from single-sector exercises to ones that are quite large, both in a geographical sense and in the sense of involving many personnel and many echelons of command. The largest exercise, known as DESK TOP, is conducted four times a year for the North American Air Defense Command (NORAD) (see Figure 8.3). Within the train-

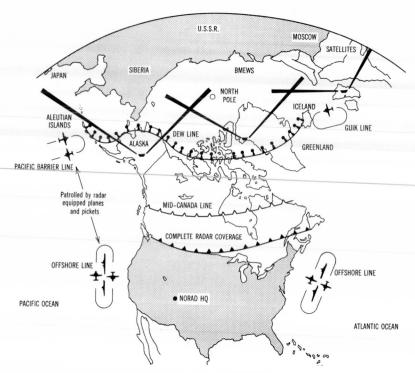

Figure 8.3 North American Air Defense Command (NORAD) warning system facilities (circa 1964).

ing program several specialized areas have been selected for specific training—battle and support staff training, disaster control training, and electronic warfare training. In addition to these specialized areas, the SAGE program provides training for so-called subsystems, such as the SAGE Direction Center Weapons Section, which can be exercised independently of other elements in the system.

The focus of system training in SAGE is upon "procedural learning," particularly in relation to the interactions of personnel, that is, teamwork. In this sense, system training is not a new idea. Teamwork training has long been basic in military activities. What is new is the technological sophistication of system training and its application to large-scale organizations of the command and control type. Army field units, Navy task forces, and Air Force flight crews can still be trained in teamwork through maneuvers and field exercises, but one cannot train command and control and electronic support systems through these traditional methods. Command organizations, such as NORAD, cannot undertake procedural learning or teamwork training by going out on maneuvers. Other traditional methods, such as war gaming and command post exercises, do not meet the full range of training needs for this type of large-scale organization. System training, by contrast, is effective for this purpose.

Philosophy Underlying System Training

A consideration of the training which is required to maximize the performance of large-scale information systems leads us into relatively unchartered and murky waters. While much is known about the training of individuals and teams, where the team is conceived as a face-to-face group, relatively little is known about the problem of training and evaluating systems involving hundreds or thousands of individuals who interact with one another, not on a personalized, face-to-face basis, but impersonally via complex communications networks encompassing, for example, a large military command headquarters building or vast geographical areas, national or even international in scope.

In the traditional approach it has been assumed that training was accomplished when personnel understood their equipment and mastered a set of procedures (standard interactions with other personnel or equipment) as defined in advance by the system engineers or analysts. This approach is adequate given a certain set of conditions: (1) that the system designer knows all the variables, both internal and external, which can affect system performance and (2) that the system's objectives or functions will not change with time. But as systems have increased in complexity, involving more variables, and as the rate of change has accelerated, such a rigid approach to training has not been adequate.

Another traditional approach to the design of a training program is to focus upon the individual or the team. One trains the pilot to fly an aircraft or the bomber crew to operate a B-52. It is a simple matter to isolate such individuals or teams as likely units for training. But if one shifts attention from the fighter pilot to the air defense system of which he is only a single component, or if one looks at the Strategic Air Command as a command and control system in which the bomber and its crew constitute only a single element, training the *system* with respect to its specific *functions* constitutes a problem of an entirely different order. The focus of our attention shifts from units (structure) to functions. What needs to be trained, in this perspective, is not an individual or a team but a function—for example, in the case of an air defense system, the function of defending a geographical area from attack by air-breathing vehicles, or the function of tracking radar returns, or the function of identifying unknown aircraft. Once attention is shifted from structure to functions, the size of the component to be trained is no longer a primary concern but becomes secondary—a matter of whether or not it is technically feasible to provide training for a given structural component of the system.

In Chapter 6, in the discussion of the role of laboratory simulation in organizational design, it was pointed out that, no matter how thoroughly and efficiently the rational process of design is carried out for a large-scale computer-based information system, there inevitably will be errors, inadequacies, and gaps in the design effort. As systems become increasingly complex, as the basic functions to be performed require intricate patterns of man-man and man-machine interaction, it becomes more difficult to design in advance the most efficient set of procedures relating men to one another, to the system hardware, and to the computer programs. *Therefore, training based upon a simulation technology becomes increasingly the means whereby an adequate set of interactional procedures can be developed.*

The fact is that, at the present stage in the evolution of computer-based information systems, the most efficient relationship between the man and the computer is largely a matter of guesswork. It is not based sufficiently, or as much as one would like, upon knowledge gleaned from experimental or experiential evidence. What is the most efficient pattern of man-computer cooperation in the performance of specific tasks? To what extent should this pattern vary, given different types of tasks? These are basic questions in the design of man-computer interactions. At the present state of the art it is not practical or desirable to eliminate human intervention in the machine processing of information. Yet we do not know how to design a system which reflects man-computer "symbiosis."[5] Until such time as these design issues can be resolved, system training may be used in the operational environment for the study of more efficient interaction patterns.

A number of investigators have described the differences between "established" and "emergent" situations[6] and "programmed" and "unprogrammed" tasks.[7] Under conditions of rapid change, it is the system's capability to cope with emergent situations or unprogrammed tasks which becomes especially critical for adequate system performance. Whereas most of the activities which occur in the daily operations of a typical organization are of the highly programmed type in established situations, provision must be made for unprogrammed tasks in emergent situations. Without such provision there can be no assurance that system innovation or adaptation to changing conditions will take place. Of special concern in this context are military organizations which may have no opportunity to operate under the condition for which they were designed, that is, warfare. Negative training, or the acquisition and reinforcement of the wrong skills, is a real and dangerous possibility in such a situation. A basic technical issue in system development, then, is providing the "resources for innovation" when the nature of the enterprise calls for them. A system training vehicle is such a resource.

For the reasons discussed in this and the preceding section, the concept of system training is applicable to nonmilitary as well as military organizations. Throughout this chapter we shall rely heavily upon SAGE system training as an illustration of the system development process for training. But large-scale management information systems in industry and commerce, no less than SAGE, are composed of hundreds or thousands of individuals interacting with one another on an impersonalized basis via geographically dispersed national and international communications networks. System training is also a means in such nonmilitary systems to develop adequate interactional procedures. Nonmilitary, no less than military, systems must evolve efficient patterns of man-computer interaction.[8] Although industrial and commercial enterprises for the most part do not require special training for wartime activities as contrasted to everyday peacetime activities, there are information systems in such areas as satellite control, weather warning, fire warning and control, public health, and civil defense which have a comparable need to train for emergency operations. Also, such systems may require exercising to teach personnel how to operate under degraded or disaster conditions. As in the case of military organizations, the full range of experience with potential environmental conditions may be provided only via realistically simulated inputs. Thus there are valid reasons for attempting to apply the techniques and procedures of system training in new computer-based systems for commercial management and control and in quasi-public and public systems of various types. Such application is feasible and has already been accomplished in the public health and civil defense areas. It would be a mistake to assume that system training is applicable only to military systems such as SAGE.[9]

System Training as Applied Science

The full significance of the development of system training since the initial experiments by the RAND Corporation has only gradually emerged as a result of practical field experience and with improvements in simulation technology. What was first conceived to be simply a more sophisticated technique for performing a type of training which had been conducted in the past by large-scale organizations has gradually become a technology, based upon the electronic digital computer, which makes possible a scientific approach to system evolution.[10] By "scientific" we mean the formulation of design and operational hypotheses which are subjected to systematic experimentation under controlled conditions for testing and revision. Although system training began as a means to study empirically organizational learning and organizational adaptation, it became evident to the personnel intimately associated with the design and use of the training medium that they were in the process of developing a rather remarkable kind of instrument. The fact that they could design via simulated inputs the specific stimuli and degree of stress to which the system responded in a training environment, and could record through computer technology indices of system response in minute detail, provided them with something new. It meant that scientific method could be applied to the creation and evolution of complex man-machine systems. It meant that at any given time a particular system configuration of men and machines could be conceived as a set of design hypotheses which, through simulation and automatic data recording, could be submitted to systematic examination, testing, and evaluation.

No claim is advanced that system training meets the *ideal* requirements of scientific method as it is conducted in the laboratory. There are obviously too many variables at work in the operational environment to duplicate the degree of control which laboratory conditions make possible. But system training is a step, a giant step, in the direction of providing a degree of scientific method in an area which in the past was conceived to be beyond the reach of science. Even more important is the fact that rigid control of single variables is not desirable for the purpose at hand. System training is valuable because it makes possible an evaluation of a particular configuration of men and machines against a system requirement under conditions in which some variables must, in the nature of the case, remain unknown, at least for the immediate future. We do not have to know exactly why configuration *A* or procedure *x* is superior, with respect to a requirement, to configuration *B* or procedure *y*. If *A* and *x* meet the requirements better under a full range of test situations in controlled exercises and we can replicate these exercises at will to ensure the validity of the results, we have then applied a scientific technique to the problem of system design.

The following sections describe the process whereby a system-oriented training program for a large-scale computer-based information system may be developed.

8.2   THE TRAINING PROGRAM DEVELOPMENT PROCESS

The determination of training program requirements proceeds through the iterative design cycle from preliminary gross concepts to increasingly detailed specifications. We have already described this process for other aspects of the system. As in the previous chapters, we shall, to the extent possible, present the training program development process as if it were a linear sequence of events. Figure 8.4 is a highly simplified schematic representation of the process. It shows in flow diagram form the inputs, the sequences of activities, and the final outputs or products. The narrative in this chapter follows the boxes in the figure.

Inputs to Training Program Development

There are three major inputs to the training program development effort: (*a*) the user's training plans and concepts, (*b*) the user's guidance on evaluation criteria, and (*c*) the preliminary training requirements as specified in the preliminary system design documentation.

The User's Training Plans and Concepts. The system user will normally have training plans and training concepts for the manual or semiautomated system which is being replaced. There may also exist a user division or department which is responsible for training the existing system personnel. In the development of the training program for the replacement system, the developer must rely heavily on the existing training operations and training organization. It is desirable to ensure a smooth transition from current to new training activities and to minimize the disruption to the current training organization. In military system development, the using command, working closely with the military training command, has the responsibility to specify

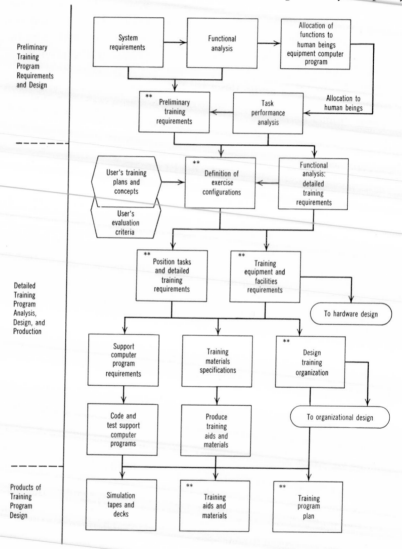

Figure 8.4 Development process for the training program. **Indicates user review and concurrence.

the types of training it desires and the scope of the effort it envisages in terms of manpower to implement the program and the frequency of training. In the development of nonmilitary systems, the user and the developer's training personnel should work together closely to ascertain the degree of possible carryover of existing training programs and concepts to the new system. In either case, whether the user is a military or a nonmilitary organization, the determination of detailed training requirements should not begin until the user has provided guidance with respect to his own training plans and concepts.

A short digression is needed at this point to note the common problem of resistance to change and, more specifically, the difficulty caused by the resentment of the user's training personnel to "interference" from "outsiders." The introduction of a new automated information system implies change. Established enterprises and institutions have built up in the course of time standard operational procedures, accepted patterns of interaction, and customary ways of doing things. Adapting these established customs to a new computer-based system does not come easily even to those who clearly recognize the need. Resistance to change is especially marked in areas such as training since the user's organization may contain a group specifically responsible for this function. Such a group is naturally resentful and suspicious of an outside organization which asserts that it will design the training for the new system. It is doubtful that any words here can dissipate this typical reaction. However, it is essential that the user management understand what is involved in this situation. The following pages attempt to explain why the developer's organization should be held responsible for the development of the training program. The design of appropriate training must be understood as no less a part of the total design activity than, say, the design of an operator console or a wall display. But this does not deny the fact, noted in the previous paragraph, that the developer should rely heavily on the existing training and training organization. If this interdependence cannot be satisfactorily achieved, the ultimate performance of the new system may be degraded.

User Guidance on Evaluation Criteria. In the typical large-scale enterprise there will exist criteria by means of which the performance of the enterprise is evaluated. In nonmilitary systems these criteria may be production, sales, profit margins, absentee rates for personnel, or employee proficiency tests. In military systems they may consist of measures of accuracy and reliability in daily status reports, frequency of equipment malfunctions, operator proficiency measures, or operational readiness measures. The measures of performance which the user regards as significant should be provided to the developer personnel responsible for the training program. These measures, which reflect the user's objectives for the system, should be incorporated with new system evaluation criteria created by the developer. The sources of these criteria are the new system requirements, new functions, task analyses, the personnel test and evaluation plan, and computer program requirements. The user's guidance data and the developer's evaluation criteria are first integrated and then designed into the training program.

Preliminary Training Program Requirements. The preliminary system requirements documents—the system operational concept, the system physical configuration, and the functional flow diagrams—will contain implications for training requirements. These implications should be made explicit as early in the development cycle as possible, ideally in the preliminary system requirements documents themselves.

Since the design and production of training programs is time consuming and costly, the earliest feasibility studies should take training variables into account. In the weighing of alternative system concepts and configurations, the need or lack of need for training can make a significant difference in the selection process. In the past, the determination of training needs, as well as of other aspects of the software subsystem, has too often been delayed until the development effort was well advanced.

It cannot be emphasized enough that contemporary computer-based information systems are *man-machine* systems. In the flow of operations men and the computer programs are interleaved; they operate in series. In the sequential flow of computer program operations there are points of human intervention. The human beings in the system insert data, request data, take switch actions, evaluate outputs in the form of printouts, wall displays, or symbolic data on console displays, and make decisions based on those outputs. Because of this tight interleaving of human and machine performance, the establishment of requirements for training whereby the performance of the human components in the system can be improved is a prime consideration in the development process.

To illustrate the nature of preliminary training program requirements we shall quote from a paper by J. T. Rowell and E. R. Streich describing the "general" training requirements for the SAGE system:[11]

"*The capability for training functionally complete units within the system, and for training the system as a whole.* In SAGE there are three levels to be trained. The basic unit is the Air Defense Sector with its computer-based information-processing Direction Center. The next higher organizational level is the division, and the third, and highest level, is the entire NORAD complex. Each level would require a separate training plan, procedures, and training materials. Training exercises at all three levels would occur on a regular basis; however, because of the immense scope of a NORAD exercise, exercises at this level would occur less frequently.

"*Training should be an integral part of continuous system operations.* Thus training should be conducted on-site in the operational setting, using normal operational equipment and communication channels insofar as possible; and it should be an on-going program rather than being limited to training for initial proficiency, with exercises conducted frequently throughout the life of the system.

"*Providing for wartime training alongside peacetime functions.* During normal day-to-day operations, operator personnel monitor the air space over the North American continent. Yet, they must be prepared to act instantaneously in case of enemy air attack. Thus, the system must be prepared to function well-nigh perfectly for an event which has never occurred and we hope never will. It is this training for the 'rare event' which presents the requirements for speed, overload, and attrition training stresses which are unique to SAGE.

"*The training program should be capable of adaptation to changes in the operational system.* From the beginning it was apparent that SAGE would undergo considerable equipment and configurational change. For this reason a built-in flexibility in the training program was imperative. This requirement also assumes that for training purposes immense quantities of data about air defense operations would be available and constantly updated to provide an information base for construction of realistic training inputs of all kinds.

"*The simulation materials should be compatible with computer and display equipment.* Since the computer is the central information processing unit and presents an entire air environment, the major simulation input materials should be capable of being processed by the computer and displayed either identically to or very similarly to 'live' operational inputs.

"*Development of other associated training input materials and equipment.* In addition to the basic simulation materials, many additional inputs such as various types of message scripts, lists, map aids, films, etc., would be required, especially for purposes of simulating external agencies. Comprehensive production facilities would be required to produce the various training materials and handle the highly complex processing of them into integrated series of exercise packages."

There are important consequences for the eventual performance of the system if training considerations are ignored during the *system-level* design and analysis and are first considered at the subsystem level of design. In the design of large-scale systems, the hardware and software subsystems are usually developed by different contractors. But in the operational configuration the hardware and software components must function smoothly *together* if the *system* is to meet its performance requirements. Training objectives and needs must be derived from these system requirements. If they are derived by the contractors responsible for subsystems, the subsystem training requirements could be achieved but without ensuring that the system performance requirements would be met. This is not just a question of obtaining appropriate coordination among the various subcontractors and developers. (In the case of military system development there is also the need for contractors to coordinate with the military training commands.) *It is a matter of studying training requirements from a system perspective.* If, for practical reasons and in spite of these strictures, the determination of preliminary training requirements is handled separately by a hardware developer and a software developer, their output with respect to training should take the form of an officially integrated system design document.

Preliminary system analysis should result in the production of a preliminary plan for the training and exercising of the system. This plan should include the following types of information: the results of the preliminary system analysis, which describes the training needs of the new system; the functions to be trained; the objectives of training; the scope of the training required; the nature of the training required, whether formal classroom training, paper and pencil training, on-the-job training, proficiency training, system training; the training configurations (definitions of component, subsystem, and system training units); the training environments, that is, simulated, operational, or some combination of both; the phasing or scheduling of different types of training or training configurations; the requirements for trainer personnel and organization; the requirements for training equipment or facilities; and the requirements for computer programs to produce simulated inputs or other training aids and materials or to perform data recording, reduction, and analysis.

The training plan should be integrated with the results of the parallel preliminary software design efforts in the areas of computer programming, personnel and organization, and operational procedures. This integrated preliminary software design document should be reviewed by the hardware contractor and by the system user for evaluation and concurrence. General agreement on the initial software design requirements should be reached before any further design work is attempted. These requirements must be based on the most up to date information on the characteristics of the system hardware. Once this agreement is obtained, the analysis to determine more detailed training requirements can begin.

Definition of Exercise Configurations

The term "configuration" refers in this context to a particular cluster of facilities, equipment, and operational personnel which is selected as the subject of a type or class of training exercise. For the designer of training the problem in the definition of exercise configurations is similar to that of the system designers who are responsible for defining the system, establishing its boundaries, and identifying subsystems and components. The objectives of the training designers, however, differ in that they are concerned with a configuration which lends itself to training.

The definition of exercise configurations involves the designer in tradeoff studies of various types. The basic variables which must be considered in these analyses include the criticality of training needs, the cost of building a satisfactory training capability, the technical feasibility of the required training vehicle, and the potentiality for isolating operational personnel and units for training purposes in the necessary environment. A particular training need may be highly critical, but the cost of designing and constructing an appropriate training vehicle involving the generation of magnetic tapes by a computer for the simulation of system inputs could be prohibitive. Similarly, the technical requirements for the provision of realistic simulation of the system's environment could be beyond the existing state of the art although the training need is imperative. The simulation of electronic countermeasures on early SAGE training magnetic input tapes is an example of this type of problem. (This is discussed in some detail in the section "Support Computer Programs," p. 264.) Thus the definition of exercise configurations requires tradeoff analyses and design decisions similar in nature and scope to the feasibility studies conducted during the advanced stages of system development. Also, as in the case of the feasibility studies, it is necessary for the developer to obtain user review and concurrence with respect to the exercise configurations which are chosen.

Although the focus of system training is upon the system as a whole, as in the NORAD-wide exercises referred to earlier, there are occasions when it is not desirable or practicable to exercise the entire system. Before a system attains its operational capability, for example, it is necessary to train individuals and work teams in the mastery of basic skills and interactions. This is the function of the Category I and II tests in the United States Air Force system development programs. After basic skills are attained, these components can then be put together for training at the system level. Also, after a system has attained an operational capability, there arise frequent occasions when training should be provided for individuals and for work teams. Even with the best planning, individuals master skills at different rates of speed. Also, in many enterprises the rate of personnel turnover is such that uneven skill mastery is the rule rather than the exception. Another source of unevenness in skills is the introduction of new equipment or the assignment of new functions to specific personnel or groups. These problems make it necessary for the designers of the training program to describe the various training configurations, in addition to the whole system, which will be required.

Another source of configurational differentiation for training design purposes is the geographical distribution of an enterprise. When a system encompasses a large geographical area, as in the case of NORAD already cited or an industrial corporation, it is frequently divided into regions or divisions (see Figure 8.2 for SAGE geographical divisions). In such cases it is likely that the installation of a new computer-based information system will also follow some sequence of regions or divisions. These distinctions lend themselves to the design of training configurations.

It is apparent from what we have said up to this point that a given training configuration may be selected on the basis of variations in skill levels, a new or critical function, an organizational unit which operates as a team, some geographical division, or the phasing-in schedule of new elements of the system. The designer must select one or more of these criteria in the determination of training configurations, depending upon the particular circumstances. These potential exercise configurations must then be subjected to detailed tradeoff analyses as noted above.

In SAGE system training the basic training unit is the SAGE sector, composed of a Direction Center and its associated radar sites. In addition, training of larger elements of the SAGE system has been conducted at the division, multidivision, and the NORAD levels. The SAGE training program also provides for the independent training of units within the Direction Center. A SAGE Direction Center is composed of four main elements—the manual data room, the air surveillance branch, an identification branch, and the weapons branch. The last-named branch became a special focus of interest in a project called Weapons Evaluation and Subsystem Training (WEST). The function of the weapons team in the SAGE Direction Center is especially critical for successful system operations. The team was composed of intercept directors, weapons directors, and senior directors. In addition to providing training for the weapons team as a whole, this SAGE effort was also employed in the training of new intercept directors and for cross-training intercept directors as weapons directors. To provide an exercise environment for weapons branch training, it was necessary to simulate the manual data room and the air surveillance and identification branches. The basic input for training purposes was provided by magnetic tape. In addition it was necessary to use human beings as simulators to act out the roles of personnel with whom the weapons team normally interacted: an air defense artillery director, an air base officer, interceptor pilots, and a tracking officer. Thus, through appropriate simulation it was possible to train the weapons branch without interfering with the other personnel and on-going activities in the Direction Center. Exercises could be scheduled at times convenient to the personnel involved, and attention could be focused upon operational difficulties which were of primary concern to the weapons personnel. In the event that the weapons branch encountered operational difficulties during the course of a sector, division, or other type of exercise, it would be possible for the branch to run through the same exercise again and again, if necessary, to diagnose the problems and develop more successful operational procedures.

The decision to develop a training capability for the weapons branch in SAGE followed tradeoff studies which indicated that the functions of this branch were critical for adequate system performance, that an exercising capability could be created within an acceptable cost factor, that the technical requirements for the exercising vehicle could be met, and, finally, that the personnel concerned could be isolated for training in the operational environment without interfering with daily operations.

Functional Analysis and Detailed Training Requirements

In the initiation of the system development effort, the definition of preliminary operational requirements will imply a set of functions. The first task of the personnel responsible for defining detailed training requirements is to determine to what extent the set of functions required to meet the system's objectives will differ from the existing functions of the enterprise. One might begin by preparing a list of two sets of functions—those currently conducted by the enterprise and those implied by the new system requirements. We will assume that adequate training for those existing functions which will be continued into the new system is being provided to personnel by the user. (At a later point it will be necessary to ensure the integration of new and old training.) For each *new* function listed, an analysis is undertaken to determine the training implications. Since each major system function is composed of a number of subfunctions and these, in turn, are composed of tasks, the job of the designer is to examine systematically each subfunction and task within the new functional area.

The list of new functions should be broken down further into critical and noncritical functions. A more detailed procedure would be to list all new functions along a continuum from critical to noncritical. Given an austere budget for training, the designer could then eliminate the least critical functions from further consideration. Of course, the user should be informed of the consequences of such decisions. The term "critical" in this context refers to those functions or tasks which, if performed below a specified level, would seriously degrade the system's objectives or mission. An example of this type of critical function is provided in some contemporary military control systems in which relatively survivable components will take over operations from nonsurvivable components in the event of massive nuclear attack upon the United States. The survivable components have the function of monitoring the operations of the nonsurvivable units and, according to the operational concept, will assume responsibility only in the event of the destruction of the nonsurvivable units.

In this case, we are obviously talking about a very critical function. There are two points to be made here with respect to training requirements for such a function. We note not only that it is critical in type but also that (1) the *transition* from the monitoring mode to the operational mode is a very critical phase and the function is not actually carried out unless there is a major attack on the United States, and (2) the experience of the survivable unit with real operations will never occur except under conditions of actual attack. Thus, in addition to perceiving the importance of training for the function of monitoring by survivable units, we can already begin to discern one of the characteristics of the training itself: there is a need to simulate attack conditions. The value of such training should be self-evident, but unfortunately there is no assurance that the *user* will view the need for training as self-evident. We cannot afford to digress, for lack of space, to the sociopsychological problem of negative training, but we will have occasion to refer to it briefly in the course of this discussion. The fact of the matter is that military system personnel become accustomed to the procedures under which they operate and the types of decisions that they make every day under normal, peacetime operations. It requires effort and imagination to consider what one would be required to do in the event of a national catastrophe such as thermonuclear war.[12]

Position Tasks and Detailed Training Requirements

In Chapter 6 we described the process of task definition and task analysis. We noted that in the course of task analysis specific training needs were identified. For example, learning to write backwards was identified as a training need for the position of plotter in the manual system of air defense. Whereas functional analysis provides general training needs, the determination of detailed training requirements is accomplished by systematically reviewing the tasks which must be performed by each position in the new system. A "systematic" review implies a methodology for evaluating or measuring the degree of training need via some scaling technique.

Each task for each position in the system may be rated on the basis of several criteria such as (1) criticality of malperformance for total system performance, (2) complexity/difficulty, (3) regularity or frequency of performance, (4) similarity to tasks in the system being replaced, and (5) the user's existing training for the task. Each task for each position may then be rated, as in the case of the training needs analysis for the BUIC system, along a five-point scale in which the assignment of a rating of 5 indicates the highest degree of need for training and a rating of 1 the lowest degree of need. (See Table 8.1.)

The procedure in applying the rating scale is as follows. Each task

Table 8.1
*A Rating Scale for Training Needs**

Scale Value		Interpretation
5	Most important	Needs at this level are paramount in terms of over-all system performance and require great emphasis in the design of the training program.
4	Highly important	Many opportunities for exercises of tasks representing these needs should be provided.
3	Important	Frequent exercising of tasks representing these needs are desirable.
2	Less important	These needs should be represented in the training program, but only occasional training is necessary.
1	Unimportant	Needs at this level should receive no specific recognition in the training program.

* From D. G. Arnold, *Training Needs Analysis of the BUIC System.* Santa Monica, Calif.: System Development Corporation, TM-783/000/02, December 18, 1962.

to be performed by each position in the system for which the software developer has responsibility (the hardware developer is responsible for the training needs analysis of equipment maintenance personnel) is assessed in turn for each of the criteria listed above, some selected number of them, or other relevant criteria. Depending upon the degree of training need estimated for each criterion for each task, the designer assigns a number from the rating scale. Thus, if the designer regards a given task as extremely critical for total system performance, he assigns that task a scale value of 5 for criticality. If he regards another task for the same position as not very complex, one of the other criteria selected, but still complex enough to require some occasional training, he may assign it a scale value of 2. Finally, the average of the ratings for each criterion for each task performed by each position is tabulated. It should be noted that the rating of tasks in the system as well as the selection of the appropriate criteria to use in any given system design effort can be done properly only if the personnel conducting these activities are thoroughly familiar with the system's operations. The system design personnel should be familiar enough with operations to make such judgments, but in addition it is desirable, wherever possible, to make use of the knowledge of the system's operational personnel as independent judges. After the system designers have made their judgments as to the rating of the training needs for each task of each position, questionnaires can be used to obtain independent assessments from system personnel acknowledged to be experts on system operations and from the user's experienced training personnel.

We can use the position of the weapons director in the SAGE system as an example of the determination of training needs via task analysis and rating. The weapons director commits interceptors and missiles against hostile or unknown aircraft and supervises their employment. Each weapons director directs the activity of a weapons team consisting of as many as five intercept directors and their technicians (assistants). A SAGE Direction Center has four such weapons teams. A basic task of the weapons director is the commitment of available weapons against hostile tracks in the system. More than one weapon (interceptor aircraft, for example) may be committed against one hostile track. If we were to assess this task by using the criterion of criticality for system performance, we would assign it the rating of 5 ("most important"). Inadequate performance of this position can affect the operations of five intercept directors; inadequate decision making can result in the overcommitment of a limited supply of weapons with possible disastrous results for the defense of the sector; and the decision to commit missiles as distinct from aircraft allows no room for error. Assessment by other criteria, such as complexity of the task and similarity to other tasks in the current system, results in all cases in a similar rating of "most important" or 5. An average rating of 5 for this position indicates the need for training the weapons director.

To identify all the training requirements and to determine the techniques for the conduct of training, the designer not only must analyze each task with respect to positions as we have noted but also must analyze the functional flow diagrams. He must examine the antecedent and parallel work stemming from personnel and organizational design which will indicate to him the new positions created, the structure of new organizational units, the interrelationships of old and new organizational units, and the organizational interfaces with other systems. From the work of the designers responsible for the development of the operational procedures he acquires the detailed descriptions of the interactions in their proper sequence between the system personnel and the hardware and computer programs. All of these inputs are studied in conjunction with the available descriptions of the system equipment—the displays, consoles, communications, and input/output devices. Out of this extensive examination there gradually emerges a listing of all the areas within the planned system where operational difficulties can be anticipated. These are integrated with the training needs derived from the analyses of position tasks. During the course of this detailed analysis of training needs, the designer also pulls out the information he needs to establish the requirements for simulation of a given task, for monitoring the performance of personnel, and for recording and reducing the data needed to evaluate individual, group, and system performance. This analysis also generates the requirements for those personnel who, in addition to the support computer programs, will be responsible for simulation and for monitoring, recording, and measuring personnel performance. Finally, this analysis generates the special equipment needed for the conduct of training operations. Each of these follow-on activities is described in the sections on pp. 262–273.

The use of rating scales for evaluating and measuring the training needs of positions in the new system is a subjective method which depends heavily upon the individual designer's skill. A subjective approach of this type is satisfactory enough during the early stages of system design, but it should be replaced as soon as possible in the development process by a more empirical procedure. In previous chapters we have discussed the role of laboratory simulation of system operations in the design process. In Chapter 6 we noted that experimentation with and evaluation of alternative design hypotheses may be conducted in a laboratory replica of the new system. In the examples cited in that chapter the focus of attention was upon organizational design. We also noted that the functional responsibilities of given positions in the system can be studied through these same methods. By playing out the role of a given position in a laboratory setting in which the variety of anticipated inputs under different operational conditions can be controlled by the designers, the training needs for the position can be derived empirically. In subsequent tests and experiments the initial training needs which are subjectively determined are gradually replaced by more empirically based and objectively determined training needs. It is perfectly possible that the most critical training needs may not be discovered until the system is installed in the operational environment.

Training Equipment and Facilities Requirements

In the previous pages we noted that, as the training requirements are established, they will usually include implications for equipment and facilities. As these equipment and facilities requirements are stated, they should be compared with the initial equipment and facilities data in the preliminary system requirements documents. If any discrepancies are found, the user and the hardware and facilities contractors must be notified. It is the responsibility of the software contractor to provide them with the additional equipment and facilities requirements necessary to accomplish the desired training.

The range of equipment and facilities which may be required for an adequate training program can be extensive. Typical examples of the types of items which may be required include storage equipment and space for training materials and aids (in military systems this may call for classified safes and the creation of a security area); office space in operations buildings for training personnel (these could be either contractor or user personnel); simulator equipment and facilities providing needed communications such as telephone or teletype; and equipment such as the AN/GPS-T2, which, in the Manual Air Defense System Training Program described in the introduction of this chapter, generated the simulated radar returns on the radarscopes of surveillance personnel. (See Figure 8.1.)

A classic example of some of the problems associated with meeting the equipment requirements for training purposes is provided by the effort to include training for electronic counter-countermeasures (ECCM) in SAGE.[13] Since SAGE is composed of electronic subsystems such as radar, digital computers, and communications networks, it is vulnerable to the electronic countermeasures (ECM) which in all likelihood would be employed by an invading force of hostile aircraft. SAGE operational personnel must be able to apply all the ECCM techniques available to them to detect and destroy such an enemy force in the disruptive ECM environment generated by it. Since SAGE personnel can acquire only limited operational experience in combating ECM under normal peacetime conditions, it was essential to provide this experience as part of the training program. The focus of the training effort for ECCM was upon the SAGE radar, not the computers or communications. The basic problem for the training designers was the creation of the equipment required to simulate the effects of the generation of ECM by the hypothetical hostile invaders on the SAGE radars. As we noted earlier, in the manual air defense system, equipment, designated the AN/GPS-T2, was designed and built to generate simulated radar returns on the radarscopes of a Direction Center. In order to simulate ECM an attachment to the AN/GPS-T2 called the ACTER (anti-countermeasures trainer) which could generate four types of simulated electronic jamming was built by a hardware contractor.

After some modifications and feasibility tests the AN/GPS-T2 and the ACTER were adapted for use in generating ECM for SAGE ECCM training. This was necessary since the earliest SAGE training in which magnetic tape was used as the source of radar inputs was not designed to include ECM phenomena. Unfortunately, when the SAGE simulation effort was initiated, the technological knowledge to simulate ECM effects on magnetic tape did not exist. Subsequent production methods for the exercise tapes did include a capability for simulating ECM.

The point we wish to stress about the determination of training equipment requirements is the importance of timely establishment of these requirements. Equipment for training should be designed to meet well-defined needs. Too often it is the practice either to ignore or delay the design of training equipment, or to design it before the purpose and the method of using it have been clearly established. In the case of the design of the AN/GPS-T2 for simulation of radar returns in the manual air defense system the proper sequence occurred. The equipment was designed in response to a clearly defined training need. In the case of SAGE, however, although the need was clear, the technological knowledge required to reproduce ECM effects on a magnetic tape did not exist. The problem was resolved by adapting the existing manual system equipment on an interim basis while a development effort was initiated to build the capability to put realistic ECM on computer-generated tape.

Support Computer Programs

At a number of points in the software development process we have noted that activities in a specific area, such as personnel and organizational design, generate requirements for related areas—testing and evaluation, equipment, training, and computer programming. Similarly, as training requirements are established they have implications for other development areas. The computer programming requirements stemming from *nonoperational* areas such as training, evaluation, and testing are collectively treated by the program designers as *support computer program requirements*.

Of crucial importance from a training point of view is the requirement that computer program designers provide for "tagging" conventions so that any simulated input can be traced as it passes through the system in the course of an exercise. "Tagging" simply means that some symbolic means for identifying an input is provided via the computer. The capability to trace the history of an input message from its initial appearance in the system through its processing, transmission, and final disposition makes it possible for operations and training personnel to recreate, after a given exercise, the history of information flow. Such a capability makes it possible to determine the sources of input errors in the system and to isolate critical decision-making points in the system operations, as well as to design and test more efficient, error-free message flows for the same inputs.

In the SAGE system training program the major stimulus in a training mission is the simulated radar picture of air traffic which is stored on a magnetic tape. This tape is produced by an IBM computer. The symbolic representations of aircraft which appear on the SAGE Direction Center consoles are generated by this tape. The data on the tape represent aircraft moving within the range of the Direction Center's radar according to realistic patterns of speed, altitude, and turns. To represent such aircraft movements in a realistic manner, the specifications must be provided to the programmers for the characteristics of actual aircraft, both friendly and potential enemy, so that these can be stored in the computer's memory. For each aircraft which will be simulated, data must be provided with regard to its maximum speed, maximum altitude, rate of climb, range, and other operational characteristics. Computer programs can then be written on the basis of these parameters. Similarly, with respect to radar coverage, specifications must be provided for the capabilities of the SAGE-associated radar equipment, that is, radar locations, range, height information, and areas of ground clutter (areas which prevent radar returns because of obstructions such as mountains or other topographical features).

In SAGE system training, many other materials must be specified in detail, some of them hand produced and others, like the simulated input tapes, generated by a computer. For SAGE training the computer-produced materials include the following:

- *Flight Information Map Book.* A reference aid providing information about events and characteristics for each flight in the training exercise.
- *Flight Plan Book.* Air Movements Identification Section (AMIS) flight plans arranged in order of call-in time.
- *Crosstell Script.* Surveillance information in message form.
- *Threat Warning and Tactical Action Script.* Early warning information on flights that originate outside the area of the exercising unit.
- *Height Input Script.* Information supplied to a simulator about altitudes of all flights in the problem.

- *Site ECM List.* Detailed information about the jamming flights which affect a site's radar during an electronic countermeasure mission.
- *ECM Jamming Summary.* Debriefing team information specifying first appearance and final fade of jamming to all sites affected by jamming aircraft. (The function of "debriefing" is discussed below.)
- *Correlation Map.* Depicts air traffic within map area at five-minute intervals.

While the purpose of some of these training aids is the same as that of the magnetic tape, that is, they are used in simulating the environment of the personnel undergoing training, other aids are used as a means whereby training personnel provide exercise participants with knowledge of results during the debriefing session which is conducted when the exercise is completed. The provision of knowledge of results is one of the basic learning principles which was so successfully applied during the RAND experiments and the SAGE System Training Program. Training aids must be produced for each exercise so that the training personnel can pinpoint discrepancies between the actual performance of the system and the expected performance. Expected performance measures are derived from the system performance requirements. Thus, for example, the Correlation Map in SAGE training exercises, which depicts the simulated air traffic within the map area at five-minute intervals, is used by the training team as a basis for comparing the air traffic picture as conceived by the exercise participants with the *actual* air picture as input via the simulation tape. Similarly, the other scripts and lists, such as the Flight Information Map Book, the Crosstell Script, the Site ECM List, and the ECM Jamming Summary, make it possible for the exercise participants, with the help of the training team, to reconstruct the pattern of events that occurred during the exercise so that errors and inadequate areas of performance can be analyzed. During the debriefing sessions ideas for new procedures and new patterns of personnel interaction are proposed as solutions to the problems encountered. In subsequent exercises these new ideas are tried out. The training exercise which gave rise to the original problem can be run again, only this time the new procedures can be used. The knowledge of results fed back to the exercise participants after this second run, and then after subsequent runs simulating other conditions, will either confirm or deny the value of the new procedures.

Training, evaluation, and testing from the point of view of the computer programmer all require similar capabilities—the capabilities to input simulated system data and to record, reduce, and display specified data in the system. Support programs provide the capability to store, sort, analyze, reduce, select, and present data. Rather than designing and producing separate programs for different functions such as training, evaluation, and testing, it is more efficient to design multiple-purpose programs. In this way the same computer programs can generate simulated data for any number of required functions. The same simulated inputs can be used to train system personnel, to evaluate system personnel and system operations, and to test the operational computer programs. This procedure makes maximal use of the limited computer storage space and is more economical than designing independent training, evaluation, and testing programs.

Training Materials Specifications

In addition to the simulation materials and data recording generated by the computer, the detailed training requirements may call for the design and production of a variety of manually produced or non-computer-generated training aids, scripts, lists, charts, forms, and other materials. The need for such materials may vary with the phase of training, with exercise configurations, and with the type of training needed for given positions in the system. The design, production, and quality control of these items, as in the case of the computer-generated training materials, may represent a major technical and managerial undertaking.

In system training for SAGE it was necessary to produce non-computer-generated training materials in order to provide adequate and realistic simulation of the operational environment. Although a major proportion of the environment could be simulated via magnetic tape, as in the case of radar returns already described, it was also necessary to simulate inputs from the environment which normally flow into the SAGE Direction Center over telephone and teletype networks. Inputs of this type included early warning information, intelligence information, weather information, and information from adjacent Direction Centers and from higher and lower echelons of command. These inputs were prepared in the form of time-phased scripts which simulation personnel transmitted over operational communications media to the personnel participating in the exercise. Of course the information transmitted to the exercise participants in this fashion had to be synchronized with the computer-generated inputs. The design of a large-scale system training exercise utilizing both computer-generated and manually produced materials, as in the case of SAGE training, requires intensive coordination to ensure consistency of content.

Design of the Training Organization

A training organization will be required to maintain and operate the training program for a large-scale computer-based information system. This training organization should be an extension of the user's current training division or department. However, it should be apparent, as we have proceeded through this description of the design of a training program, that some new functions, such as the design of computer-based training exercises and the conduct of debriefings, and some new technical skills, such as the construction and use of simulation aids, must be acquired. There must, therefore, be (1) a design effort to plan the training organization and (2) a training plan for the user's training personnel.

The requirements for the training organization emerge in the course of the analysis of training needs. As decisions are made with respect to the training methods to be utilized, the exercise configurations, the characteristics of the simulation necessary for exercise stimuli, the nature of the feedback information, and the operational positions which may constitute foci of training interest, the requirements for the training organization are gradually delineated. These requirements must be organized and then analyzed in terms of the following types of questions. How many people will be required to simulate external agencies? Are the nature of queries made to external agencies such that multiple tasks can be performed by one simulator position? Will it be necessary for the simulators to communicate with one another during the exercise? Is visual monitoring of operational personnel necessary during exercises? How will the performance of operational personnel be visually monitored and by whom will this be done? Who will determine on-going training requirements for the user organization? How and by whom will future training exercises be designed and constructed? Who decides how frequently exercises should be run and what type of exercise to run? How will knowledge of results be presented to the exercise participants—will each simulator and monitor present individual results, or will the results be summarized and presented by one individual? If one individual is to have this responsibility, what shall his rank or status be?

As these questions indicate, the design of the training organization is an effort which deals with the same problems and follows the same steps as the personnel and organizational development activity described in Chapter 6. Indeed, the requirements for training personnel, as we noted in that chapter, must be fed into the personnel and organizational design effort. We noted, for example, that in the design of the BUIC system, since system training was to become a military rather than a civilian contractor responsibility, as it had been in the SAGE system, it was necessary for this to be studied as part of the determination of new qualitative and quantitative personnel requirements information.

Figures 8.5 and 8.6 show the organization and composition of the

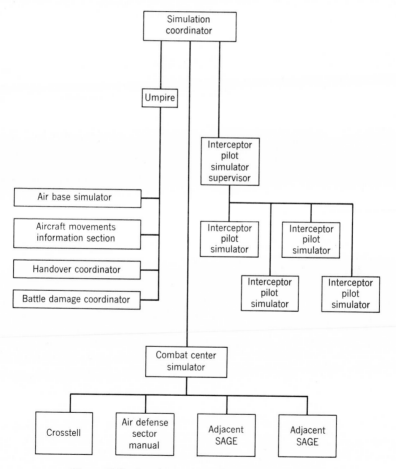

Figure 8.5 Simulation team for a SAGE sector.

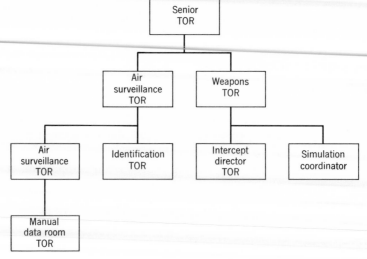

Figure 8.6   TOR (training operations report) team.

simulation team and the training operations report (TOR) team, respectively, for SAGE system training. As the titles of these teams indicate, the simulation team is responsible for all the simulation, other than the preplanned simulation on the exercise magnetic tape, which is required to maintain a realistic environment during an exercise, while the TOR team is responsible for monitoring the exercise and providing the knowledge of results data to be utilized during the post-exercise debriefings.

The Training Plan

In addition to designing the training organization, it is the responsibility of the developer to design a plan for training the user's training personnel. If system training is to play a major role as a training method for the new computer-based system, as was the case in SAGE, planning the training of the trainers is a major task in itself. The importance of such training cannot be overemphasized. In any type of training where simulation via either magnetic tape inputs or manual inputs, or both, plays a major part, those responsible for its conduct must be familiar with simulation technology and must understand the relationship between simulation and training objectives. Simulating the environment realistically is one of the basic training principles derived from the RAND experiments and SAGE training experience. To simulate a role realistically—for example, the role of the Aircraft Movements Information Section of the FAA (see Figure 8.5)—requires on the part of the simulator an understanding of AMIS operations and the standard operating procedures linking the aircraft identification personnel in a SAGE Direction Center to AMIS. The AMIS simulator must undergo some training before he can perform his role adequately in the training exercise.

The development and implementation of the training plan must be phased in as a major component of the over-all development phasing. Since the training of operations personnel must begin before the operational date of the new system, training for the trainers must necessarily start still earlier. Thus the beginning of such training may require a lead time as much as six months before the planned operational date. Since training in general is regarded as less important than operations (an attitude which is no longer tenable for military systems making use of thermonuclear weapons), it is commonplace to find simulation personnel not properly trained for their very important tasks and selected from the least qualified of available personnel, least qualified in the sense that they may be new personnel unfamiliar with operations.

The training plan for the trainers should spell out in detail the following kinds of information: a description of the training organization and its operations; a detailed description with flow charts of the tasks of training personnel; a description of the training needs of training personnel; a design for meeting these training needs, including descriptions of the training methods; and a schedule for the accomplishment of all training requirements for training personnel.

The training plan should also provide for the production of training manuals. These manuals perform the same function as the operational procedures handbooks for the operations personnel, that is, they are essentially step-by-step descriptions of the tasks which, in this case, would be carried out by training personnel in the conduct of training exercises. In the case of SAGE, for example, training manuals were produced for the simulators and for the training personnel responsible for presenting operations crews with knowledge of results.

Like other aspects of system design, the training plan may go through a number of iterations as more detailed information becomes available to the designers. As each iteration of the plan is published, it should be reviewed and concurred in by the system user, by other system contractors, and by other organizations, such as military training commands or the user's training organization, which will be concerned with various aspects of training for the new system.

Training Exercise Design and Specifications

A point is reached in the development of the training program at which it becomes possible to design the specific content of training exercises. On the basis of previous design activity the training needs and objectives have been established; the exercise configurations have been defined; the training methods have been selected; and the capability to produce simulated inputs via computer programs and other types of training aids and materials has been designed. If the training method chosen has been simulation in the operational environment at the system level, design decisions have to be made with respect to such questions as the level of difficulty of stress to incorporate in the exercise, the pattern of change in the level of difficulty over a given series of exercises, the priority of types of functions or situations to include, the degree of realism required for adequate training, the duration of each exercise, the frequency of exercises, and the most appropriate time to conduct exercises.

The answers to these questions require many tradeoffs between learning theory, cost (of realistic simulation via the computer, for example), and practical problems associated with the user's daily operations. For some of the questions, such as the level of difficulty to incorporate in exercises, there are no clear-cut answers. Traffic studies and information flow analyses will indicate the approximate levels of simulated inputs that the system will be required to accommodate for different types of operational conditions. These analyses and studies can provide a basis for estimating the degree of difficulty which can be designed into exercises at various stages of training. Obviously, in the pre-operations, system shakedown stage, the level of difficulty should deliberately be kept low so that individual operators can master basic skills before they are overwhelmed with complex system problems.

The issues with which the training program designers are faced at this stage of design can be illustrated by describing the characteristics of the training exercises for the SAGE system when it replaced the manual air defense system. We shall confine our remarks to the installation phase. For the installation of system training at manual radar sites, a training package consisting of ten two-hour exercises was generally developed. The exercises provided for the simulation of basic air defense functions in three types of environment: peacetime, transition from peace to war, and wartime. The level of difficulty was low in the first exercise in the package and gradually increased throughout the series of ten. The SAGE installation package for the New York Air

Defense Sector (NYADS), the first SAGE sector to become operational, also contained ten two-hour exercises. The selection of exercise content for NYADS, however, was based on criteria which differed somewhat from those of the manual system. Since the SAGE system was introducing air defense personnel to computer-based operations, there were new operator positions and new operational patterns, particularly patterns of interaction with the computer, for such basic system functions as air surveillance, identification of unknown tracks, and weapons control. Thus the initial SAGE exercises were designed to provide training for all critical operational positions as well as indoctrination for all personnel. Figure 8.7 shows the relative level of complexity and basic content of the NYADS installation package of exercises. Problem 1 was a relatively light-load peacetime problem; Problem 2 was a light-load war problem. This exercise was used for basic indoctrination. Problems 3 through 8 increased gradually in complexity, varying with respect to peace, war, and peace to war environments. Problems 9 and 10, as the figure indicates, were the most difficult exercises and dealt with wartime massive air attack conditions.

The detailed content of each exercise should be established through a series of conferences involving the developer's exercise design personnel and the user's training and operations personnel. The ideal training exercise is a product of the specialized knowledge that both of these types of personnel can bring to an exercise design conference. The developer personnel are familiar with the potential areas of difficulty inherent in the system that they are designing, while the user personnel are most familiar with their current areas of operational difficulty and the nature of the external environment to which the system must respond.

The SAGE Sector Training Exercise Cycle: An Example

The success of a training program whereby maximum system performance is achieved is dependent upon a cycle involving in sequence (1) determining training needs, (2) designing exercises to meet these training needs, (3) exercising, (4) analyzing the results of the exercises, and (5) reassessing training needs. To accomplish this cycle, a typical SAGE exercise is composed of four phases: a prebriefing, exercising, feedback, and a debriefing. A SAGE document describes the cycle:[14]

"*Prebriefing.* The prebriefing gives each crew an opportunity to

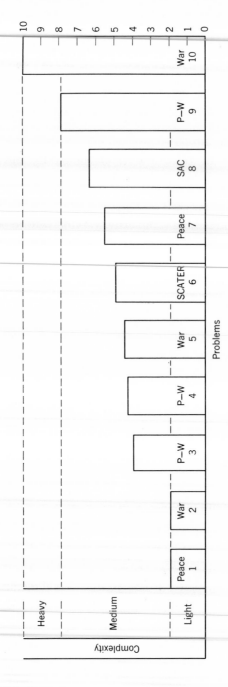

Figure 8.7 Installation training problems. Complexity estimated in terms of loads to be processed, critical incidents, regulations applicable under various states of alert, etc.

274

review difficulties encountered during previous exercises and to plan for the approaching exercise.

"A review of previous problems and the suggested solutions made by the air defense team makes it possible for them to try out new problem-solving techniques during the approaching exercise. Further, it gives continuity to the many training exercises received by the team.

"Following this review, training personnel brief the crew on such things as the potential threat as evaluated by intelligence personnel, the expected weather conditions for the next several hours, simulated conditions of alert, early warning of the impending attack, and the air defense weapons available to the unit for the defense of its area. These facts furnish the crew with planning information prior to the simulated attack. The information also 'warms up' the crew to a realistic, although simulated, battle condition.

"*Exercise.* From the information furnished by the prebriefing, the commander plans a defense of the sector. He and his team are presented with a simulated environment consisting of everything from scope presentations to a variety of real-time message inputs. The radar returns are in actuality coming from a magnetic tape, the other inputs from simulation personnel [Figure 8.5] who are specifically trained to simulate any aspect of a dynamic real-time environment. The defense team "scrambles" aircraft; reacts to telephone, teletype, and radio information input by the simulator personnel; initiates and identifies new tracks coming within radar coverage; commits aircraft or missiles to intercept those tracks identified as 'hostile'; reacts to minimize the effects of bomb damage and fallout effects from enemy action; takes actions to deploy and resupply all defensive weapons; and interacts with higher and lower echelons within the system. To a considerable extent, each crew member is experiencing a realistic battle. If a successful outcome of the battle is to be realized, each crew member must contribute a maximum performance to the crew effort. Most simulated battle phases last three hours. However, they are frequently preceded by a planning phase and followed by a discussion phase.

"*Feedback.* Knowledge of results is considered to be one of the prime requisites for the system training program. Exercise results serve to relate the training goals for each exercise to the team performance and thereby facilitate learning.

"Information for feedback is collected by the training operations report (TOR) team [Figure 8.6]. The members of this team observe the battle from critical positions throughout the Direction Center. The TOR team records such facts as the degree and accuracy of staff planning prior to the attack, the proper use of communications facilities, and the time periods and places throughout the system where overload conditions develop. Information concerning the initiation, continuity, identification and interception of hostile tracks is recorded automatically on magnetic tape.

"At the conclusion of the exercise, this information is consolidated by the TOR team and formally presented to the air defense team when it assembles for the debriefing.

"*Debriefing.* A debriefing is a discussion session held by the team following the exercise. It is led by the senior officer of the crew being trained and is oriented toward identifying and solving problems encountered by the team.

"Even though the debriefing leader is ultimately responsible for deciding the course of action taken to solve problems encountered by the team, the debriefing is conducted in a nonthreatening atmosphere where full participation by all members of the team is encouraged.

"The debriefing leader first attempts to uncover the problems encountered during the exercise, then encourages suggestions for their solution by the team members. Once a full discussion of each problem is concluded, a course of action is chosen by the team leader for future exploration. Each problem encountered, its suggested solution, and the decided course of action are logged by a team recorder for use at the prebriefing of the next exercise. Thus, a circular pattern of exercise continuity is established."

8.3 SUMMARY

This chapter described the process of developing a training program for an information system and located this aspect of system design in the over-all development cycle. In the introduction to the chapter we reviewed the empirical origins of system training and discussed the philosophy underlying its emergence.

The bulk of the chapter was devoted to a description of the training program development process. This began with a review of the inputs to the process from the system user and from preliminary design activities. The process of determining the detailed training requirements was then described. This entailed discussion of the analyses of new system functions and position tasks. The establishment of other training requirements was reviewed with respect to the definition of exercise configurations, training equipment and facilities, training materials and aids, support computer programs, the training organization, and the training plan. Some of the considerations going into the design of training exercises were then discussed, and, finally, the SAGE sector training exercise cycle was described to illustrate the application of system training and its *modus operandi*.

In the course of the chapter several generalizations pertaining to system training were stated. These generalizations are summarized here:

System training provides a capability for overcoming the "degradation factor" in the operation of computer-based information systems.

The basic training principles which evolved from the RAND experiments and the SAGE System Training Program are as follows:

- Exercise at one time as large a part of the system as possible.
- Provide a simulated environment which is as realistic as possible.
- Observe and record selected aspects of system performance.
- Provide system personnel with knowledge of results.
- Exercise the system at a frequency which is consistent with high learning motivation.

The inherent complexity and interdependent nature of the man-machine-computer program components of information systems make some form of system-oriented training essential if maximum system efficiency is to be achieved.

A training program for the development of individual, group, and system capabilities in information systems is most efficiently and economically designed if all training is conceived and planned from a total system perspective.

The overlapping technical requirements for system evaluation, testing, and training in information systems are such that it is neither efficient nor economical to develop them as independent entities.

When a particular system configuration is conceived as a set of design hypotheses, training in a simulated environment provides a means whereby scientific method can be applied to the study of alternative design concepts, the improvement of system performance, and system evolution.

REFERENCES

1. J. L. Kennedy, *A Preliminary Diagnosis of RAND's Psychological Problems*, Memorandum to the Man-Machine Panel LOGS-88, August 15, 1950.
2. For a description of the RAND research see R. L. Chapman et al., "The

Systems Research Laboratory's Air Defense Experiments," *Management Science,* **5**, No. 3 (April 1959), 250–269.

3. L. F. Carter, *The Principles of the System Training Program.* Santa Monica, Calif.: System Development Corporation, SP-9, September 12, 1957.

4. For a description of system training in SAGE see J. T. Rowell and E. R. Streich, "The SAGE System Training Program for the Air Defense Command," *Human Factors,* **6**, No. 5 (October 1964), 537–548.

5. J. C. R. Licklider, "Man-Computer Symbiosis," *IRE Transactions on Human Factors in Electronics,* March 1960, pp. 4–11.

6. R. Boguslaw and E. H. Porter, "Team Functions and Training," in *Psychological Principles in System Development,* R. M. Gagné (ed.). New York: Holt, Rinehart, and Winston, 1962, pp. 395–396.

7. J. G. March and H. A. Simon, *Organizations.* New York: Wiley, 1958, Chap. 6.

8. On the application of system training concepts and procedures to business situations see C. H. Kepner and B. B. Tregoe, "Developing Decision Makers," *Harvard Business Review,* **38**, No. 5 (September-October 1960), 115–124.

9. For examples of the potential application of system training concepts in school emergencies, operations of a mail-order house, fire fighting, and executive training see E. H. Porter, *Manpower Development: The System Training Concept.* New York: Harper & Row, 1964, Chap. 7.

10. See, for example, the adaptation of the early RAND experiments for the conduct of a business game known as "Project SOBIG" in J. L. Kennedy, "The System Approach: Organizational Development," *Human Factors,* **4**, No. 1 (February 1962), pp. 25–52.

11. J. T. Rowell and E. R. Streich, Ref. 4, pp. 541–542.

12. For an elaboration on this theme see Herman Kahn, *Thinking About the Unthinkable.* New York: Horizon Press, 1962.

13. H. M. Parsons, *The Development and Installation of a System Training Program: The SAGE ECCM Example.* Santa Monica, Calif.: System Development Corporation, TM-537, September 28, 1960.

14. *System Training: Its Growth and Development.* Santa Monica, Calif.: System Development Corporation, TM-1263, June 1, 1963, pp. 34–40.

Chapter Nine

The Installation Phase

P. E. Rosove

9.1 INTRODUCTION

The purpose of this chapter is to describe the general characteristics and objectives of the installation phase. To begin with, we must explain why the installation phase for an information system development effort is of critical importance; second, the transitional and overlapping nature of this phase between the antecedent and the subsequent phases requires emphasis; and, finally, we need to review the major activities which are conducted during the phase and the rationale underlying them.

As the term "installation phase" implies, this is the first period of time in which the physical components of the system are placed in their operational environment and, in conjunction with the user's personnel, both are readied for the assumption of operational responsibility. The phase is that period of time encompassed by the completion of the production of the system components and the beginning of operations. The duration of this period is customarily specified in advance by administrative fiat, that is, both the delivery of products by the developer to the user and the beginning of operations are assigned dates which appear in contractual agreements. However, the beginning and end points of the installation phase for an information system are much less determinable than is generally realized by typical users and procuring and administrative agencies. System testing, for example, continues as a sequence of specific tests from the production phase into the subsequent installation phase. As a result of testing, deliverable items may be modified or replaced. Thus, it is difficult to say with any precision, from a technical or developmental point of view, where production activity ends and installation activity begins. Similarly, as we hope to make clear in this chapter, installation and operational activities cannot be sharply demarcated. Like the changing of the seasons, these phases and types of activities merge imperceptibly into one another. Thus, the installation of an information system should not be thought of in terms of the traditional "turn-key" concept of system handover from the developer to the user.

In the simplest terms, the following sequence of activities must be conducted during the installation phase:

- The instruction of the users in the characteristics of the system.
- The conduct of a period of trial use of the system by the users.
- The test and verification of the system design.
- The detection and correction of errors, inadequacies, and gaps in system operations.
- The development of an operational system capability.

The length of time which should be devoted to system installation varies with the nature of the system, such as its size and complexity, the number of locations which must be installed, the strategy of development employed, and the presence or lack of a precursor system. An installation phase may be a periodic activity, or it may be a continuous activity merely shifting its locale from site to site.

When computer programs are added in increments to an existing information system, as is frequently the situation in commercial enterprises, it may be possible to install the new programs and test them under operational conditions without conducting a formal period of installation. Where systems are built by using an inductive strategy upon the foundation of a well-established semiautomatic information system, and the users have participated heavily in the development effort, the installation phase may be accomplished in a few weeks with relatively little effort or long-range planning. However, when a large-scale system which differs drastically from its predecessor is being installed, as in the replacement of the manual system of air defense by the SAGE system, an installation activity comparable in scope to the SAGE variety may be essential. It is important to realize that the installation phase for a large-scale information system may last for many months or actually extend over a period of years. In the case of the SAGE system, in which pieces of the system at different geographical locations were installed in sequence, and of systems which are built via a strategy of evolution, the installation activities may occur periodically at various sites as system models replace one another, or they may occur continuously as different versions of the same system are installed in sequence at a variety of locations.

The installation phase is, without question, the most exciting and difficult period of information system development. There is tremendous pressure on the developers to demonstrate that they have successfully met their contractual commitments on schedule; and there is corresponding pressure on the users to have the new system, on which they have spent so much money and placed such high hopes, assume operational responsibility at the earliest moment. Both users and developers feel anxiety over the capability of the new system to meet their expectations. At the same time, such systems are so complex that a trouble-free installation is unknown. Thus, excitement mounts as errors are found, time runs out, and tempers flare.

Within the scope of a chapter we can only hope to touch on some of the more significant aspects of the installation phase. We attempt to establish at the outset the unique nature of installation activities for information systems as contrasted with hardware systems. In Section 9.2 we review the irrelevance of the "turn-key" concept of system handover for information systems. The remaining sections of the chapter deal in sequence with the following subjects: the importance of the installation phase; phase-over planning, that is, the planning by the user and the developer for the physical replacement of the existing system or unintegrated information-processing elements by the new system; the orientation program; the system shakedown; and feedback to system design. In this last section we shall also discuss system change. The subject of introducing changes to the system will be treated in terms of feedback to design during the installation phase. We shall review in this section the problems associated with system change proposals and the need to establish a change review organization and associated administrative procedures. It should be understood, however, that change proposals are not restricted to the installation phase but may occur at any stage in the development effort.

9.2   THE IRRELEVANCE OF THE "TURN-KEY" CONCEPT

In the established hardware system development process, the completed system, after it has met its acceptance tests, is presented by the developer to the user who, on some predetermined date, turns the system on—declares it operational. This has been referred to as the "turn-key" concept. A simple illustration of the turn-key approach to the handover of a system by the developer to the user is the presentation of a new automobile by a dealer to its owner. The new owner turns the ignition key, starts the engine, and proceeds on his way. Maintenance, as guaranteed by the manufacturer's warranty, is provided over some specified period of time or mileage traveled. As hardware systems have increased in complexity and technological sophistication, as in the case of jet aircraft, nuclear submarines, missiles, and space vehicles, this handover process has become increasingly critical for adequate initial system performance and has required an increasingly longer period of time to accomplish. For such complex systems, the turn-key concept of handover is no longer accurate. Rather than an abrupt switch in responsibility for the system from the developer to the user, there is a varying period of time in which the system is gradually phased into operational status through the combined activities of the developer and the user working as partners in a common endeavor. The turn-key concept is even more irrelevant for information systems. The handover process is qualitatively as different between information systems and sophisticated weapons systems as it is between such weapon systems and an automobile. Two main reasons for the irrelevance of the turn-key concept for information systems need to be discussed: (1) the nature of the development process for information systems, and (2) the strategy of development via evolution.

The Nature of the Development Process

In the preceding chapters of this book we have seen how close the relationship between the user and the developer must be throughout the development effort if a successful system is to be created. We have defined the desirable role of the developer as that of an intimate advisor and consultant to the user. It is a fallacy to believe that this intimate relationship can be terminated suddenly at some hypothetical operational date. An information system is not an automobile, and it cannot be made to operate at a satisfactory level of performance simply by throwing a switch which turns on the computer.

The relationship between the user and the developer begins during the requirements phase, as we have seen, with the involvement of a handful of personnel representing the two organizations. The number of persons involved from both groups gradually increases, as does the frequency and intensity of their interaction, after the establishment of the initial system requirements and during the system design work. This interaction pattern declines during the production phase, since the developer is producing subsystem components to a set of *temporarily* frozen specifications, but then builds up again and *reaches its peak during the installation phase.* After the handover period, it gradually declines again. There are, then, two peaks in the intensity of interaction between the user and the developer during the development process—one during the design phase and the other during the installation phase. *Maximum interaction and interdependence occurs during the handover period.* After this period, the interaction between the user and the developer gradually declines as the users become familiar with the system, learn how to operate and improve it, and develop confidence in its capacity to meet their operational needs. The extent of the decline, however, varies, depending upon which organization assumes responsibility for on-going system maintenance.

An information system, no less than a weapons system, requires on-going maintenance if it is to be kept at maximum performance. However, the newness and sophistication of computer technology are such that a question remains as to the capability of the user to maintain an information system with an in-house staff after the system attains an acceptable operational performance level. When machines are replaced by other more sophisticated and more complex machines, it is still possible, through retraining, for the mechanics of the user organization to assume responsibility for on-going system maintenance. But the most capable mechanics in the user organization obviously cannot maintain an information system. This is not just a question of retraining. The skills of computer programmers, system designers, system analysts, procedures designers, behavioral scientists—all the sundry persons who contribute to the development of an information system—cannot be acquired overnight. Thus, the relationship between the user and the developer should not be terminated arbitrarily upon the handover of the system; in the future this relationship will vary to the degree that the user has the in-house resources capable of assuming the responsibilities of the developer. If he has no such capability, he must continue to rely upon the developer for on-going maintenance.

The Strategy of Evolutionary Development

It will be recalled that a strategy of evolution in information system development calls for the installation of a low-cost, minimal operational configuration, using off-the-shelf equipment, which is scheduled to assume operations at the earliest possible date. This initial capability represents an experimental or prototype system. It provides a means for the involvement of the users in the development of the system, in the generation of additional and changing requirements, and in the eventual design of a system that will meet their continuing needs.

A strategy of evolution means that a relatively small group of developers with the assistance of the user's in-house technical personnel can initiate the first modest operational system configuration. Subsequent system configurations, conceivably more complex and sophisticated, may call for an increasing number of developmental personnel from external sources, such as an outside contractor, and a relationship to the user characterized by growing intensity and frequency of interaction. Design in an evolutionary development strategy does not terminate with the initial operation of the system. On the contrary, the initial operations of the prototype configuration signal the initiation of an intensive feedback process from the user to the developer whereby improvements can be incorporated into subsequent system configurations. In the evolutionary strategy, therefore, there is no point in time when it can be said that the developer has turned over to the user a finished product and has bowed gracefully out of the picture. Again, the exception to this statement is found when the user has the technical in-house capability to assume responsibility for the design and production of subsequent system configurations. But such a capability has been extremely rare in the past, particularly in the military area.

The SAGE system may serve to illustrate the continuing intimate relationship between the user and the developer. The model concept in SAGE, described in Chapter 3, has meant that, since the initial SAGE system configuration became operational in 1958, the developer has continued to design and produce a series of successive system configurations as military air defense requirements have changed. Since each system model essentially alters the flow and the content of information in the system, extensive and costly maintenance activities on the part of the developer are required.

Development personnel must track down all the changes to computer programs, for example, which might be affected by new requirements, additional requirements, or the deletion of requirements. These modifications to requirements can arise as a result of the introduction of a new jet interceptor or of changes in the tactics used by interceptor aircraft. Such modifications were introduced when missiles, as well as jet aircraft, became elements of the defense system. Since all computer programs are tightly integrated among themselves and with other elements of the system—equipment, displays, operational procedures, and personnel—any change to a computer program can have an extensive ripple effect throughout the system. Changes to the programs may require a reassessment of storage allocations in the computer or a re-evaluation of the allocation of system functions among computer programs, equipment, and personnel. The conduct of such activities presumes a detailed knowledge of the system elements and their operations which only the developer possesses. When the developer and the user are one and the same, the problem is minimized. But, as we have noted, this is relatively rare.

Existing budgetary and financial management practices are incompatible with the concept of system evolution. These practices are based on traditional hardware development concepts, such as unchanging requirements, predetermined and fixed completion dates, and predetermined and fixed budgets. Such financial procedures are based on a turn-key concept of system handover. The notion of a gradual phase-over or an extended period of transition from system production to operations is foreign to contemporary finance administrators. Thus, the turn-key concept is perpetuated by nontechnical administrators despite its irrelevance to both the nature of information system development and the strategy of evolutionary development.

9.3 THE IMPORTANCE OF THE INSTALLATION PHASE

We have thoroughly reviewed in Chapter 2 the more significant differences between hardware systems and information systems. In that chapter we described some of the consequences of these differences for the system users, the developers, and procurement agencies. The installation phase constitutes an additional and very important area of difference between the two types of systems. There are three main areas of importance with respect to the installation of information systems: (1) the test and verification of system design concepts *in an operational environment,* (2) the accomplishment of psychological acceptance of the system by the user, and (3) the development of an operational capability. As these subjects are reviewed in the following sections, the differences between the handover process for hardware systems and that for information systems should become increasingly evident. These differences are of degree rather than of kind.

Test and Verification of System Design Concepts

One of the most traumatic points in the development process occurs when the initial computerized system is installed in its first operational version. Why is this such a traumatic period? It is analogous to the situation of the test pilot putting a new jet aircraft through its final test phase before handover to the customer. The best design work available has gone into the creation of the aircraft; it has been carefully built according to the design specifications; but an agonizing question must still be answered: will it fly? This question must also be asked, figuratively, of the new information system. Testing and verification of design decisions have been carried out throughout the development of the system. But the key question—will it fly?—cannot be finally answered until the information system, like the jet aircraft, is tested in the operational environment. Unlike the case of jet aircraft (and here the analogy breaks down), the test for an information system must be made, not by unusually qualified personnel, but *by the actual users of the system.*

The importance of the installation phase, then, is that it provides, for the first time, the environment for the most critical series of tests and experiments which the new system will be required to face—tests in which it is put through its operational paces, involving operational personnel, operational computer programs, operational facilities, and operational equipment. In these tests system performance is measured by the highest-level performance standards—the formally specified system requirements. Thus, these tests supersede all other prior tests which have utilized lower-level standards of performance—the component and subsystem standards. The system may have passed all such tests with flying colors and still fail when measured against the system level requirements.

The Psychological Acceptance of the System by the User

The installation phase is critical since in this phase the majority of user personnel are exposed to the system as an operational entity for the first time. This is a period in which the basic attitudes of personnel who must operate and depend upon the system are formed and solidified. If negative attitudes are established, if the users do not acquire confidence in the system, if they are less than cooperative in ensuring that the system accomplishes its goals, if they reject the system out of hand and refuse to use it, the result may be a disaster from both the users' management and the developer's points of view. Such disasters can and do happen. They can be prevented if appropriate steps are taken as part of the development planning to ensure the psychological acceptance of the system by the users.

A hypercritical attitude on the part of the users toward the system is likely under the following conditions: (1) if they are relatively unfamiliar with information system technology; (2) if they have not participated in the development process; (3) if they have not participated in the phase-over planning for the replacement of the old system by its successor; and (4) if they have not been prepared to accept the new system through a comprehensive and thorough orientation process.

Throughout this book we have insisted at many points on the critical importance of the participation of the user in the more significant design decisions which must be made by the developer. We have specified at key points in the development process the requirement for review and concurrence by the user's representatives of the developer's design documents. If the user understands why a particular alternative design was chosen, he will be more likely to accept the product of that design decision as necessary and desirable. This notion of the importance of user participation in the work of the developer as a basis for psychological acceptance of the final product is not an impressionistic hypothesis but is based upon a considerable amount of experience in information system development and research in the behavioral sciences.[1]

Psychological acceptance of the system by the user, particularly the development of confidence in the capability of the system to perform the user's mission, cannot be accomplished overnight. This is another reason why the turn-key concept of system handover is inappropriate for information systems.

Contributing to the psychological acceptance of the developer's efforts by the user, which follows logically from the comments above, is the participation of the user in the formulation of the phase-over planning. This will be reviewed in Section 9.4.

Another contributing factor to acceptance of the system is an appropriate introduction to it. This is taken care of, or should be, in an orientation program. This topic is discussed in Section 9.5.

The Development of an Operational Capability

During the installation phase, system personnel are interacting with one another in unfamiliar patterns. They are interacting with computer programs in a manner which is different from anything in their previous experience. The interactions of personnel with the computer and with other equipment, such as displays and consoles, are new and strange. The arrangements of work spaces may involve many unusual elements, and the physical facilities, as such, may be peculiar to the uninitiated, as in the case of the SAGE windowless block houses and blue interior lighting. The operators and decision makers must carry on their operational responsibilities in a strange environment—an unfamiliarity which pervades almost every area of their past experience.

The development of an operational capability by the user means that he must understand how the system works. This understanding is based upon many elements, all of which are interrelated. Operators must understand their equipment—the use of switches, light guns, display request panels, printers, tape units, keyboards, etc.; they must understand the computer programs—the structure of the programs, the tables, the data base, and the operational functions performed by the programs; they must understand how information gets into and out of the data-processing elements of the system and the format of both inputs and outputs; they must understand the communications network by means of which information flows through the system from remote locations as well as the communications which link them to their colleagues in the organization. The decision makers must understand what kinds of information the system can provide, the frequency with which information of different kinds can be obtained, the relationship between information in the system and the types of decisions they have to make, the format of the displays and printouts so that they can interpret the information provided by the system, the kinds of requests for information they may make of the system, and so on.

An operational capability for a complex, large-scale information system can only be achieved as a result of an extensive period of system "shakedown." This shakedown includes a phase of pre-operational exercising of personnel in the operational environment, system testing, and the alteration of the designed operational procedures as experience indicates that this is necessary. These subjects are discussed in Section 9.6. The point to be made here is that the user must recognize the importance of the installation phase for the system shakedown.

It is the system's incubation period. Hatching without proper incubation will produce a monster rather than a good system.

The requirement for a period of incubation is another reason why the turn-key concept of system handover is inappropriate for information systems.

9.4 PHASE-OVER PLANNING

Why Phase-over Planning Is Important

One of the responsibilities of the developer, in close cooperation with the user, is to develop a phase-over plan whereby the successor system can assume operational responsibility without incurring a period of performance degradation. This implies some period of time in which the precursor unintegrated data-processing elements or the manual system is gradually phased out and the replacement system is phased in. To prevent operational degradation during the phase-over period, a plan to accomplish this must be created as one element of the developmental task. Of course, phase-over planning is not as critical in cases wherein the new system is being installed as an entity in a physical facility unrelated to existing data-processing elements. But planning is still necessary for the shift in operational responsibility. During the period of phase-over, normal performance levels may be jeopardized. In the case of military command and control systems, jeopardizing normal performance capabilities is not to be tolerated. For most types of "real-time" information systems, nonmilitary as well as military, as in the case of airline reservations and material processing and control systems in industry, an indeterminate period of system degradation is not tolerable. Hence, the phase-over must be as short a period as possible; it must be carefully planned; and it must be implemented with precision.

To illustrate some of the typical problems encountered during the phase-over period, as well as other points made throughout this chapter, we shall quote at some length from a study of an electric light and power company by F. C. Mann and F. W. Neff[2]:

"About five months after the 705 computer was installed, the conversion of daily operations to the new equipment system began. Unlike a change in car model in the auto industry, no stock-piling could occur. It was necessary to operate three systems simultaneously: the old system for accounts not converted; a transitional system for accounts being converted; and the new system for those which had been converted. Forty thousand bills had to go out daily, and an equal number of payment postings had to be made.

"The operation of these three systems meant that additional personnel had to be borrowed, hired on a temporary basis, and secured from commercial agencies. Permanent employees were reluctant to stay with the old system, yet skilled and experienced people were needed to keep it functioning properly. The company therefore declared that all appointments made during the transition period would be temporary, and informed employees that no preferences for the new jobs would be given to the people who manned them during this period. Final assignments of personnel to jobs in the new system would not occur until after the change was completed.

"Many 'bugs' showed up in the EDP program and related clerical procedures, and these were found to be costly to remove. It was found that the 705 computer demanded a higher degree of accuracy than had been anticipated, and additional checks had to be built into the machine system. Responsibility was highlighted and errors could now be traced directly to the clerk who made them.

"The pressures accompanying this phase of the change process had important effects on personnel at all levels. Hundreds of people had to be trained (about 90 per cent of the jobs in the departments at the vortex of the change were wholly or partly modified). Some people had to put in so much overtime that they had to give up most of their outside community and family activities. The continued physical and mental strain began to affect employees and supervisors. Evidence of this ranged from an occasional unexpected flood of tears from women supervisors to illnesses stemming from stress by some of the principal persons responsible for the change. The head of Accounting ordered more frequent physical examinations for top level Accounting personnel. In addition to the pressure created by the conversion schedule, the desire of non-supervisory employees to know what their new permanent jobs would be increased the urgency of completing the change-over.

"Before the conversion began, the impact of the change had been felt entirely by employees within the company—mainly within the Accounting and Sales Divisions. Now, the customers were affected by the new system. Some billing errors got to customers. Since it took time to make the necessary changes in programs, the same errors went to some customers two and three times. Irritated customers took their complaints to Sales personnel in the field. Since the field staff did not adequately understand the system, they blamed the 705 computer and sent complaints to Accounting. Conflict between personnel in Sales and Accounting—now in more frequent direct contact than ever before —began and grew. Sales sent more and more complaints to Accounting personnel regarding the new system.

"The difference between the extent to which the key line officers in Accounting and Sales had been involved in the change process now began to appear. In the past, the two Divisions had been relatively independent of each other, particularly at the higher levels of management. There had been limited interaction between their personnel, and neither group adequately understood the work of the other. Top management from Accounting had been heavily involved in the design and execution of the change-over plan; top management from Sales, having asked one of their key staff men to keep them fully informed about the progress of the change-over, went on with their usual activities expecting that they would be able to handle whatever coordination requirements were necessary as they occurred. Lower level personnel in the two divisions now had to exchange much information more frequently—and their 'conversation' had to be in what was essentially a new language. Personnel in Sales, at the top and at most other levels, had not been involved enough in planning for the new system to understand how it worked and what its problems were. They could not explain the difficulties to customers.

"These customer complaints, and other problems of the new system, soon began to reach the president and others in the top management group in the company. As these appeared to become more frequent, it was decided to suspend further conversion to the new system for one month primarily to give programmers time to make a backlog of corrective changes to the system. At about the same time, the president called in some management consultants to evaluate the system in regard to its effect on customer relations. The consultant studied the situation for several months and finally reported back to top management that customer complaints had increased but seemed to be about normal for this kind of a change, and that the system was fundamentally sound. One error could be traced to the machine. The rest were about evenly divided between Sales and Accounting personnel. The consultants also recommended other changes similar to those embodied in the original study report which had not been adopted.

"One of the steps which was taken to reduce tension between the two Divisions was to establish a program for all personnel in Sales and Accounting who were involved in the change. This program began with joint meetings conducted by the heads of Sales and Accounting with their department managers, staff and supervisors. These meetings demonstrated unanimity at the top of the two Divisions and did much to stimulate cooperation and understanding down the line. Personnel from Sales and Accounting were then given tours of each other's Divisions. Heads of district Sales offices were also asked to spend more time with Accounting personnel in their offices. These several steps were designed to provide the base of understanding which was needed to enable personnel in both areas to perform in the coordinated fashion required by the new system."

A phase-over plan is also essential for an information system since many organizations and agencies are normally involved in its development and installation. The system has been designed and built by a variety of procurement agencies, users, and contractors. During the installation phase, the culmination of all the efforts of these diverse organizations is reached. For the first time, all the physical components of the system are brought together as a functioning entity in the real-life environment. The phase-over plan must ensure adequate coordination and control over the many components; it must ensure that these components are appropriately scheduled for delivery, installed, and tested. This must be accomplished without a chaotic situation in which the representatives of the various organizations attempt to install and test different elements of the system at the same time in the same space.

An invariable problem is the scheduling of computer time for the many development contractors who need time during the installation phase for testing and checkout purposes. The computer manufacturer is concerned with checking out the computer itself and its utility programs. Other contractors are concerned with testing data transmission equipment which is linked to the central computer. If another contractor is responsible for computer-driven display equipment, he will want to check it out through tests run in conjunction with the computer. The software system developer wants to test out his operational, utility, and support computer programs on the computer. The user will also be interested in testing the computer, both for hardware operation and for the operation of computer software. To prevent confusion, inadequate testing, and the waste of valuable computer time, it is essential that the utilization of the computer be appropriately scheduled by some central planning and administrative unit established by the user. All the interested parties should participate in this planning activity to ensure that their interests in obtaining sufficient computer time are recognized. A guarantee of a minimum amount of computer time should be provided and stated in contract form for each participant. In the installation of SAGE, unfortunately, no such guarantee was provided for the software system developer with the result that tests of computer programs had to be conducted in time left over by other participants whose contracts provided for priority usage of the computer.

The User's Responsibilities for Phase-over Planning

An effective phase-over plan cannot be created without the full participation of the top-echelon managers of the user organization. In some situations, the new system may be planned for a completely new facility, separate and distinct from the manual system it is replacing. In such cases the phase-over difficulties may be minimized since the two systems may be able to operate in parallel. Thus, the replacement system can be brought up to an operational capability without affecting the quality of the existing system (assuming personnel are available for both), and the old system can continue to function as a backup capability in the event that the new system encounters operational difficulties.

By contrast, we must consider the situation in which the replacement system is planned to fill the same physical facility which contained the old system. In this case existing equipment must be pulled out and new equipment put in while operations personnel carry on with their daily tasks. Without a plan of phase-over by the user which meshes with the developer's installation plans chaos will result.

A great proportion of the time required by the installation phase is devoted to system testing, system evaluation, and training. It will be recalled in our review of system training that the user is responsible for the provision of personnel for exercise monitoring and simulation tasks. The importance of these tasks is such that only the most highly qualified people should be selected for them. This means that the user must detach some of his most competent personnel from daily operations and make them available for some period of time before the installation phase to undergo indoctrination on the new system and training in monitoring and simulation. Similarly, in order to conduct adequate system testing and evaluation, some of the most competent user personnel must be exposed, before the installation phase, to a period of intensive training on system testing methodology and procedures.

A major responsibility of the user is to inform lower-echelon units, especially those at dispersed geographical locations, of the phase-over plans. In the case of military systems, it is essential for commanders to notify all field units of the phase-over activities sufficiently in advance of the installation so that the necessary preparations can be made. Nothing can be more disastrous for good user-developer relations and a successful phase-over period than having a team of installers descend on a military unit without advance warning—this will invariably happen in the midst of a major military operation.

9.5   THE ORIENTATION PROGRAM

Why an Orientation Program Is Important

The orientation program is important in that it establishes for user personnel the foundation of knowledge about the system upon which all their future learning will be built. The conduct of the orientation and the substantive knowledge presented to the users also serve to contribute to the establishment of basic attitudes toward the system.

Orientation is differentiated here from training. In Chapter 8 system training was conceived in terms of exercising or rehearsing operations in a partially simulated environment. Other types of training were also mentioned. The objectives of these varieties of training were the acquisition of basic skills by personnel, the development of satis-factory personnel, man-machine, and man-computer program interac-tions, and, in general, over-all improvement in system performance under all varieties of potential real-life situations. Orientation, by contrast, is a learning situation in which the users of the system are *introduced* to it. The larger and more complex the information system, the more essential is the requirement for user personnel to be intro-duced to it at a general level before the installation phase and then again at an intensive, detailed level during this phase. It is the inherent complexity of information systems which compels this distinction be-tween orientation and training. Experience has shown that user per-sonnel must have an opportunity to attempt to comprehend such systems intellectually and as total systems before they undertake more mechanical efforts to make the system work in an operational environ-ment.

The importance of the orientation activity is associated with the several objectives of this activity. One of the more obvious objectives is, of course, the provision of knowledge about the system to the future users. Another, equally important objective is to prepare high-ranking personnel in the user organization for the managerial and administrative planning which must be accomplished for the installation phase and for the proper conduct of the major activities which take place in that phase, such as system testing, system training, and system shakedown. It is also during the orientation program that the developers can bring home to the users the critical nature of phase-over planning for successful system installation.

In addition to transmitting basic knowledge about the system, an important objective of the orientation program is to assist the highest echelons of user management in understanding the objectives and intent of the system, the development strategy which was followed, and the nature of information systems with respect to such features as changing requirements, maintenance, and replacement. In essence, the orientation program must convey to the managers of the enterprise *their* responsibilities for the continued life and satisfactory performance of the system. After handover occurs, it will be the user's responsibility to plan for system evolution, design modifications, and the alteration of system requirements to meet the changing objectives and goals of the organization.

The developer's personnel who plan and conduct the orientation activities usually will also be the ones who will participate in the system installation. The orientation program, therefore, serves to introduce developer and user personnel to one another, assuming that they have not already worked together during the course of system design and production. It is during the orientation program, then, that rapport must be established if a smooth and efficient handover of the system is to be accomplished. This program serves to establish feelings of mutual trust, understanding, and confidence which facilitate the handover process.

Varieties of Orientation Programs

In Chapters 2 and 3 we reviewed the kinds of systems, types of development situations, and varieties of development strategies which complicate the system development process. These factors affect the nature, scope, content, and organization of orientation activities. Each orientation effort must be custom-tailored to the requirements of the particular development.

Whether or not a formal orientation program is needed at all is a question which is related to the selection of a development strategy. If the new system is being designed upon an inductive approach, for example, in which the developer is merely automating existing methods and procedures, there may be no requirement for orientation. Introduction of user personnel to the new procedures may be conducted as the development occurs. Formal orientation requirements will be more essential, by contrast, where a deductive approach has been followed, since this may result in profound changes in the nature of the user's operations. In this event, the orientation effort must review for the user the deductive process undertaken by the developer as well as the consequences of that process for system design and the production of system components.

The number and frequency of orientation efforts, and therefore the extent of planning for such efforts, will vary with the number of system iterations or configurations. Where the system is built as a single configuration, with no anticipation of a successor configuration, the orientation effort is also necessarily a single-shot affair. However, where an evolutionary strategy is followed, a series of orientation activities is called for since each system configuration will have to be introduced to the users before installation. In evolutionary development, the scope of the orientation will vary with the degree of change reflected in successive system models or configurations. The introduction of the SAGE system, for example, required a major orientation program when the first model was installed. The installation of subsequent models called for orientation activities also, but on a much less extensive scale.

The extent to which a formal orientation program is needed also varies with the experience and knowledge of the users. Some users have unintegrated information-processing elements; others are already operating manual or semiautomatic information systems; and, in the future, users will be replacing automated information systems with more powerful and more tightly integrated ones—for example, systems which combine management planning, managerial control, and on-line materiel processing. When users are uninitiated into the mysteries of computers, computer programming, and the other aspects of software and have had no prior experience with information systems as systems, the content and scope of the orientation program must necessarily be detailed and cover the complete range of software elements.

The complexities and variations in orientation program planning may be illustrated by the treatment accorded to the war planning and control functional areas of the SAC Control System. The differences in the nature of planning and control operations and organization meant that different orientation approaches had to be developed for each functional area. The differences in the functional areas can be briefly described. SAC war planning is largely concentrated at one geographical location. Control operations, by contrast, are conducted at all SAC headquarters and bases. Whereas planning is basically a non-real-time activity, control is a real-time function. Planning is conducted periodically, whereas control is a continuous, everyday operation. As far as the new system was concerned, planners had to learn the input/output procedures for utilization of the planning computer programs. They were primarily interested in the data-processing subsystem; the controllers, on the other hand, were concerned mainly with the communication network—the data transmission subsystem. As a result of these differences, the orientation program for SAC planners included instructional periods in classes conducted by developer personnel. Since control personnel could not readily be detached from their posts for periods of classroom instruction without disrupting normal operations, their orientation was limited to an instructional manual which was produced by the developer and published by SAC.

Planning the Orientation Program

It should be apparent from what has already been said about orientation activities that the orientation program requires intensive and careful planning comparable to that carried on for the other aspects of the installation phase. In creating the orientation program, the planners need to consider the following areas:

- The requirements of various types of users for information about the system.
- Development of the appropriate techniques for the dissemination of the necessary types of information to the various classes of users.
- Study of the user's organization and operations so as to select the most suitable procedures for conducting the orientation without interfering with on-going operations.

Planning the development of an orientation effort follows the phases of development in general; that is, there must first be a study of orientation requirements—who needs to know what about the new system—then the design of the orientation content and structure, the production of orientation materials (manuals, briefings, lecture courses, films, slides, etc.), and, finally, the installation of the program in the field. The personnel responsible for the orientation effort should establish a work plan which schedules and defines each of these sequential activities and provides for the acquisition and training of appropriate personnel to conduct the program.

The brunt of the planning for the orientation program must necessarily fall upon the shoulders of the developer, although knowledgeable user personnel should participate to the extent possible. Ideally, user personnel should conduct the orientation activity since this would facilitate acceptance of the system by their co-workers. However, it is usually developer personnel who are most familiar with the nature and characteristics of the system and are best qualified to introduce it to others.

The problem for the developer is determining how best to create a group within his own organization to assume responsibility for orientation planning. The personnel who best understand the system are usually too involved in the design and production of the system to be used for this purpose. Orientation program planning is itself a major undertaking, calling for specialized skills such as familiarity with the design and use of visual aids and areas of knowledge such as learning theory. Frequently, therefore, a group will be created specifically for the creation and implementation of the orientation program on a full-time basis. Such personnel, however, may be plagued by the problem of obtaining current information about the system since they are not directly involved in the development process. It is the function of the developer's management to ensure either (1) that information on the system is passed promptly to orientation personnel through formally established communication channels, or (2) that technical development personnel are made available to participate in the orientation program as sources of knowledge for the preparation of manuals and course curricula or as field instructors.

It has been an unfortunate practice to delay the establishment of orientation program planning until relatively late in the development effort. But we have noted that one of the important functions of the facilities which are used early in the development process, such as laboratories and other experimental setups, is the orientation and training of user personnel. Thus, consideration of orientation needs for user personnel should be undertaken from the inception of the system development project. The initial feasibility studies for laboratory and experimental facilities should take into account their value for user orientation as well as for their primary purpose. The initial cost estimated for a simulation facility to be used for experimental purposes may seem much more reasonable when it is realized that the facility can also serve to introduce the system to its ultimate users early in the course of the development effort. SIMFAC, the simulation facility used in the experimental studies for the SAC Control System, described in Chapter 6, provides an example of the multiple purposes which such a facility may serve.

9.6 THE SYSTEM SHAKEDOWN

Pre-operations Exercising

Before the scheduled operational date of the system (there will be such a scheduled date regardless of its lack of meaning) it will be necessary for user personnel to undergo a period of exercising with the system in a nonoperational mode in order to achieve an acceptable level of performance when the system assumes responsibility for operations. This period is referred to as the system "shakedown." As the term implies, the system at this point is not yet a functioning totality; it is, rather, a conglomeration of elements—people, computer programs, and equipment—which do not interact smoothly and efficiently. The computer "hangs up" or halts when it is not supposed to; personnel are not sure how to request information from the computer; a procedure for displaying data takes more time than the minimum required by system performance specifications; an excessive number of errors are transmitted via the input keyboards; decision makers are unable to interpret alpha-numeric information; and equipment breaks down. All of these elements must be shaken down through exercises which simulate real operational conditions.

The capability for conducting pre-operations exercising is provided by the simulation vehicle which has been developed for training purposes. Pre-operations exercising represents, then, the first phase of system training in an orientation program environment. Since the developers and the users can control the simulated inputs, the activity level in the system can be kept at a minimum sufficient to provide a learning experience for the novitiates, but not high enough to overwhelm them. Since the level of activity is simulated, it can be considerably lower than that normally experienced in everyday operations.

The process of user review of and concurrence with the developer's design documentation periodically throughout the development effort contributes to conceptions of the emergent system. However, there will inevitably be some discrepancy between these conceptions of the system and actual system operation. It is likely that the user's expectations of the system will deviate more from the reality than will the developer's. One of the functions of the shakedown period is to facilitate convergence between the expectation and the reality for the users. During the pre-operations exercises, the users, at all levels of the enterprise from top management down to the lowliest operator, will have the opportunity to comprehend the actual capabilities of their new system.

One of the functions of the developer's installation personnel, working closely with the users, is the isolation of the causes of system malfunctions. This is a surprisingly difficult task. Information systems in which performance is the outcome of complex interactions among men, computer programs, and equipment do not lend themselves readily to the identification of the causes of less than acceptable performance as defined in design specifications. System performance is the outcome of manifold actions, events, and decisions. In the debriefing following a typical SAGE system training exercise, for example, the operations personnel will, during their initial exposure to the system, invariably blame the equipment or the computer programs for human failures. Experience has shown that only gradually, as operations personnel become more familiar with the system and as they find that they are allowed to express themselves without fear of sanction during postexercise debriefings, do they begin to observe that system malfunctions may be a result of their own inadequacies, such as a lack of understanding of the system or an ignorance of operational procedures. Tracking down the causes of system malfunctions requires experienced development personnel who understand the characteristics of the system in minute detail. They must also understand the nature of the user's operations and organization. Through the close cooperation of the developer and the user, each of whom brings his own specialized knowledge to bear on the issues, and through intensive system exercising, debriefings, and feedback, the isolation and accurate identification of the causes of system malfunctions can be accomplished.

It should also be noted that the users will report "errors" and "malfunctions" which, upon close examination, will turn out to be accurate interpretations by the developer of the originally stated requirements and design specifications. The difficulty here is that the user was not completely able to foresee the total range of consequences of his original requirements statements, nor was the designer able to foresee all the consequences of the design.

System Testing

In the previous discussion of the importance of the installation phase, we pointed out that one of the major objectives of this phase is the test and verification of the system design. We have also taken note of the fact that the most critical and traumatic series of tests occurs during the installation phase for the first configuration of a new, automated system. These tests can be conducted either by themselves or in conjunction with the pre-operations exercises, depending upon the test objectives. The testing should include preplanned tests and evaluations of system performance based upon the system operational requirements. It should also include tests and evaluations which are developed as needed following indications of specific trouble spots in system operations. Pre-operations exercises will usually reveal operational areas in which an unusual and unanticipated degree of malfunction is occurring.

In multiple-location systems in which operational computer programs and operating procedures must reflect a variety of local conditions, as in the case of SAGE or of corporations with a number of dispersed plants, tests must be devised not only to ensure that the system is error free but also to ascertain that it meets local requirements. In such instances, the parameter and assembly tests of computer programs conducted by the developer during the production phase will have to be supplemented by additional tests in the operational environment. For adequate control over the inputs and outputs of such tests, special test vehicles must be constructed.

The Development of Procedures

The handbooks describing the recommended sets of procedures which the developer hands over to the user during the installation phase represent a collection of hypotheses about how the interactions among men, machines, and computer programs *ought* to take place. Furthermore, since the system will undergo changes during the course of its development, there will always be discrepancies between the content in the handbooks and the actual system operations. An information system is simply too complex in terms of its components and their interactions for all such interactions to be prescribed by the designers of operational procedures and the handbook writers.

It is during the system shakedown, specifically during pre-operations exercises, that the most important tests of the procedures occur. Earlier tests of operational procedures have been made only in simulated test environments and by highly trained developer personnel. As the pre-operations exercises are conducted by operations personnel, and as the range of operational conditions and traffic loads on the system are simulated, the users will discover, with the help of the developers, the errors, inadequacies, and gaps in the existing procedures. The training vehicle makes it possible to experiment with alternative procedures. It is used to develop and test new procedures. Out of this process, as described in Chapter 8, more efficient and satisfactory procedures are created.

9.7   FEEDBACK TO SYSTEM DESIGN

Improvements, both minor and major, to the system design cannot be accomplished without the provision of formally defined procedures whereby the results of system tests, system evaluations, and pre-operations exercises are transmitted from the users to the developers. Feedback with respect to minor improvements may simply require alterations to procedures; feedback calling for major improvements may involve, on the other hand, new design concepts of such a magnitude that they can be incorporated only in a second system configuration.

It can be anticipated that the developer will be deluged with requests for changes from system users during the installation phase. Some of these requests can be accommodated with little difficulty. Changes which do not affect the computer programs, the format and content of displays, and the equipment, such as proposed changes in operational procedures, operator interactions, and personnel and organizational responsibilities, may possibly be made with relatively insignificant consequences for other elements of the system. By contrast, proposed changes which do affect the programs, computer-driven displays, and equipment may require long-term studies of the system before the feasibility and cost of such alterations can be determined.

If the users of the new system are naive where information systems are concerned, this may be a period of great disillusionment to them.

If they do not understand the process of system development which we have described in this book, they may be chagrined to learn that major changes to the system cannot be undertaken lightly. If they do not understand the precise nature of the instructions in a computer program and the interdependence of a series of such programs for the conduct of a system task, they will have some unpleasant surprises in store. This, in fact, has frequently been the experience of both military and nonmilitary users of the first generation of information systems.

System Tests and Feedback to System Design

A few additional comments about testing will be made here. (Chapter 10 is entirely devoted to system testing.) These pertain to the organization and administration of tests at the system level and the establishment of formal procedures for the feedback of test results to system designers.

The design and conduct of component- and subsystem-level testing is *relatively* simple since at these levels each contractor involved in development can carry out his test requirements independently of other contractors and of the user. This is not the case with system-level testing. Here all elements of the system are to be tested as interrelated components. The designing of the tests, the planning for their conduct, and the actual testing in the operational environment, therefore, demand the participation of all agencies and organizations involved in the development effort as well as the users. To carry out a system testing program, then, requires a high order of organization and administration. The administrators of the system tests must apply measures of system performance derived from the operational requirements and the design specifications. Thus, as was pointed out in the earlier chapters of the book, the system tests should be designed at the same time in the development process as the operational system itself is designed. The system test plans must include the standard procedures for the feedback of the results of the tests to the respective development contractors—results in the software area to the software developer, and results in the hardware area to the hardware developer. The flow of this information back to the system designers signals the beginning of the second iteration or cycle of system design.

Perhaps the most important point to be made pertaining to the relationship between system testing and system design is the need to establish formal procedures for the feedback of test results to designers.

A formal feedback procedure is essentially a method for documenting all requests for changes to the system. Establishing these procedures is an important responsibility of the testing organization and administration. The concept of a strategy of evolution is meaningless without such a formal feedback procedure. The formally specified feedback procedure serves to close the loop in the system development process and permits this process to cycle as long as the system remains in operational status.

Pre-operations Exercising and Feedback to Design

The process of transmitting feedback information from the users to the developers for the test and verification of design is also accomplished via pre-operations exercises. This process has been described in terms of operations in the review of system training in Chapter 8. In the presentation of the example of a SAGE sector training exercise cycle, it was noted that training teams observe and monitor the performance of operations personnel, while the computer automatically records radar track data. After each exercise, a discussion session or debriefing is held in which the operations personnel have an opportunity to review with their group leader the difficulties and problems encountered. The solutions to problems which are proposed by operational personnel in the debriefings are transmitted through formal communication channels to higher authorities for consideration. If these proposals involve design changes, and if they are approved by the higher authorities, they are then transmitted to the developer for his study via the formal system change procedures described in the following section.

System Change Proposals and Administrative Procedures

Problems associated with requests for design changes plague the user, the developers, and the procuring agency throughout the history of a development effort. Contemporary enterprises, both military and nonmilitary, are dynamic entities—their environments and their internal operations are constantly changing. Hence, the information systems which support these enterprises are also subject to frequent change requirements. Since an information system is a tightly integrated system in which operational functions and tasks are interdependent, as are also the various physical components of the system, a large number of changes will require additional work, increased system costs, and schedule slippages. Significant design changes may require not only the redesign and recoding of computer programs, for example, but also the reallocation of functions among the men, machines, and computer programs that make up the system.

In regard to their causes, design change requests fall into three general classes: (1) those due to changes in the external environment of the system, (2) those due to changes in the internal environment of the enterprise using the system, and (3) those due to changes growing out of the development process itself.

The design of an information system may be affected in the course of development by a number of external factors—technological breakthroughs; changes in the definition of strategy or doctrine (such changes would, of course, be significant for military command and control systems); alterations in competitive relationships (these would affect both military and industrial enterprises); and changes to budgets, schedules, or development planning by procurement or other administrative agencies. In the course of the development of the SAC Control System, for example, while design activities were proceeding, missiles were introduced into the SAC weapons inventory, and the doctrine of controlled response replaced that of massive retaliation. These externally induced events, plus others of an administrative nature, such as requests for additional system capabilities in the area of SAC war planning and alterations in budgets and schedules for the delivery of specific items, required changes to the system design.

Changes in the enterprise of the user may also cause severe requirements for changes to the system design effort. The user's goals and objectives may change during the course of the development effort. There may be major changes in the top management of the enterprise, with subsequent alterations of expectations and requirements for the system. A new commander or a new president of a corporation may express his personal desires for the kind of information he wants to receive via the system and the way in which he wants to receive it. The user's enterprise may undergo extensive reorganization, such as a shift from centralization to decentralization, or carry out mergers with other enterprises. New departments or divisions may be created within the organization, or there may occur major shifts in departmental responsibilities during the course of the development effort. Each of these events may have profound implications for the nature of the system design.

The development process itself will normally give rise to requests, within the developer's organization, for significant system changes. If laboratories and experimental facilities are funded in the development effort, new design concepts may evolve with respect to equipment, computer programs, or the utilization of personnel. Testing at all phases of the development process may result in the generation of change proposals. Tests may reveal, for example, that storage facilities are inadequate to handle the number of data required for essential system tasks. Changes may be required to the system design as a result of the failure of specific components to meet performance requirements. Changes may be desired by the various subsystem contractors to the components under their jurisdiction in order to achieve suboptimization of these elements. And, particularly during the installation phase, system testing and training in the operational environment will reveal many inadequacies in the system design with a subsequent flood of change proposals.

Given all these possibilities, and assuming that we are dealing with a system such as SAGE or a large industrial corporation with multiple locations, the potential number of change requests may run into the hundreds. The total accumulation of such requests, even when each one is minor in nature, may have profound implications for the system and may overwhelm the design and production capabilities of the developers.

An information system, after it has been produced, reflects the design requirements which are defined in the operational specifications documents. This documentation must be an accurate description of the system at any given point in time. Only in this way can the developer and the user mutually understand what the system is and how it is supposed to operate. This understanding is a necessary condition for managerial control. If either the user or the developer is allowed to make changes to basic elements of the system at will, the system itself and the documentation describing it will degenerate into chaos.

To prevent such disintegration of the system and yet accommodate the inevitable requests for changes, there must be a centralized agency for the receipt, coordination, processing, and disposition of all change requests. In the SAGE system this agency is called the SAGE Program Review Committee. The user (this is Headquarters, Air Defense Command, in SAGE) should formally authorize a review committee and define the procedures which are to be followed by all organizations for the introduction of changes to the system. Figure 9.1 shows the general steps followed in SAGE for the processing of design change proposals originating with the user.[3] The procedures should

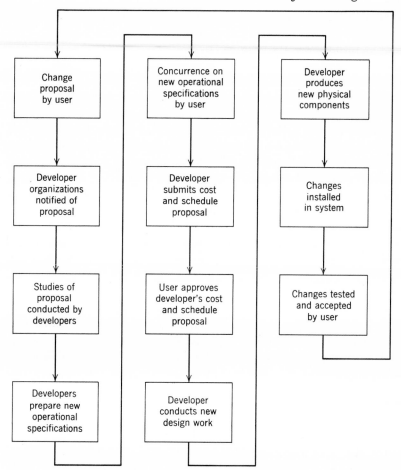

Figure 9.1 The design change process.

specify the following: (1) the personnel who may originate change requests; (2) the personnel who must authorize further study and implementation of the request; (3) the form of documentation—letter, memorandum, or technical document—for each step in the change process; (4) the charter for the organization of a change concurrence committee which will represent all interested parties; and (5) the definition of the communication channels to be used by each organization for the transmission of official change requests.

The user should also establish a format for change proposals. This format should include the following types of information: (1) a statement of the problem; (2) the justification for the proposed change; (3) the proposed solution, if this is known; and (4) a statement of the desired priority for the change. In the case of SAGE, each change request is identified by letter designators and a numerical index which indicates the priority assigned to the proposal. This procedure facilitates communication and coordination among the organizations concerned, it facilitates cross-referencing of system documents and change proposals, and it ensures that the identified change proposal will receive specified and routine consideration before its final disposition.

In addition to the formal procedures for the consideration and disposition of design changes as described above, it is desirable, where many contractors are involved in a development effort, as well as users and procurement agencies, to establish regular conferences for the review of change proposals. Another method for ensuring necessary communication and coordination of change proposals is the exchange of liaison personnel among the parties involved. Each of these methods can, of course, be used alternatively or concurrently, depending on the situation.

Since proposed changes may vary extensively in scope from minor ones which affect no other element of the system to major ones which may affect the basic design of the system, there is no single adequate method for dealing with them. In general, three classes of changes are differentiated and reflected in SAGE development schedules. Minor changes are handled as they arise on a continuous basis; a large number of minor changes may be batched for implementation as a change "package"; or a large number of minor and major changes may be deferred for inclusion together in a replacement system model.

There are, unfortunately, no across-the-board definitions of "minor" and "major" changes which would be applicable to all information systems and all change proposals. It is the purpose of the administrative procedure for the review and concurrence on change proposals, of user-developer conferences, and of liaison relationships to attempt to secure agreement among all the organizations involved in the development effort as to what constitutes an insignificant and a significant change.

9.8 SUMMARY

This chapter has described the general characteristics and objectives of the installation phase. It reviewed the reasons why the installation phase is of critical importance in the development of an information system. A major purpose of the chapter was to emphasize and describe the transitional nature of the phase and its typical overlapping with the antecedent production phase and the subsequent operational phase. After defining the installation phase, the irrelevance of the turn-key concept of system handover by the developer to the user was discussed. It was shown that this irrelevance was due both to the nature of the information system development process and to the strategy of system evolution.

Three main reasons for the importance of the installation phase were described: the need for the test and verification of system design concepts in an operational environment, the need for the psychological acceptance of the system by the user, and the need for the development of an operational capability.

Other sections of the chapter were devoted to phase-over planning, the development and planning for an orientation program, and the requirement for a period of system shakedown. The final section reviewed the sources of feedback to system designers, the problems associated with system change proposals, and the requirement for the establishment of an organization and administrative procedures for the processing and disposition of change proposals.

REFERENCES

1. See, for example, L. Coch and J. R. P. French, Jr., "Overcoming Resistance Change," *Human Relations,* **1**(4) (1948), 512–532; E. Ginzberg and E. W. Reilley, *Effecting Change in Large Organizations.* New York: Columbia University Press, 1957; R. Lippitt et al., *The Dynamics of Planned Change.* New York: Harcourt, Brace, and World, 1958; F. C. Mann and F. W. Neff, *Managing Major Change in Organizations.* Ann Arbor, Mich.: Foundation for Research on Human Behavior, 1961.
2. F. C. Mann and F. W. Neff, Ref. 1, pp. 43–45.
3. Figure 9.1 is adapted from N.E. Willmorth, *System Programming Management,* Santa Monica, Calif.: System Development Corporation, TM-1578, draft, March 13, 1964.

Chapter Ten

System Testing and Evaluation

H. Sackman

10.1   INTRODUCTION

This chapter is a critical overview of system testing as related to computer-based information systems in real-time applications. System testing is defined in the context of a taxonomy of testing. The inchoate status of current system testing is briefly reviewed. Scientific system design is subsequently described as a type of longitudinal system testing. The emerging methodology for system testing is reviewed with special emphasis on recent developments in the collection and reduction of digital data. A detailed example of SAGE system testing is given, illustrating many aspects of an applied experimental approach. This is followed by an exposition of the central role which is and should be played by system testing within the total testing process in the evolution of real-time systems from manual precursors, through initial computerization, to successor systems. The final section introduces the concept of "experimental realism," which exploits the on-line capabilities of the central computer as a more generally powerful testing approach for man-machine digital systems than the classical laboratory techniques embodied in experimental idealism.

Definition of System Testing

Before proceeding to historical antecedents and some approaches and attitudes toward system testing in the literature, an introductory definition is offered. This definition is elaborated more fully in a later section in the broader context of a taxonomy of testing.

System testing refers to experimental measurement of system performance in a credible setting involving an adequately large complex of the men, equipment, and data-processing facilities of the object system, so that the results can be used to make generalizations regarding current and future system effectiveness.

Note the close affinity of the definition of system testing with the characterization of system training in Chapter 8. The overlap is considerable, with system testing somewhat more general in emphasizing the over-all system and its performance effectiveness as the unit of discourse rather than focusing primarily on people, as is the case with training. More will be said about these relationships throughout this chapter.

The Historical Setting

System testing is a very recent phenomenon as far as large man-machine systems in a computerized setting are concerned. SAGE is the first system of this type, initial operations having commenced in June 1958 for the New York Air Defense Sector. Therefore it has the longest historical perspective in system testing, with seven years of operational experience in 1965. Other military command and control systems have evolved and are currently at different conceptual, design, production, and operational phases. Civilian applications are extremely recent in the airline reservation and banking areas with many more under active investigation and development in fields as diverse as law, medicine, and education. As a result of the predominance of military applications, there is a paucity of unclassified and nonsensitive literature on testing for computer-based information systems.

There is, however, considerable literature on man-machine test and evaluation and on computer program testing. These were the historical antecedents for computer-based information system testing. This literature, with the exception of that dealing with program testing, which started later, has been growing rapidly since World War II. Selected publications from engineering, programming, and human factors points of view will be reviewed here to illustrate the needs and purposes served by system testing, the diversity of approach, the technical problems, and the pervasive lack of agreed structure for this field. Although these selections are necessarily limited and may be subject to some misinterpretation out of their original context, they do provide some indications of historical trends leading to the current status of system testing.

An Engineering Approach

H. H. Goode and R. E. Machol, in one of the first textbooks on system engineering, emphasize the economic and technical difficulties in conducting full-scale tests to evaluate large systems.[1] In a section entitled "Impracticability of Evaluation by Test" they express the view that test design and operation may be excessively costly and often more difficult than the design and operation of the object system. In a very brief treatment of this area they describe the need for high-load test situations, special test equipment, and adequate data recording and reduction facilities. Test crews are considered separately from equipment as providing two separate sources of performance measurement in independent tests. The concept of over-all system performance is not made explicit for an over-all system test. System reliability, viewed as a probabilistic function of continuous operation, is considered as an integral part of system test and evaluation.

The purpose of system testing is described as an attempt to check theory against actual practice in order to evaluate and improve field performance. The position taken by these authors is that the usually ambiguous results of system testing are generally not worth the cost and effort for complex man-machine systems.

Human Factors Approaches

Some selections from *Psychological Principles in System Development,* edited by R. M. Gagné, are indicative of human factors viewpoints concerning system test and evaluation.[2] In one of the chapters, R. Glaser and D. J. Klaus describe the broad spectrum of human performance testing, ranging from on-the-job tests, through simulated situations, to correlated behavioral testing (such as paper-and-pencil techniques).[3] They stress the necessity for testing in the operational situation and the prior need to incorporate performance measurement and recording instrumentation into the original design of the object system.

R. H. Davis and R. A. Behan emphasize the heavy cost of testing large systems and the great difficulties in collecting and evaluating data.[4] They are highly critical of the alleged validity of completely simulated tests, such as all-computer simulation for man-machine systems. They emphasize the advantages of "operational simulation," using personnel and equipment at operational facilities, together with specially designed simulated inputs to provide partial experimental control over system inputs.

J. L. Finan distinguishes between applied or empirical system testing and theoretical or laboratory testing.[5] Experimental tests in applied systems are inductive in character, follow the variability of the operational setting, have minimal experimental controls, and yield results useful for short-term system forecasts of limited generality. Theoretical or conceptual systems, according to Finan, are based on formal models, are characterized by a hypothetico-deductive process, are conducted in simplified laboratory environments with rigorous controls, and give fruit to systematic predictions of broad generality.

A Programming Approach

W. A. Hosier's informative article on real-time digital systems is indicative of testing from the programmer's point of view.[6] Hosier also considers large-scale system testing prohibitive in cost, particularly for tests involving realistic peak input loads to measure computer running time in relation to system capacity. Hosier's comments are directed primarily at the computer system rather than man-machine system testing. He stresses the importance of including long lead-time specifications on acceptance testing as part of the original system requirements and initial design specifications.

Practical advice is offered on the mechanics of program testing and digital data collection and analysis: adequate high-speed storage for anticipated testing needs; the availability of a computer clock for "timeout," or interpolated non-real-time operations; simulated tape inputs from minimum to maximum load levels; adequate association tags in simulated inputs to control, trace, and identify program processing of these inputs; sufficient tape drive and buffer suport facilities to handle simulation inputs and data storage requirements; selective recording and summarized data reduction to avoid overwhelming numbers of digital data; and on-line monitoring, printout, and display facilities during the live test run for immediate feedback of selected test results.

A basic change in point of view toward test data is reflected by Hosier, in marked contrast to the previously cited comments from engineering and human factors approaches, which were primarily derived from manual or noncomputerized system experience. The problem is not how to get enough test data, but rather how to fish for the best catch from the torrent poured out of the computer. The power of the computer to tap voluminous data from on-line operations is a key characteristic which sharply distinguishes computerized systems from their manual precursors. This leads to many implications for experimental testing which are developed throughout this chapter.

10.2   A TAXONOMY OF TESTING

The definition of system testing provided earlier served to introduce the topic of this chapter and to provide a focal point for a brief look at the literature. There are many types of system testing. Although it is beyond the scope of this chapter to cover all types of testing in computer-based information systems, it is necessary to sketch their broad relationships to system testing. A taxonomy of testing is outlined to place the kinds of system testing described in this chapter into better perspective. Four classification categories are described: test level, developmental phase, test approach, and chronological trends, covered in the same order.

Test Level

Six general levels of testing, including system testing, may be specified:

Multisystem	Functional
System	Component
Subsystem	Omnibus

Multisystem testing refers to tests of supersystems, such as the planned National Military Command System (NMCS), which contain disparate systems such as SAGE and Polaris Command and Control as integral components. It may also refer to mixed manual and computerized system testing, such as a joint NORAD (425L), SAGE, BUIC (Backup Interceptor Control) and manual air defense exercise. System testing logically includes the multisystem level, but the term is commonly used to describe tests of single systems such as any one of the above component systems considered separately.

Subsystem testing breaks down into the major areas of hardware, software, and personnel. Functional testing refers to related groupings of equipments, programs, and people to perform particular tasks. For example, console equipment, display programs, and command staffs represent functional groupings for man-computer communication in command and control systems. Component testing gets down to a particular piece of equipment, a subprogram, or the individual operator. Omnibus testing refers to any combination of two or more types of the above tests incorporated into a single effort. Generally speaking, any test at a higher level may include numerous tests at the lower levels. System testing, for example, is frequently a type of omnibus testing which may serve to spin off many types of lower-level tests.

The listed test levels are not presented as orthodox archetypes. They are convenient descriptions indicating the relative focus of test emphasis. The classification is not mutually exclusive or exhaustive. The overlap between adjacent categories is unavoidable, and conceivable combinations of omnibus tests cut across the entire classification scheme and are too numerous to mention.

Developmental Phase

The second broad classification category refers to the development phase in which the object test is embedded. This category is presented as any logical combination of the three sequentially ordered classes shown below.

	A *Evolutionary* *Stage*	B *Operational* *Version*	C *Production* *Status*
1	Manual system	Initial operational version	Design
2	Initial computerized system	Second operational version	Installation
3	Successor digital system	Third operational version, etc.	Operations
4	Mixed transitional states	Mixed versions	Combination

The three types range from most general to most specific, reading from left to right, and are ordered chronologically within columns, reading from top to bottom. "Evolutionary stage" and "production status" are probably self-explanatory. "Operational version" refers to successive models or mutations of operational configurations within a given evolutionary stage. One of the most traumatic points in system evolution is characterized by the system test involving A-2, B-1, and C-2, which represents the initial installation of the first operational version of the first-generation computerized system.

The classification scheme for developmental phases is also not mutually exclusive or exhaustive, as indicated by the "mixed" and "combination" entries. Any rational combination of these developmental phases in system evolution may be matched with any level of testing, as previously described, to obtain a phase-differentiated test type. The "traumatic" system test mentioned above is one such type. These types may become extremely complex, as indicated by matching omnibus testing with the "mixed" or "combination" categories. For example, NMCS multisystem testing with various reporting systems in different stages of evolution might fall into the omnibus test level and combination developmental phase categories to take advantage of simultaneous testing at different levels.

Test Approach

Four different types of test approach are distinguished:

Formal	*Ex post facto*
Informal	Combination

Formal tests refer to specially scheduled, officially budgeted, and carefully planned efforts, usually requiring formal reports. Informal testing includes the borderline case of pilot tests, and the obviously informal processes of spontaneous observation, anecdotal reports, and intuitive analysis. Even though informal testing is not rigorous, it should not be disregarded since it typically represents the greatest proportion of total test activity in defining, building up, preparing, and developing tools and measures for formal testing. The unwritten or subjective impact of informal testing may often influence managers and decision makers more than the written results of formal testing.

Ex post facto testing refers to testing after the fact. This may occur when some trouble develops during live operations. The symptoms may be equipment failure, computer hangup, or an overloaded crew. The troubleshooting, analysis, and remedial action after the breakdown occurs may be described as *ex post facto* testing. Crew debriefings and examination of operational printouts to analyze unanticipated critical events or emergency situations occurring in live operations are another form of *ex post facto* testing. Exploratory testing in both formal and informal tests in which unexpected events take place, requiring follow-on study, is a borderline variety of this type. The combination category is included to indicate that these test approaches are correlated rather than independent and may well occur together.

The test approach classification qualifies and multiplies the types of tests defined by the two prior classifications, test level and developmental phase. An example of the manner in which this classification scheme may begin to have the flavor of a real test is as follows: a system test (test level) may occur in a first-generation computerized system in the installation phase of the second operational version (developmental phase) and be conducted primarily as a formal test (test approach), but perhaps secondarily on an informal and *ex post facto* basis for certain functional areas which lead to unanticipated follow-on studies.

Chronological Type

Three types of time trends are differentiated:

> Cross-sectional tests.
> Longitudinal tests.
> Combination tests.

These concepts are borrowed largely from the psychological test literature, but with some modifications. In this context, cross-sectional refers to single or one-pass tests to accomplish immediate goals, such as the acceptance of a program, equipment, or a system package. Longitudinal testing refers to iterative efforts in which previous performance is compared against current performance in the context of standardized experimental controls. Longitudinal testing may be long-term or short-term. The short-term varieties may overlap with cross-sectional testing in that a short series of related tests may also be considered as variants of one cross-sectional test. Longitudinal testing may refer to comparative testing of the performance of a given operational feature in an ascending series from component to functional to subsystem and system testing. This constitutes a powerful technique of multiple and interlocking design verification of hypothesized performance for the referent operational feature.

The extreme long-term case may be described as evolutionary longitudinal testing. It consists of comparisons of system performance within successive versions of manual, first-generation, and second-generation computerized systems and between these gross system mutations with respect to a set of standardized system test situations. Combination cases are possible, such as cross-sectional testing of transient features versus longitudinal testing of stable features. The general value of this classification category lies in the objective evaluation of trends in system performance, which can be done only in a longitudinal test series. Such testing permits standardized comparison of earlier with later system effectiveness.

The four classification categories are brought together in Table 10.1, where they are listed in the same order as described in the text. This taxonomic exercise has accomplished its purpose if the three following conclusions are borne out.

1. Total testing is a pervasive evolutionary process occurring at many levels throughout the life cycle of the object system.

2. The varieties of system testing are legion. They serve an equally great variety of needs and goals pertinent to the given developmental point in system evolution.

3. Although system testing may be distinguished from other types of testing with regard to certain characteristics, it frequently overlaps and occurs together with many other types as a kind of omnibus system testing.

10.3   SYSTEM TESTING AND SCIENTIFIC SYSTEM DESIGN

In this section, system testing is advocated as the vehicle for scientific system design. Longitudinal system testing is described for different phases in system evolution. The problems of changing performance criteria are considered in following the evolution of external environments. Finally, methodological tools are reviewed for implementing system testing as an applied science.

System Testing as Applied Science

The notion of scientific system design is one of the recurrent themes of this book. It is more fully elaborated here in the context of system testing. The main thesis is straightforward: operational specifications should be cast in the language of experimental hypotheses concerning system performance which can be verified by system testing. In other words, purely verbal or qualitative operational descriptions should be supplanted by quantitative statements specifying a measurable level of performance for the given design feature which may be tested under standardized experimental conditions. If there is no empirical verification of purported capability, there is only a system technology with unknown effectiveness, not an applied system science. It is feasible, economical, and highly desirable for computer-based

Table 10.1
A Fourfold Taxonomic Structure for Testing

I. TEST LEVEL

Multisystem	Functional
System	Component
Subsystem	Omnibus

II. DEVELOPMENTAL PHASE

Evolutionary Stage	*Operational Version*	*Production Status*
Manual system	Initial operational version	Design
Initial computerized system	Second operational version	Installation
Successor digital system	Third operational version, etc.	Operations
Mixed transitional stages	Mixed versions	Combinations

III. TEST APPROACH

Formal	*Ex post facto*
Informal	Combinations

IV. CHRONOLOGICAL TYPE

Cross-sectional	Longitudinal	Mixed types

information systems to be operated as an applied scientific enterprise through longitudinal system testing. It is further alleged that system operation as an applied science may provide an unprecedented degree of objective control for managers and users.

System testing should serve as the empirical conscience of system design throughout the life cycle of the object system. When over-all system requirements are first drawn up, system testing should be part of the formal requirements and test support should be integrated into the operational features. Detailed operational specifications should be spelled out as testable hypotheses for empirical verification. This involves specification of quantitative measures of performance, standardized test controls, and appropriate statistics within a critical experimental design. The initial quantitative performance estimates may prove to be unrealistic, depending upon the complexity and novelty of the system, but these hypothetical estimates will be empirically corrected toward realistic performance by the initial prototype tests evolving from component, through functional, through subsystem, and finally to system test levels. System test performance provides the best estimate of system operation and, as such, serves as the ultimate validation for prior results in the test series. To express the same idea in another way, teamwork is required between all types and varieties of tests with system testing as the focal point.

Once test performance results start coming in, the empirical data gradually replace the educated guesses, and systematically observed performance levels provide the groundwork for new hypotheses involving proposed design changes. At any point in time, the operational specifications should include the latest and most valid test performance results together with scheduled design changes and the hypothesized improvement in performance. The initial crude system tests will correspondingly evolve in a longitudinal series toward more sophisticated system testing with increasing credibility of results.

This applied science approach to system development involves some basic changes in technological outlook. System managers, designers, and users would become more familiar with the language of standardized tests and controls, the variability within and between test situations, and the probabilistic confidence intervals for quantitative performance levels, and they would grow to appreciate the variety of system behavior in different stress environments. An elementary knowledge of applied experimental design and introductory statistics would be required for managers and users, with more advanced training for designers and analysts. Operational language would tend to displace arcane technological language since performance evaluation is most meaningful when expressed directly in terms of the achievement of system goals in operational environments. Evaluative performance data, properly used, may critically summarize masses of detailed operations that would otherwise be a meaningless conglomeration. System testing tends to make the system operation more the public province of all participants in the system and less the specialized bailiwick of technicians who, without standardized testing, are not really answerable to external validation of their work in meeting system goals.

The experimental testing approach to system evolution will meet with resistance and antagonism as long as managers, users, and designers are not trained or familiar with experimental methods, and as long as those who are so trained remain aloof from realistic, practical testing in the hurly-burly world of live operations. The experimental approach will also have to prove its versatility and long-range economy by actual example. The assertion of the primacy of experimental test-ing does not in any way guarantee useful, definitive, and worthwhile tests. It is all too easy, as the experimental literature will demonstrate, to conduct poor tests or exorbitantly expensive tests. For these reasons, the concept of scientific system evolution through experimental testing may remain a utopian dream requiring fundamental changes in the pre-vailing technological culture before it can become a reality.

System Performance Measures

Useful and reasonably valid system performance measures are frequently hard to establish and may constitute a stumbling block for system testing. Large computer-based information systems are noto-riously complex. As a result, measurement calls for approaches radically different from classical laboratory procedures dealing with simplified models of dependent and independent variables. Military performance measures may illustrate many of these problems.

Military command and control systems have to deal with the now familiar spectrum of coordination, negotiations, cold war, brushfire wars, limited wars, national emergencies, and many conceivable types of nuclear wars. System response and performance measures are different for each case and have many subvarieties, depending upon the concrete circumstances of a given situation. This complexity points up the requirement for defining the varieties of system environments to be used as normative standards for gauging system performance. As S. B. Sells points out, although the area has been receiving increas-ing attention, a taxonomy of environmental situations has not been adequately developed by the social and behavioral sciences.[7] The type of contingency thinking required to come to grips with multiple stan-dards of performance runs counter to the natural human tendency to simplify and stereotype. It is clear that performance measures should be situationally defined and that pluralistic situations mean pluralistic system performance.

The pluralistic performance problem is further complicated by the great diversity of performance measures that may evolve for complex command and control systems. This may be briefly illustrated by some SAGE experience. From a comprehensive review of the SAGE litera-ture, J. M. Baker reported a total of 2,291 performance measures.[8] Of these, 802 were equipment and computer program measures, and the remaining 1,489 concerned man-machine performance. These figures are somewhat inflated since redundancy was not eliminated in the count, but the totals are still impressive.

The growth of the computer program system for SAGE operational data reduction is equally revealing. From very meager beginnings, the programmed data reduction capability has expanded so that it will handle over 1,000 variables related to system performance. This program serves kaleidoscopic applications covering design testing, training evaluation, and operational field tests at local and system-wide levels. These continually changing needs required new types of performance data. The result was an unmistakable historical trend toward increasingly diversified and specialized performance measures. Flexibility in adapting to changing system needs seems more sensible than the panacea of ultimate and absolute performance measures, conceived through a priori insight, which will be good at all times for all users.

Methodology for System Testing

The basic tools for system testing may be subsumed under three generic categories: the collection and analysis of digital data, simulation, and experimental design. These are only very briefly sketched below from the viewpoint of key problems in current testing since they are also described in the more concrete setting of the example on system testing presented later in the chapter.

The Collection and Analysis of Digital Data. There seems to be little interest in the computer science literature in the issue of recording digital data, although there is acknowledgment of the need. For example, the author was not able to find any studies devoted exclusively to the relationship between experimental design and digital recording in the abstracts of the *Computer Reviews* up to 1965. C. W. Churchman comments that most scientific talent seems to be intrigued with the problem of modeling, experimental design, and analysis to the relative neglect of the anterior process of data collection, which seems dull by comparison.[9]

Analysts, programmers, and test and operational personnel are frequently hobbled by antiquated recording techniques which severely limit their access to digital data. Inefficient use of packed tables in high-speed memory is frequent, although a preferable method of direct storage on magnetic tape is possible. Some recording systems stop cycling through the operational program to dump data onto tape when the input-output facilities would permit overlap of tape transfer with central computer operation. Computer running time for recording may be excessively high as a result of inefficient program control. Greater attention to recording needs would quickly correct the more obvious deficiencies.

Ideal digital recording for on-line operations should fulfill three general requirements.

1. *Maximum capacity and flexibility.* An ideal system should be capable of recording all data in high-speed memory with flexibility to select desired data subsets from this total data base.

2. *Reliability and economy.* The over-all recording system should be accurate, reliable, economical in operating time and storage space, and easy and convenient to use and maintain for current and projected operational requirements.

3. *Regenerative capability.* There should be a facility for unlimited playback of complete computer system runs. The regenerative capability permits replication or controlled variation in a rerun mode for digital test events and for spontaneous live events as they occur in operations. This effectively amounts to a built-in laboratory for controlled experimentation and *ex post facto* analysis of operational digital events in computerized information systems. Regenerative recording for command and control systems has been described by H. Sackman.[10]

These ideal recording requirements are probably within the state of the art for many systems and will become easier to meet as computing speeds and storage capabilities increase and the sophistication of input-output facilities grows. SAGE comes potentially close to meeting these ideals. The development of regenerative recording in SAGE began in 1961 and has proved its versatility and economy. Total recording of core data is feasible. Selection of data subsets offers no outstanding technical problems in SAGE with current recording systems. Thus, civilian and military personnel working with SAGE have the capability of getting at practically any digital data in core memory and of rerunning any type of test or live operation as often as desired.

As mentioned earlier in connection with Hosier's article, the exploitation of digital data recording may result in such numbers of data as to disillusion the most avid enthusiast of analysis. Some of the recommendations listed by Hosier for digital data reduction and analysis may be expanded to the broader operational setting. The following ideal characteristics may be cited for digital reduction and analysis systems:

Comprehensive data	Selectivity of output
Economy in operation and maintenance	Adequate user documentation
	Human-engineered output formats
Reliability of outputs	Statistical outputs
Evaluative measures	Graphical capability
Fast response time	User indoctrination

There should be more emphasis on human engineering of the reduction and analysis support system for the various types of users. This would involve appropriate documentation, specialized training, understandable outputs in operational language, pictorial and statistical summaries, evaluative rather than descriptive measures, and fast response times. A common pitfall is the tendency for data reduction programs to be designed as programmer utility systems, oriented toward the programmer but too abstruse for others. The instruction-chasing trap and trace needs of a programmer interested in debugging his routines calls for a different type of recording and data reduction from that required by the user or manager interested in system performance.

The various users should be able to obtain operational performance reports in natural language and in hard copy format suitable for open dissemination. The analyst and designer should have adequate statistical routines to perform a variety of quantitative analyses on recorded performance. These routines should include, at a minimum, simple descriptive measures of frequency distributions, measures of dispersion and central tendency, and elementary bivariate correlation and regression techniques.

Simulation. Simulation as a basis for the test and development of man-machine and computer-based systems has had an erratic history since World War II. Hundreds of papers have been published on this topic.[11] In an unpublished survey of simulation presented by J. W. Singleton in 1964 (part of a series of lectures, "Information Sciences in Command and Control," sponsored by UCLA), he listed twenty-five simulation laboratories and facilities which were initiated after World War II. Of these, seventeen perished and eight survived. Singleton attributed this mortality record to the high cost of laboratory simulation, the predisciplinary nature of this field, and the fast obsolescence of a specific-purpose simulation capability for rapidly changing systems. Three more recent simulation laboratories, established in 1963, are general-purpose facilities which hopefully will escape quick obsolescence.

It was of special interest in this survey that the System Training Program described in Chapter 8, now operational on a world-wide basis in the Pacific, North American, and European military theatres, is the only simulation-based program which has survived for over a decade, and which seems to have favorable prospects of continuity. (The System Training Program will be presented as a system test vehicle in the example described in this chapter.)

The close affinity between system testing and operational simulation follows the common-sense injunction that system testing should use the most realistic operational setting possible, within economic and time constraints. Veterans who have witnessed the early evolution of several systems will object that anything approaching operational simulation or live testing is an impossibility in the incubation period when the system prototype facility is unavailable. Early decisions must often be made, freezing hardware and software commitments, on the basis of whatever evidence is available. In this incubation period, many types of computerized simulations, scenarios, subsystem simulation, people-only simulations, and a host of other simulation approaches are very useful for exploring new alternatives, role playing, unearthing unforeseen problems, and providing initial leads on system performance.

Simulation without people may be used to perform studies of the sensitivity of one set of variables versus another as it sweeps through a range of values. Simulation with people may serve in developing and evaluating operational procedures and information-processing and decision aids for a system before its active development. Both types of simulation may provide the means for conducting controlled experiments in which all events are observed easily, data are recorded objectively, and many replications are made quickly and inexpensively to obtain statistically significant results, within the constraints of the necessary assumptions. Conditions can be simulated that could not be introduced into live system testing because of safety risks, unavailability of operating forces, political considerations, and other sensitive factors.

The great value of many nonoperational approaches to simulation for very early system planning and design would be difficult if not impossible to refute. But any serious acceptance of these types of simulation results should nevertheless be tied to a chain of empirical validation, leading to experimental verification with the best type of system testing available, and ultimately to the live operation. At any stage of simulation, findings should be subjected to the empirical corrective of the next evolutionary level of testing. The collective results should form part of the evolutionary test series with longitudinal system testing serving as the highest level of validation.

For example, the programmer's initial estimates from flow diagrams concerning the performance of his subprogram in terms of capacity, error levels, and running time should be empirically checked against parameter testing of the coded product. These performance estimates should be revised on the basis of the parameter testing experience and extrapolated to assembly test performance. The assembly test results, incorporating interprogram features, should lead to computer system test estimates of subprogram and package performance. These estimates should be empirically verified at the more convincing level of system testing. Finally, system test results should be continually adjusted by feedback from the payoff test of live operations.

Experimental Design. Experimental design is too often a neglected and misunderstood area in the development and use of computer-based information systems. Few managers, users, designers, and programmers have received formal training or applied experience in empirical experimental techniques involving people as well as equipment in computerized applications. Experimental methods in computerized settings and associated statistical techniques are rarely recognized as essential tools requiring formal indoctrination for personnel responsible for data processing and operational procedures in object systems.

One of the current difficulties faced by programmers is the obscure nature of their product from the point of view of the user. Programmers have yet to learn how to include the needs of the human user in their testing procedures. Engineers are frequently trained in applied statistics and experimental design, but primarily for the evaluation of equipment systems, frequently shunting out the human user. The behavioral sciences have an experimental tradition of over a century, dating back to Fechner's pioneering work in psychophysics, in testing and measuring human performance. But psychologists are prone to err in the opposite direction, focusing on the man, and often on the man and machine (engineering psychology), but rarely on the computer program or on the entire system. The emergence of operations research since World War II initially provided the integrative basis for systems generalists, but, in the opinion of the author, practice has tended to veer away from empirical experimentation such as system testing and to relapse into the formalism of mathematical modeling. Despite timeworn and tiresome appeals for the "system" approach, we do not yet have a generation of applied systems generalists. As a result, there is a hiatus between principle and practice which may be termed the "systems lag."

The overriding quest of experimental design in system testing is for accelerated exposure to the varieties of system experience to permit more rapid evolution toward more powerful and capable systems. This open-end approach establishes the need for formal exploratory elements in experimental design in addition to the traditional needs of preconceived hypotheses regarding selected features of system performance. The availability of a central computer makes comprehensive exploration of system performance much more feasible through selective collection and analysis of digital data. The recording and reduction system should include diagnostic and quality control data for flagging potential trouble spots. The unlimited capability for *ex post facto* analysis of digital events in regenerative recording was mentioned earlier. Simple paper-and-pencil techniques, including open-end questionnaires to be answered by participating personnel, provide exploratory probes leading to unforeseen problems.

An omnibus approach should be employed in the design of system tests. The same tests should serve many users at component, functional, and subsystem levels, all the way up to over-all system performance. The common test situation permits standardized and direct comparability of performance from different facets of the system. Omnibus system testing has obvious cost advantages in combining what might have been many separate tests with separate overheads into a unified and usually a more credible test with just one overhead.

Testing the limits is a critical requirement in the experimental design of any study purporting to test system performance and effective capacity. The type and rate of deterioration in system performance under increasing and extreme input loads must be known if the bounds and limits of variation in system capacity are to be understood. In military systems survivability and continuity of command require tests of degraded and remnant systems, including empirical explorations of possible types of decentralized command and control. Testing the limits is commonplace for equipment but has not yet been widely accepted for combinations of people and software.

The above approach to experimental design indicates the close kinship between system training and system testing: not only do they both benefit from the best operational simulation available for credibility and optimal validity of results, but also they have economic ties in that both purposes may often be accomplished at the same time with an over-all savings in system costs. The recording, reduction, and analysis support systems should be economically consolidated to serve simultaneously the needs of system testing, system training, and live operations.

10.4   AN EXAMPLE OF SYSTEM TESTING

This section is a condensed account of a SAGE system test conducted by H. Sackman and J. B. Munson.[12] It illustrates many aspects of the approach toward system testing outlined in this chapter. The study is described in some detail to counterbalance the somewhat abstract and hortatory nature of the preceding material.

The broad problem was to measure SAGE computer operating time and associated system capacity in a credible combat setting. It grew out of a lack of definitive data as to what extent computer cycle time would slow down with increasing load, and just how much system performance would deteriorate with slower cycle time under combat conditions. In real-time systems, as load increases, the computer takes longer to cycle through the inputs and performance tends to deteriorate. As the computer program cycle slows down with increasing load, storage capacity may be exceeded, program and equipment synchronization may be disrupted, errors may increase with slower extrapolation and correlation of data, and human control may be compromised by drawn-out and erroneous computer response.

A characteristic which designers have as a goal is a "graceful" or relatively gradual deterioration in system performance with increasing input loads. It is undesirable to design a system so that performance degenerates in a highly erratic, uneven manner because of weak links in the chain of system events. Graceful degradation, however, is a myth, since experience shows that different system functions will deteriorate at different rates. The problem is to design the system in such a way that subsystem performance will deteriorate within known and tolerable limits as input load increases. This problem can be attacked through system testing. Early exposure of problem areas and detection of errors through system testing permits corrective program design and compensatory training of operational personnel for improved performance at high loads approaching rated system capacity.

Methodology

The methodology covers general project goals and techniques for the collection and analysis of test data.

The four major goals were as follows:

- To develop specialized tools to measure computer operating time as a function of input load and associated system performance.
- To measure frame time and system performance in a SAGE system training program setting to provide a simulated wartime environment at nine Direction Centers and two Combat Centers (higher headquarters) participating in a multidivision field exercise.
- To develop and cross-validate regression equations from the empirical data to predict frame time as a function of a small set of input variables which may be applied over a wide range of air defense situations.
- To assess operational air defense performance against a wide range of frame times and system input load levels.

The Chronos or "time" program complex, consisting of three parts, was developed. The first program, Chronometer, permitted real-time measurement of subprogram operating times for all SAGE Direction Center subprograms, as well as over-all program cycle time during test runs. Chronometer also recorded system load and performance variables such as track composition, radar inputs, operator actions, and tracking effectiveness. These timing and system load measures involved 89 quantitative variables automatically collected every frame. The standard frame in SAGE involves a program cycle of 15.7 seconds, a nominal time interval which rises with increasing system inputs. The second Chronos program, called Chronograph, processed the Chronometer data in non-real time to provide data printouts and punched card outputs suitable for subsequent statistical processing of the recorded test data. The third program, called Chronicles, was designed to permit playback of computer test runs. This regenerative capability permitted us to "can" computer test runs on tape for *ex post facto* analysis of any part of the computer test operation after the field tests were completed.

The playback notion is ancient history in data processing. However, successful regeneration of computer runs for complex systems such as SAGE has been a difficult technical problem. It has been solved only recently. The Chronicles program records initial core content and then records all computer program inputs during the test run. Then, by resetting initial core memory conditions and playing all inputs back into the operational program in the rerun mode, the computer follows the same steps in the same sequence as they occurred in the original test. This amounts to total recording of the entire computer operation. The investigator may analyze any part of the test run as often as he wishes and at any time.

Because of efficient overlapping of core to tape transfer with central computer operation, Chronos recording never consumed more than 3% of total frame time, maintaining the real-time integrity of the operational program. As a general rule, recording tools should be efficiently designed to provide adequate but not excessive statistical sampling of data for economical recording with minimum interference in the on-line operation.

Concurrently with the design of the Chronos system, a questionnaire was developed to obtain operational performance and experimental control data not available from digital recording, as well as military evaluations of operational problems at individual positions. The questionnaire performance data included simulated hostile kills, ratings of individual operator load, and ratings of computer system support. The experimental control data covered the number and types of participating military personnel, crew experience levels, and sector weapons status. The military evaluations consisted primarily of open-end responses describing the most serious operational problems which occurred at individual stations and recommendations for dealing with these problems.

Test Procedure

The test procedure included a specially designed pilot test, administrative and technical preparations for the large field test, selecting the scope of and conducting the actual multidivision test, and the processing of results.

A system pilot test was conducted at an operational Direction Center to accomplish two goals. One was the shakedown and checkout of the Chronos program system and the questionnaire in the setting of a SAGE System Training Problem (SSTP) in preparation for the multidivision test. The second goal was to use extremely heavy simulated wartime track loads to test the limits in generating high frame times and to observe and measure associated air defense performance.

The general purpose of the multidivision test was to achieve the maximum realism possible within the framework of the SSTP vehicle. The test environment was designed to provide heavy hostile attack loads for frame time and performance measurement over an extensive geographical area.

There was a four-hour emergency warning buildup, with all battle staffs participating, before simulated hostile aircraft penetration of division boundaries. This was followed by a three-hour combat period, roughly corresponding to the time required for the hostile fly-through in the tested geographical area. According to test plan, two sectors became inoperative in the last hour of the test, and three adjacent sectors took over responsibility for the disabled areas. This was part of the experimental strategy to obtain heavier traffic levels for testing system limits. It also permitted a wider range of operational and emergency test modes for more comprehensive results.

Over 5,000 frames of automatically recorded Chronos data were collected from the nine Direction Centers involved in the test series. There were 724 questionnaire forms completed by participating military personnel. These data were processed with statistical routines.

Results

The results are considered under two general areas: the statistical measurement and prediction of computer operating time as a function of input load obtained from the Chronos recording programs, and the questionnaire.

Statistical Measurement of Frame Time. The general goal of the statistical measurement of SAGE computer operating time was to reduce the enormous complexity of factors contributing to computer load to a simple, sensible, and easily manageable set of statistical predictors which would hopefully show useful validity for a wide range of system loads and a variety of credible combat situations. The concrete goal was to arrive at multiple regression equations estimating over-all frame time and component subprogram time as a function of a small set of input load predictors.

The regression analysis involved formal and informal techniques to arrive at the "best" set of input predictor variables. These techniques included:

- Inspecting the 89×89 empirical correlation matrix of Chronograph variables.
- Using a routine to correlate frame time against recorded system

load variables and to subset the best predictors in rank order of contributed correlated variance.

- Trying out logical and rational combinations of variables in contrast to rank-ordered statistical predictors.
- Testing linear versus curvilinear equations.

After some trial and error in interweaving these approaches, a six-predictor linear solution was arrived at and cross-validated for the nine Direction Centers. It is not surprising that combinations of track and radar return variables ended up as the "best" system input predictors for computer operating time. This set of predictors covers all tracks and radar returns which should satisfy rational requirements for meaningful and inclusive variables. Combinations of these six variables can cover a wide range of air situations.

The six predictor variables are as follows:

Interceptor tracks	Correlated returns
Friendly tracks	Uncorrelated returns
Hostile tracks	Rejected returns

Multiple linear regression equations were obtained for over-all frame time and subprogram operating times as a function of the six input variables for nine Direction Centers. The average multiple correlation of frame time against the six predictor variables was .965 for the nine Direction Centers. This high level of correlation indicated a smooth, linear, and highly predictable increase in computer operating time with rising system input loads.

Further analysis showed frame time to be relatively insensitive to differences between sites, including differences in operational crews and local defense configurations. The regression coefficients were also quite similar for Direction Centers with highest and lowest track and radar input load levels. These findings indicate that one set of regression equations may be used as an effective norm for all tested input load levels and for all Direction Centers for the given SAGE computer program model.

Questionnaire Results. The questionnaire data covered three areas: experimental controls, chronological rating scales, and open-end responses.

Average crew experience levels in SAGE and at operational positions were essentially equivalent for all sites. Operational manning levels were fairly uniform. There were considerable variations in simulation team size, and numerous difficulties with simulation were reported in the open-end questionnaire results. We concluded that operational experience and manning levels were fairly well controlled, but that differences in simulation support at the test sites represented a significant uncontrolled influence in the test results.

The individual operator load scale and the computer system performance scale contain fivefold rating schemes as shown below. The military participants in both Direction Centers and Combat Centers filled in their ratings every ten minutes over a maximum three-hour test period. These are simple, general-purpose scales which may be useful for fast and economical exploratory tests for other systems.

Individual Operator Load Scale		*SAGE Computer System Performance Scale*	
Score	Description of Load	Score	Description of System Performance
1	Light	1	Very good
2	Moderate	2	Good
3	Heavy	3	Fair
4	Very heavy	4	Poor
5	Breakdown	5	Breakdown

The rating scales provided some insight into individual evaluations of operator load and computer system performance. The reliability of these scales was established by finding significant individual and time differences for all Direction Centers and Combat Centers, with only one exception, in a total of twenty-four analyses of variance tests (two rating scales for each of twelve sites). That is, individuals gave consistently different ratings, and ratings varied systematically with different time periods throughout the field tests. The uniqueness of the two scales was demonstrated by very low intercorrelations, indicating that they were measuring different attributes. The validity of the scales was established by significant correlations against frame time and switch action levels. That is, higher frame times were associated with ratings of reduced computer system performance; and high rates of operator actions were accompanied by ratings of heavy work loads.

The open-end portion of the questionnaire was the response to the following question: "What was the most serious operational problem occurring at your particular station at your heavy load periods during this test?" With respect to the grand total of 724 military personnel, 38% did not respond and 62% responded to this particular item. Responses were classified into four general problem areas: equipment, simulation, man-computer communication (console actions and displays), and human communication. Sectors with heaviest loads had fewest null responses. Simulation, human communication, and man-computer communication frequencies were almost equivalent, ranging from 16% to 18%. Equipment problems were somewhat lower at 10%.

In particular, "serious problems" in the man-computer communication area accounted for about 30% of the actual reported difficulties, or 18% of the total sample including the null category. This finding helps place the man-computer area in proper system perspective as a major problem area, but not the dominating consideration. Another noteworthy finding is that simulation problems in field tests are extremely difficult to handle successfully on all fronts and usually result in an uneven pattern of support for large-scale tests involving hundreds of people in geographically dispersed areas.

A key finding in man-computer communication involved a direct relationship between operator switch actions and frame time. Computer response to operator switch actions takes longer as frame time increases. Individual operator load also rises with increasing frame time. As a result, the computer system responds more slowly at a time when the operator has more work to do and needs a faster response. The recognition of this problem and associated ones led to further studies concerned with improved switch processing systems to permit more rapid computer response and provide more extensive computer feedback for all operator actions.

The open-end portion of the questionnaire was useful in uncovering unanticipated problem areas, in presenting a picture of the test from the individual operator's point of view, and in providing independent guidelines for a balanced interpretation of test results. These responses were instrumental in generating changes leading to improved design for many areas of the program system.

Interpretation

The interpretation covers classification of the reported test, following the taxonomy described earlier. System test characteristics of this study are then reviewed with the final discussion on incurred costs.

Test Classification. The reported test permits an exercise in applying the taxonomic scheme described previously to a concrete case. The classification of the test within the four major categories is shown below.

    1. TEST LEVEL. Primarily a system test with some omnibus features

at subsystem, functional, and component levels; it might be described as an omnibus system test.

2. DEVELOPMENTAL PHASE. Initial computerized system; Model 8 version in the SAGE computer program series; test conducted in the operational status of this version.

3. TEST APPROACH. Primarily a formal test which was planned, budgeted, and authorized well in advance of the actual testing; secondarily an *ex post facto* test in that several follow-on studies were initiated by the findings.

4. CHRONOLOGICAL TYPE. Cross-sectional, since this test stood alone without a comparable test preceding or succeeding it.

System Test Characteristics. The definition of system testing given in Section 10.1 cited five distinguishing characteristics, considered in the order shown below. The reported field test is matched against these.

1. Measures of system performance.
2. Experimental tests.
3. Credible setting.
4. Adequate man-machine and computer system complex.
5. Useful generalizations for future system effectiveness.

1. Both digital recording and manual data were required to relate computer operating time to man-machine system capacity. The measures included computer operating times, system performance variables such as hostile kill ratios and target defense levels, and experimental controls as anticipated in test design. The combination of objective (e.g., switch action frequencies) and subjective (e.g., rating scales) measures provided a more comprehensive approach to the study of system performance than either one taken alone, and permitted methodologically independent checks on the internal consistency of the results.

2. A great variety of experimental tests was used, each appropriate to a particular hypothesis and its associated empirical data. The linear regression equations for frame time proved to be a powerful multivariate approach for the observed data. The separate samples provided by the nine test sites permitted independent cross-validation checks and generalization of the regression results. These independent tests ruled out the possibility of artificial inflation of the significance of the results because of selection of chance fluctuations in directions

favorable to the given hypothesis. The large sample size (over 5,000 frames) resulted in stable statistical findings.

Different types of experimental tests were employed for the questionnaire data. Analysis of variance permitted tests of temporal and individual differences. Simple bivariate correlations were employed to check reliability and validity measures. The tabulation of open-end responses was an exploratory technique involving simple response frequencies.

3 and 4. The third and fourth distinguishing characteristics of the definition of system testing, the credibility of the test setting and the adequacy of the man-machine and computer system complex, go hand in hand. The SSTP simulation involved the actual operational defense facilities of the northeastern portion of the United States. The crews were the actual operational personnel at these sites. The simulated combat problem was originally designed in conjunction with the military staffs of the participating Air Defense Divisions. There was a four-hour intelligence and warning buildup before hostile aircraft penetration of division boundaries. These features were convincing arguments as to the inherent credibility and the adequacy of the operational complex for the multidivision system test.

Even with this formidable array of positive factors, the credibility of the findings had to be carefully qualified with respect to certain limitations. The simulated air attack represented only one of a variety of conceivable penetration patterns. As noted in the results, there was uneven simulation support at the various sites. For example, equipment for simulated electronic jamming was not working effectively at all Direction Centers. Nearly all of the tested parameters—for example, the SAGE computer program model, crew composition, types of switch actions, and the nature of the hostile threat—change in time. All these factors tend to make any generalization of the results more approximate and conditional than is the case for more static and stable entities. In this study the major antidote to counteract these effects was the use of nine independent sector samples. This extended sampling permitted greater confidence in cross-validated and generalized results but did not eliminate the conditionality of many of the findings. From a practical point of view, these are relatively unavoidable limitations which accompany the impressive advantages of live testing at operational facilities over a large geographical area.

5. In regard to the fifth characteristic of system testing, the results proved useful for future operations. Standardized norms were available for subprogram as well as over-all program running times as a function

of the six track and radar input variables. The experimental test tools, such as the Chronos program system, were available as checked out and standardized capabilities for future testing. Programmers were better able to test subprogram operating times for the next computer program model, which resulted in significant savings in running time. The regenerative test run for the successor computer program model permitted accurate estimates of new program operating time under controlled conditions. Numerous improvements were made in areas such as hostile track telling, switch processing, manual inputs, and simulation, in response to the errors and inefficient procedures detected in the test results. Finally, the primary goal of the system test was accomplished: the relationship between computer operating time, input load, and associated system performance was objectively matched against operational requirements.

Cost. The cost factor for system testing was frequently mentioned as exorbitant and prohibitive by most authors cited in the early part of this chapter. This was not the case for these SAGE field tests, and the reasons are instructive in demonstrating how to cut system test costs. The SSTP multidivision problem and the single-sector pilot test problem were "free" since they were selected from off-the-shelf, available training problems best meeting the test needs. Although the Air Defense Command paid for the original production of these problems for training purposes, no additional costs for materials were incurred for system testing. Since the test was run as a training mission, the participating crews obtained the benefits that accrue from training exercises. The same problems were used later by other crews. The complete operational facility—men, computers, and equipment—also came "free" under the rubric of training. This again bears out the close relationship between system training and system testing which has been a recurrent theme in this chapter: not only do they both benefit from the best operational simulation available for credibility and optimal validity of results, but they also have economic ties in that both purposes may often be accomplished at the same time with an over-all savings in system costs.

The design, development, and checkout of the Chronos program complex took only about half a man-year of programming effort, with all of the computer testing time absorbed in the normal overhead of operational computer facilities. As a result, the SAGE system acquired checked-out and standardized tools to measure and output program running times and computer load indices, and it also gained an efficient regenerative recording system. Great numbers of recorded data were economically processed by available statistical routines for the 7090 computer. Only one man, the principal investigator, was tied up full time, less than a year for the total elapsed period between the project proposal and the final report.

The over-all box score amounted to a total of approximately two man-years of professional time and a few hours of 7090 statistical running time, with the rest coming out of normal overhead for training and field operations. This type of system test did not involve prohibitive costs, nor was it as difficult to design as the operational system itself, as Goode and Machol, cited earlier, would lead us to expect. Consolidation of testing, training, simulation, recording, reduction, and operational facilities can result in highly economical system testing simultaneously serving a variety of users.

10.5   EVOLUTIONARY SYSTEM TESTING

The positive aim of this section is to elaborate upon the outline of the taxonomy of testing in terms of an evolutionary process which permeates the development of information systems, and which effectively results in a great variety of testing activities occurring in series and in parallel through time, at many different levels up to system testing, and including live operations. The negative goal is to dispel the persistent stereotype of the climactic, grand-slam system test that magically integrates, evaluates, and shakes down the disparate elements of a system at the end of the production process to launch it successfully into mature operations. This stereotype is an anachronism carried over from weapons system development which does not apply to computerized information systems. An evolutionary test approach, spanning the period from the antecedent manual system, through the initial man-machine digital system, to successor computerized versions, is useful in conveying the notion of the diversity and continuity of testing and the value of cooperation and coordination between the different types of testing.

Testing Manual Precursor Systems

In antecedent manual systems, testing may be well developed at man and machine component levels, and operational testing may be a formal institution, the whole comprising a testing subculture. This is especially characteristic of military systems with:

- Their detailed procedures on equipment design, development, and testing.
- Regulations regarding personnel selection, training, placement, evaluation, and promotion.
- Long-standing operational regulations which involve various types of quality control checks and field and readiness tests.

Civilian man-machine organizations tend to have analogous functions on a reduced scale.

As mentioned earlier, experience with manual systems seems to indicate that experimental system tests are difficult to establish, controls are only partial, performance data are hard to obtain, the test effort is usually very costly, and the final results are often ambiguous. These problems have tended to discourage extensive system testing and have encouraged equipment bench testing, simplified laboratory tests, and inexpensive paper-and-pencil techniques—that is, testing at subsystem, functional, and component levels. Field tests often become feasibility demonstrations of gross effectiveness levels of system behaviors rather than controlled experimental measurements under standardized conditions.

Nevertheless, people in systems continually evaluate effectiveness from their own points of view. Total testing is like an iceberg with only a small portion visible above the surface. Most testing is intuitive, informal, and essentially invisible, as indicated by the taxonomic distinction between formal and informal testing. Decisions are made at all levels, modifying the system in gross and subtle ways, on the basis of performance imputed from the typically uneven mix of stingy amounts of objective evidence with generous portions of subjective conviction. Compilations of available data with complete listings of performance measures, test situations, and descriptive statistics of system operational parameters, including contradictory and ambiguous findings, critically reviewed and updated by independent analysts, would provide an invaluable source of information for personnel working in and with the object system. Such compilations of manual system performance would be especially valuable as a reference point for the design and testing of initial computerized systems.

Testing Initial Computerized Systems

A fundamental assumption in the decision to evolve from a manual to a computerized system is that the performance tradeoff in the digital version will more than offset the over-all additional costs. Ideally, if there were credible performance standards from controlled experimental situations for the base manual system, and equivalent experimental tests for the computerized version, the performance differential between the two systems could be objectively measured. Comparative or longitudinal system testing in manual systems and their computerized successors comes closest to achieving this ideal.

System testing has its origins in the manual precursor system and should be strongly established as far as economic feasibility and the state of the art will permit. Computerization does not change basic system goals or bedrock performance measures, unless, of course, the new system is redefined and emerges as a different type of system. Air defense is geared toward destroying invaders and protecting our targets; banking institutions are interested in fast, economical, and accurate processing and analysis of financial transactions; hospitals are oriented toward expeditious and effective support of doctors and patients; law enforcement is concerned with the optimal protection of life and property; etc. System technology may change dramatically with the introduction of computers, but not system teleology.

With an established manual system test and evaluation technology, particularly longitudinal system testing, the initial computerized system can build upon an existing test structure. This would provide a starting point for critical tests to measure manual to computerized improvement (or degradation, as the case may be in the earliest operations of the computerized version), providing a springboard for subsequent exploitation of the digital test data well beyond manual system capabilities. This evolutionary approach is quite different from starting almost from scratch in creating new performance tools and tests for the prototype version of first-generation computer-based information systems. Much of the sting would be taken out of the traumatic experiences of the first system test efforts if the heritage of system testing were transmitted from manual systems to their computerized offspring.

Managers and users should take a close look at manual system test procedures and findings before proceeding toward a first-generation computer-based system. This information provides the most objective empirical base for projecting cost-effectiveness tradeoffs against proposed computerized alternatives for the object system. The follow-on requirements of the selected computer-based system should include corresponding empirical tests of system performance to verify the actual cost-effectiveness improvement. This approach was essentially recommended by Hosier and implied by the other authors in the historical review presented earlier. The applied scientific approach requires that cost-effectiveness criteria as well as design specifications should be defined so as to be testable when facilities become available.

To return to the iceberg theme, the total testing process, at least as defined by the taxonomic scheme, occupies a much larger share of the total design and operational effort than is commonly supposed. Usually, only a small portion of the testing iceberg is made visible, separately funded, and formally documented. Perhaps the major share of the design effort is spent in informal and semiformal tests of proposed designs. For example, a programmer may spend less of his time in writing code than he uses in parameter checking and debugging his initial program version until satisfactory performance and usable instructions are achieved. Computer time may be almost wholly devoted to program testing as distinguished from program production. The process is repeated at assembly testing, program control, and computer system checkout levels. Great efforts are expended in support facilities to provide the required tools for testing, including simulation, recording, reduction, and adaptation programs; and these in turn require their share of testing. Program production tools, such as assemblers, compilers, and data dictionaries, also require continual testing. L. Farr and B. Nanus estimate that in military command and control systems up to 50% of software costs are spent in test activities.[13] J. P. Haverty also estimates that typically half of the programming effort is expended in testing activity for such systems.[14] He indicates that probably no one has taken a serious look at the general nature and problems of program testing. Equipment and human testing follow similar paths with pervasive checking and testing at all levels, separately in the early design phases, conjointly in functional subsystems, and finally as a whole in system testing. In this sense, system testing serves to polarize and organize the anterior types of component, functional, and subsystem testing.

Nor does the process stop here. Well.before the first operational system is assembled, many postinitial design changes are released in an unending stream for men, equipment, and the computer program complex. These changes, either separately or in related clusters, require some form of acceptance test and evaluation before they are incorporated into the system. And ultimately, such changes must demonstrate system compatibility either in system testing or by acceptable performance in on-line operations. System operation constitutes the final link and is in fact part of the testing chain. Inadequate operational performance of any element or complex, even if informally detected, will generate another system requirement, demanding an additional cycle of modification and retesting.

It would be interesting to have objective data on total testing costs in the design, development, and operation of different types of computer-based information systems. Comparable cost data obtained under controlled conditions are virtually nonexistent for computer program development.[15] If all testing costs in system development were to be made visible and formalized, fiscal attitudes toward the necessary economic support for effective testing at all levels might take a new turn. The emphasis might shift toward the creation of more powerful and versatile testing facilities, more expensive during initial design but more economical over the lifespan of the system, and with higher transfer to successor systems. Many types of isolated, redundant, and primitive testing, much of it following individualistic and anarchistic paths, might be centralized and standardized with more public dissemination of results, particularly in the corrective form of longitudinal testing to check earlier against later findings. System tests would be increasingly employed as economical omnibus vehicles for simultaneous testing of men, machine, and program features which may have been inadequately tested in isolation at previous times. System tests could thus, in principle, reduce total test costs and improve the quality and credibility of total test results. It might even turn out that testing would be viewed as a continual corrective in system evolution and not as a distasteful one-shot job to get over with as soon as possible.

Testing Successor Computerized Systems

BUIC (Backup Interceptor Control), in the dual role of a successor and backup system to SAGE, is one of the few current examples of second-generation computerized systems with at least an incipient history. BUIC is specially notable for the heavy borrowing of many operational and design concepts from SAGE, in many ways a chip off the old block. But unlike SAGE, BUIC had to be designed under an austere budget and with short lead times. The existence of a viable, working predecessor in SAGE simplified the design and production job, permitting positive fallout of many notable improvements, including performance testing harvested from SAGE experience. This example illustrates another hidden cost factor in total system evolution: the relatively high cost of developing many first-generation computerized systems may grossly amortize much of the lead time and dollar cost of developing and operating successor systems.

System testing for successor computerized systems may assume a more grandiose scale than that for initial systems. There are more likely to be requirements for the second-generation computerized system to communicate with other computer-based systems and to be compatible with them. System tests and exercises may, in fact, become multisystem in scope, as indicated in the taxonomy of testing, requiring different and more powerful approaches to test and evaluation. The National Military Command System will constitute an extremely complex type of supersystem with a remarkably rich mixture of component manual and computerized systems, at different stages of evolution. R. L. Kirby and H. L. Wright have anticipated and outlined some of the interface problems in the NMCS as more and more military information systems become computerized.[16] The increasing proliferation of computer-based systems and the obvious advantages of digital intercommunication and compatibility between such entities will diversify the need, enhance the value, and accelerate the requirements for increased testing at multisystem levels.

10.6   EXPERIMENTAL REALISM

The problems and techniques of system testing in computer-based information system environments appear to involve a reorientation of traditional approaches to the experimental method. This section sketches one such reorientation, termed "experimental realism."

Digital Data and Experimental Method

The existence of a large, central computer in information systems has a profound impact on the basic nature of the experimental approach to such systems. The computer effectively amounts to a built-in, semiautomated laboratory for the system, making it possible to experiment with living, operational events in real time as they occur in the "real world." Computers have been operating at 100,000 dynamic instructions per second (SAGE), may now execute a million instructions, and will, admittedly in the somewhat distant future, be approaching a billion machine orders per second (nanosecond speeds). This capability, with increasingly sophisticated man-machine, input-output coupling, makes it possible to efficiently collect and analyze vast numbers of digital data on real-time system behavior both in a controlled setting and spontaneously in live operations without recourse to an abstract laboratory environment.

For example, regenerative recording in SAGE only requires, on the average, about 1% of the dynamic instruction flow to be diverted to recording to permit complete reproduction of a computer test run. It only takes some 3% of the dynamic instruction flow to record completely the changing elements of core memory in SAGE, permitting direct capture of core data without a regenerative rerun. Thus, by tapping only a fairly small fraction of its operating capability, the relatively middle-aged SAGE computer can be made to tell all or replicate all it contains for the interested investigator.

Extrapolation from live events to similar live events is generally much more direct and credible than extrapolation from an artificial laboratory environment to the full man-computer setting. This comparison is not meant to deny the usefulness of the classical laboratory approach, which will and should remain the method of choice for many important types of experimental problems. But the comparison does imply that preliminary laboratory experiments for computer-based information systems should be successively tested through component, functional, and subsystem levels, and finally in the actual system setting, for proper validation. Corrective longitudinal testing should be employed, culminating in system testing. System testing in the operational environment is thus the method of experimental choice if it is feasible and economically available for direct study of actual system events.

A major shift in the nature of experimental inquiry from the classical laboratory to live system testing lies in the formulation of hypotheses. The shift is in the direction of greater formalization and increased visibility of exploratory and open-end techniques, in contrast with and in addition to, preconceived hypotheses. Unexpected or new findings derived from exploratory probes may overshadow or reconfigure the original hypotheses that led to the system test.

Experimental Realism versus Experimental Idealism

The computer thus permits an unparalleled experimental opportunity to record essentially all its own data and, in particular, to regenerate or replicate its own operation in real time either for direct reproduction of digital events or for controlled experimental variations. When this experimental control and replicability is considered in conjunction with the staggering complexity of diverse human and hardware inputs from a large embedding system and its environment, the increase in experimental scope and power cannot be considered as trivial or as a transient novelty. Live system testing constitutes an on-line experimental approach which may be described as "experimental realism." It is contrasted with the classic laboratory procedure in which dependent and independent behavior variables are relatively isolated with other factors controlled or held "constant," in an idealized and simplified model of the object system. This traditional approach may be designated as "experimental idealism." Recall the earlier review of Finan's article, in which similar approaches were contrasted.

The relationships and distinctions between experimental realism versus experimental idealism reflect basic philosophical values. The differences between the two points of view are impressionistically suggested in the following lists:

Experimental Realism	*Experimental Idealism*
Real world	Laboratory world
Real time	Non-real time
Heuristic	Algorithmic
Open-end systems	Closed systems
Pragmatic	Rationalistic
Inductive	Deductive
Pluralistic	Monistic
Probabilistic	Deterministic
Eclectic	Systematic
Holistic	Reductionistic
Interdisciplinary	Specialized
Exploratory experimentation	Controlled experimentation
Operational simulation	Mathematical modeling
Psychological	Logical

The lists of contrasting attributes are an updated extension, with some modifications, of an analogous list from William James,[17] in which he distinguishes between "tough-minded" pragmatism and "tender-minded" idealism. The main differences are essentially a stronger emphasis on experimental method and the more powerful types of experimentation offered by the· advent of computerized systems. But the pragmatic predilection is the same.

The listed distinctions between experimental realism and experimental idealism are only indicative of tendencies which probably represent nonexistent extremes when considered in their pure form. Many pairs of attributes are noncontradictory and may well occur together. No experimenter represents all the characteristics of one camp, and every investigator probably has some significant admixture of both elements of all contrasting traits. Nevertheless, the distinction between experimental realism and experimental idealism is believed to be a fundamental issue which has been brought into new focus with the possibilities of system testing in computer-based information systems.

10.7 SUMMARY AND CONCLUSIONS

Definition. System testing refers to experimental measurement of system performance in a credible test setting involving an adequately large complex of the men, equipment, and data-processing facilities of the object system, so that results can be used to make generalizations regarding current and future system effectiveness.

Taxonomy of Testing. System testing is located within the perspective of a general taxonomy of testing for computer-based information systems. The taxonomy includes four major classification categories: test level, developmental phase, test approach, and chronological trends.

Status. System testing is an applied discipline for computer-based information systems, now in its infancy.

System Testing as Applied Science. Operational specifications should be cast in the language of experimental hypotheses regarding system performance which can be verified by system testing. If there is no empirical verification of purported capability, there is only a system technology with unknown effectiveness, not an applied system science.

Pluralistic System Performance Criteria. System performance measurement is complicated by the problem of pluralism: numerous and different types of system environments, large numbers of qualitatively different performance measures, temporal changes in system environments and in relevant measures of effectiveness, and pluralistic norms for performance.

Credible Simulation. System testing and system training require credible simulation in an operational environment. More realistic simulation should serve as empirical verification for less realistic simulation in a longitudinal test series culminating with system testing and continually modified by live operations.

Digital Data Collection. Ideal digital recording for system testing should permit access to all data in high-speed memory, selective extraction of any subset of digital data, and a regenerative capability to play back any computer test.

Reduction and Analysis of Digital Data. Ideally, reduction and analysis of digital data for system testing should be optimally adapted to the needs of the human user. This involves comprehensive coverage of operational variables, human-engineered formats, graphs, statistical summaries, printouts in operational language, on-line or rapid user feedback, and flexible selection of content subsets, in addition to the usual standards of economy and reliability.

Applied Systems Generalists. System testing requires contributions from engineering, programming, human factors, and operations research which should be harmoniously blended to form the interdisciplinary background for a new breed of applied systems generalists.

Example of System Testing. A detailed example of system testing is taken from SAGE. The example illustrates parts of the approach described in this chapter and emphasizes the value and economy of certain applied testing techniques.

Evolutionary System Testing. Total testing and test support activities are massively embedded in all phases of system evolution at both overt and implicit levels. System testing serves as the ultimate level of validation for other types of tests. It should be well developed in manual precursor systems, highly elaborated and increasingly sophisticated in the successive stages of growth in first-generation computerized systems, and diversified further in succeeding computerized generations for multisystem testing.

Experimental Realism. A preliminary statement of a neopragmatic philosophy of system testing, exploiting the on-line capabilities of computer-based information systems, described as "experimental realism," is presented as a more powerful approach than the classical laboratory techniques embodied in "experimental idealism."

REFERENCES

1. H. H. Goode and R. E. Machol, *System Engineering: An Introduction to the Design of Large-Scale Systems.* New York: McGraw-Hill, 1957.
2. R. M. Gagné (ed.), *Psychological Principles in System Development.* New York: Holt, Rinehart, and Winston, 1962.

3. R. Glaser and D. J. Klaus, "Proficiency Measurement: Assessing Human Performance," in R. M. Gagné (ed.), Ref. 2, pp. 419–474.

4. R. H. Davis and R. A. Behan, "Evaluating System Performance in Simulated Environments," in R. M. Gagné (ed.), Ref. 2, pp. 477–515.

5. J. L. Finan, "The System as a Principle of Methodological Decisions," in R. M. Gagné (ed.), Ref. 2, pp. 517–546.

6. W. A. Hosier, "Pitfalls and Safeguards in Real-Time Digital Systems with Emphasis on Programming," *IRE Transactions of Journal Engineering Management,* **EM–8, 2** (June 1961), 99–115.

7. S. B. Sells, "An Interactionist Looks at the Environment," *Journal of the American Psychological Association,* **18**, No. 11 (November 1963).

8. J. M. Baker, "Taxonomic Analyses of The Compendium of Air Defense System Performance Measures." Santa Monica, Calif.: System Development Corporation, D-3463, N-16892/000/00, November 2, 1961.

9. C. W. Churchman, *On Inquiring Systems.* Santa Monica, Calif.: System Development Corporation, SP-877, July 13, 1962.

10. H. Sackman, "Regenerative Recording in Man-Machine Digital Systems," *Proceedings* (PTGMIL 64), National Winter Convention on Military Electronics, Vol. III, February 1964.

11. H. H. Harman, *Simulation: A Survey.* Santa Monica, Calif.: System Development Corporation, SP-260, July 1961; Bibliography 7, "Uses of Computers in Simulation," *Computing Reviews,* **3**, No. 6 (November-December 1962).

12. H. Sackman and J. B. Munson, "Investigation of Computer Operating Time and System Capacity for Man-Machine Systems," *Journal of the Association for Computing Machinery,* **11**, No. 4 (October 1964), pp. 450–464.

13. L. Farr and B. Nanus, "Cost Aspects of Computer Programming for Command and Control," *Proceedings* (PTGMIL 64), National Winter Convention on Military Electronics, Vol. III, February 1964.

14. J. P. Haverty, *The Role of Programming Languages in Command and Control: An Interim Report.* Santa Monica, Calif.: The RAND Corporation, RM-3292-PR, September 1962.

15. See L. Farr and B. Nanus, Ref. 13, and J. P. Haverty, Ref. 14.

16. R. L. Kirby and H. L. Wright, "Information Systems Integration," *Proceedings* (PTGMIL 63), National Summer convention on Military Electronics, September 1963.

17. W. James, *Pragmatism: A New Name for Some Old Ways of Thinking.* New York: Longmans, Green, 1907.

Chapter Eleven

Retrospect

P. E. Rosove

In this final chapter we intend to make some summary remarks which, although philosophical in tone, reflect our thinking about the information system development process as it has been presented in this book. There are essentially four points which must be made. These include (1) the fact that computers (and other hardware) are only components of information systems; (2) the need to be sure that we ask information systems to solve the right problems; (3) the recognition that technological changes in the information sciences have not altered the general nature of the system development process; and (4) the fact that information systems, if they are well designed, can provide some of the needed responses to the profound challenges of the contemporary era.

11.1 COMPUTERS ARE COMPONENTS OF SYSTEMS

The literature of contemporary information science deals endlessly, it seems, with the capabilities and limitations of computers. There are interminable debates on the differences and similarities between the computer and a human being. These are, of course, important issues. But if it is true that the value of the computer lies in the interaction between it and human beings, or what has been called man-machine symbiosis, then attention must be directed toward the process whereby *information systems* based upon such symbiosis are created.

When the IBM/360 computer system was unveiled in April 1964, an enthusiastic official of the company was quoted as saying that the high speed with which the new system could deliver information to a user made it comparable to "drinking information from a high-pressure fire hose."[1] The analogy is a useful one insofar as the purpose of this book is concerned. The reader may, perhaps, picture a hapless user of this system attempting to keep from drowning in a rising tide of data as he is deluged with information at speeds ranging from one-millionth to two-hundred billionths of a second! Potential users of information systems should be cautioned that the fantastic operational speeds of a computer cannot solve their informational problems. Furthermore, the constantly increasing capabilities of the hardware only add to the problem of the *system* designers since they must determine how to make maximum use of these capabilities.

In celebration of the Massachusetts Institute of Technology's Centennial Year a lecture series was offered on the subject "Management and the Computer of the Future."[2] During a panel discussion following one of the lectures, Norbert Wiener is reported to have said that he could build a computer that would be able to duplicate itself. Vannevar Bush commented on this remark, "But it is possible to visualize a machine in the desert, surrounded by its numerous progeny, busily computing all sorts of things to which no one is paying any attention whatever."[3] This story illustrates the point of view expressed in this book. Computers are fabulous machines, as we all know; and they will perform even more astonishing feats in the future, as Norbert Wiener indicates. But in an information system, as we defined such a system in Chapter 1, the computer(s) and associated equipment are merely components of a *system*—and it is the *design* of the system, rather than the physical attributes of its components, which is critical. If there is no such design, but merely components endlessly reproducing themselves, we must ask with Vannevar Bush, will anyone be paying attention?

The ultimate potential of the mechanical devices of the cybernetic era will be realized when we recognize more fully that the basic problems and difficulties in using such devices are to be found in two related areas: (1) the nature of the information system development process, and (2) the attitudes, customs, and institutionalized inertia of the users of the new technology. As we have seen in this book, particularly in Chapter 2, many of the problems and difficulties encountered in the typical system development activity are traceable to the attitudes, customs, and institutions of the users. John Diebold[4] has noted this relationship in the businessman's approach to the creation of information systems. He writes:

"Truly fruitful results from information handling systems require a fundamental change in approach, an understanding that the best applications come not from the mechanization or streamlining of existing procedures, but are based on management's willingness to rethink the problems of an *entire business* in terms of ultimate goal and final product. These are not technical problems. They are problems of definition of objectives and assessments of markets, of method, organization, and attitude."

It follows that before the potentialities of the revolution in information technology can be realized there must also be revolutions in the social or institutional realm. The inability to grasp this fundamental point, an inability fostered all too often by special interests (computer salesmen) and by the typical manager's lack of familiarity with information science, impedes a more rapid and more successful utilization of the new technology.

In Chapter 2, for example, we found that frequently there is a lack of correspondence between the jurisdictional area of an enterprise and the information system that it requires to meet its needs and objectives. This is a widespread dilemma of our time. Highways cross city, county, and state lines; polluted rivers are no respectors of political boundaries; crime is notoriously interstate and even international in its operations. In the business world the need of top management for information critical for long-range planning and decision making cuts across the boundaries separating decentralized operating product divisions and functional departments. And in the military realm we have seen in recent years the general trend toward centralization, first in such areas as logistics and supply but more recently in planning and in operations: the National Military Command System cuts across and integrates the various service and command information systems. As a result of these trends, the development of information systems requires coordination and planning extending across existing organizational jurisdictions and through several levels of government. We are impaled, then, on a three-horned dilemma—there are operational needs, jurisdictions determined by organizational boundaries, and the information sciences. As yet we have not found the way to ensure the most effective correspondence among these three elements.

11.2   LET US ASK THE RIGHT QUESTIONS

Perhaps we can now see why much of the apprehension over the possibly harmful consequences to society of the use of computers is misdirected. The electronic digital computer, like any other machine, is only a tool. Like any other man-made instrument, a rifle for example, it can be used for good or ill. But this is not the issue. The question with which we ought to be more concerned is not how shall we use the computers so that evil consequences can be avoided, but how shall we develop information systems which will be commensurate with our values, which will achieve our stated objectives, and which will accommodate our institutional structure?

It may well happen that the widespread use of computers in information systems will decrease the number of persons who will participate in high-level policy decisions, as D. N. Michael fears.[5] It is possible that the use of computers will contribute to unemployment in certain fields and for certain categories of personnel. But these are not inevitable calamities; they are not inherent either in computers as such or in information science in general. Whether or not democratic processes are jeopardized or social dislocations result from the employment of computers in a given institutional area will depend upon the decisions made during the system development process. To illustrate this point, if we design an information system which no longer requires a particular skill or task, thereby making someone unemployed, the system's computer can also be used, with appropriate programming, to find another task which *is* required for that same individual either in the same institution, in another one of the same general type (e.g., a federal hospital, a university library, an automobile factory), or in another kind of institution. Perhaps even more important (and this requires us to look at the consequences of introducing computerized systems into one enterprise for other areas of society) is the fact that we can create new information systems which will automatically match job seekers with jobs available. Thus, the problems lie, not in the machinery of the cybernetic era, but in the ability of human beings and their institutions to adapt to the requirements of this new era.

Another potential danger in the application of computers is not so much in the social dislocations which their use may entail, although these are unquestionably painful and costly, but *in putting them to the wrong use*. The critical questions, and these are embedded in the system development process, are as follows: What is the system being asked to do? What problems is it being asked to solve? As E. E. Morison notes in this respect, it is "much harder to ask the right question than it is to find the right answer to the wrong question."[6] In our review of the system development process, particularly in Chapter 3, we have stressed the importance of obtaining the right questions from the potential users of the system. If it is true that a computer will answer a fool according to his folly, then the function of the system developer is to try to prevent the user from making a fool of himself.

We have attempted in this book to describe the major characteristics of the development process for large-scale, computer-based information systems. Although each information system is unique (since each system is custom-built to satisfy the needs of a particular enterprise), it is possible to indicate the typical stages or phases through which every system must pass as it is being created. It is possible, as we have done in this book, to review the typical types of problems—administrative and technical—which occur in the various phases of development. It is our conviction that, if managers and administrators who are about to acquire a computer-based information system understood this development process, particularly the earliest phases when the right questions must be asked, many of the disappointments and disillusionments which users of newly designed systems have experienced in the past could be avoided in the future.

11.3   SYSTEM DEVELOPMENT AND THE PROBLEM OF CHANGE

The information sciences underwent a major revolution during the few years in which this book was written, rewritten, and finally published. There is always the possibility of producing an obsolete product when one writes a book under such conditions. While this book may indeed become obsolete in the future, we believe that the basic issues dealt with here are still very much part of the contemporary scene. However, in the long run (and we cannot predict how much time that term may encompass) this book will, of necessity, be an object of historical interest only. Such must be the fate of any work dealing with a technological process while it is in a state of revolutionary transformation.

The book was begun at a time when the first generation of large-scale, "real-time," military computer-based command and control systems had reached operational status, as in the case of SAGE, or, like the SAC Control System (465L) and the North American Air Defense

Combat Operations Center (425L), were nearing such status. Since the authors of this book participated in the development of these systems, it was inevitable that their thinking about the system development process would be influenced by this experience. The lessons we learned as we labored to develop those systems are reflected in this book. Since the operations of these military systems were of necessity during their development (or even now) shrouded in secrecy, no small service is performed for the public, we believe, by the publication of the material in this book. We have also tried, wherever possible, to make use of information on the system development process from the nonmilitary area and to incorporate such information into our over-all view of the process. Thus, although we recognize differences between military and nonmilitary computer-based information systems, this book has focused, rather, on the typical problems and issues derived from their underlying and basic similarities.

What stands out above the changes in technology is the relatively stable character of the system development process. Similarly, despite technological progress, the problems associated with system development have remained. Thus, in the few years since 1963 we have seen the development of such techniques as computer "time sharing" by multiple users, "general purpose" data management systems, natural language data processing, the capability for "on-line" program error detection and correction, the application of "real-time," "on-line" concepts of system design to nonmilitary enterprises, microminiaturization, computer operating speeds of a billionth of a second, relatively unlimited data storage capacities, and many other revolutionary developments too numerous to mention. Yet the striking fact remains that for *new* large-scale systems the system development process, as such, is basically unchanged. The user must still cooperate with the developer to determine the objectives and goals of the enterprise; the basic information system configuration must be conceived and its operating requirements determined; the system must be designed; its component elements must be designed and produced; the system must undergo testing and evaluation throughout its history; training must be provided for the users; and the system must be installed and brought up to operational capability. Finally, through a formally defined feedback process, the system must change and evolve in response to altering internal and external events and conditions.

Certainly one of the major developments in recent years from a strictly technical point of view is the time-shared system in which multiple users, linked to a central computer from remote input/output devices, "simultaneously" utilize the computer. But it should be made clear that such technical creations do not eliminate the need for system design or the system development process as described in this book. The design issues in the development process are simply different. The potential user and the developer must first determine whether or not a time-shared computer would meet the user's needs; then, if it is decided to apply the concept of time sharing, the attention of the designers must be directed to associated issues. For example, since input/output technology lags behind the capabilities of the central computer, the selection of the appropriate input/output devices becomes critical. Deciding how these devices will be apportioned among the user's personnel and how they will be utilized for transmitting data also become vital issues. Another example of the shift in design problems is meeting the requirement in a time-shared system to protect the reliability of the data base when multiple users are interacting with it. For example, in airline reservations systems, many remotely located ticket agents modify the record of available seats. Furthermore, as a larger number of users with varying interests and functions interact with the computer, the need for data storage shifts from off-line to on-line auxiliary facilities. SAGE, SABRE, and similar systems have demonstrated that batch processing can be performed on-line; with the advent of time-shared systems, the design issue is no longer deciding whether an on-line operation would be better than a batch processing operation but, rather, which functions of a hybrid system should be performed on-line. Also, on-line, time-shared operations require the design of a different data base structure from that for batch processing operations. All these problems and many others must be resolved by the system designers.

It is true that in recent years many of the largest business corporations have created their own in-house capabilities for computer-based information system development. In such cases the user and the developer are one and the same, but only in an abstract sense. For, as John Diebold points out, the controller's conception of the enterprise may be parochial. In the military realm, prodigious efforts are being made to create in-house capabilities for information system development. But the military must compete in this realm, as in so many other technical fields, with the higher salary inducements of the commercial world. And in the quasi-public and governmental areas, in-house capabilities for information system development are virtually nonexistent.

Thus, at least in military, quasi-public, and governmental institutions the user-developer relationships described herein will persist for some time into the future.

11.4 CHALLENGE AND RESPONSE

In the opening pages of this book we referred to the crises which beset many contemporary institutions and enterprises. Since those pages were written, the Watts riot wracked the city of Los Angeles and the far-ranging power failure of November 9, 1965, plunged the northeastern part of the United States into primeval darkness. In South Vietnam, the expensive B-52's of the Strategic Air Command are used anachronistically to drop conventional bombs on dense tropical jungles, a task for which they were not conceived or developed. The so-called "biggest construction project in history," the great Interstate Highway System, still in the process of being built, was described in 1965 as inadequate although it was designed to carry an amount of traffic projected through the middle of the 1970's. Hospitals, already unable to accommodate a rising tide of patients, are struggling to find facilities and staff to cope with the flood of elderly people taking advantage of Medicare. Our schools and universities, still with roots in the Middle Ages, seek to meet the problems attendant upon ever-rising enrollments and the soaring costs of new buildings, administration, and operations. Scientists in all fields, limited by frail human capabilities, attempt valiantly to keep abreast of the most recent discoveries in their disciplines. As smog clogs the air, as pollutants of every kind turn once beautiful rivers into reeking quagmires, as junked automobiles and other discarded debris offend the eye everywhere, reference to our nation as "the effluent society" does not seem farfetched or even facetious.

Contemporary problems multiply and proliferate in such areas as law enforcement, the administration of justice, education, city and regional planning, information storage and retrieval, air and ground traffic control, and the administration and control of large-scale enterprises of all types in the military, governmental, and business realms. Indeed, it does not seem farfetched to view this period in which we live as a race against disaster. Norbert Wiener has stated that "there is a real possibility that changes in our environment have exceeded our capacity to adapt."[7] Kenneth Boulding asks, "Where are we going, if anywhere?"[8] On the one hand, problems of extraordinary magnitude close in around us; while, on the other hand, we struggle to employ whatever rational skills we possess to resolve those problems. Science and technology are the progenitors of our dilemmas, but science and technology also contain the hope for the resolution of these problems.

Information systems technology and the computer sciences have led to the problems of information system development described in this book, but this technology and this science contain also the seeds of regeneration. We have our "time of troubles"; yet we also have the means at hand to transform crisis into triumph. It is possible, as some pessimists predict, that western civilization as we know it is doomed. It is equally possible (and, we believe, more probable) that western civilization, as well as the rest of the world, stands at the edge of a new era—a new historical epoch. Central to this new epoch in man's history is the potentiality inherent in the information system built upon the foundation of the electronic digital computer. We have only just begun to apply what has been learned in the creation of military and commercial information systems to the overriding dilemmas of our time. It is not surprising that war and the desire for profit have been the prime movers in the creation of information system technology. It has been ever thus. But the application of this technology to assist in the resolution of the critical problems of our time will be a great act of creation.

The contemporary revolution in the information sciences and the social revolutions call for imagination and the willingness to explore new areas for the application of computerized systems and new ways of conceptualizing information systems per se. We need the kind of thinking that can conceive a "national research library" built around computers and other hardware which would serve the information needs of both the federal government and the universities; we need new approaches in which the information system as a national public utility does not seem farfetched; we need to be able to design entirely new kinds of medical information systems of the type illustrated in Figure 6.2. This is the kind of thinking which is required if we are to survive our time of troubles.

A word of caution must be added. Technology by itself can solve nothing. Implied in this book is a set of values; at the core of these values is a belief in man as the creator of his own destiny. Furthermore, we believe that institutions, also, are the creations of man and exist for his benefit; they are not sacrosanct. The truly effective use of information system technology will require a re-examination of all types of accepted institutional forms, from the operations of the Congress of the United States to the management of waste disposal. Today our armament for survival includes the information sciences. These sciences can be one of the instruments in achieving the next evolutionary stage of mankind.

REFERENCES

1. Reported in the *Los Angeles Times*, April 8, 1964, Part III.
2. M. Greenberger (ed.), *Management and the Computer of the Future*. New York: Wiley, 1962.
3. *Ibid.*, p. 307.
4. J. Diebold, *Beyond Automation: Managerial Problems of an Exploding Technology*. New York: McGraw-Hill, 1964, p. 64.
5. D. N. Michael, *Cybernation: The Silent Conquest*. Santa Barbara, Calif.: Center for the Study of Democratic Institutions, 1962.
6. In M. Greenberger (ed.), Ref. 2, p. 16.
7. *Ibid.*, p. 27.
8. K. E. Boulding, "Where Are We Going, If Anywhere?" *Human Organization*, **21**, No. 2 (Summer, 1962), 162–167.

Bibliography

Adams, E., *An Introduction to Data Processing in Trial Courts.* Santa Monica, Calif.: System Development Corporation, SP-1409, October 28, 1963.

Adamson, R. E., *Implementing and Evaluating Information Processing Systems.* Santa Monica, Calif.: System Development Corporation, SP-1294, November 6, 1963.

"Advances in EDP and Information Systems," *AMA Management Report No. 62.* New York: American Management Association, 1961.

Alexander, L. T., et al., "The Effectiveness of Knowledge of Results in a Military System Training Program," *Journal of Applied Psychology,* 46 (1962), 202–211.

Alexander, L. T., and E. H. Porter, *Terminal Air Traffic Control and Problems of System Design.* Santa Monica Calif.: System Development Corporation, TM-639/008/00, October 1, 1963.

Almendinger, V. V., *SPAN: A System for Urban Data Management.* Santa Monica, Calif.: System Development Corporation, SP-1862, November 11, 1964.

Anshen, M., and G. L. Bach (eds.), *Management and Corporations: 1985.* New York: McGraw-Hill, 1960.

Ashby, W. R., "General Systems Theory as a New Discipline," *General Systems: Yearbook of the Society for General Systems Research,* Vol. II, 1957, pp. 1–6.

Asimow, M., *Introduction to Design.* Englewood Cliffs, N.J.: Prentice-Hall, 1962.

"A Steel Company's Date with a Data Machine," *Business Week* (May 4, 1963), pp. 142–146.

A Summary of Lessons Learned from Air Force Management Surveys, Air Force Systems Command, AFSCP 375-2, June 1, 1963.

"A Survey of Airline Reservation Systems," *Datamation,* June 1962, pp. 53–54.

Automated Data Processing in State Government: Status, Problems, and Prospects. Chicago: Public Administration Service, 1965.

Becker, G. M., *The Elusive Criteria in Command and Control.* Santa Barbara, Calif.: General Electric Company, SP-198, November 1962.

Becker, J., and R. M. Hayes, *Information Storage and Retrieval: Tools, Elements, Theories.* New York: Wiley, 1963.

Belden, T. G., *The Language of Command: Final Report,* Studies of Command and Control, Study No. 2, Technical Report No. 62-17, Institute for Defense Analysis, August 1962.

Bello, F., "How to Cope with Information," *Fortune,* September 1960.

Bennett, E., et al. (eds.), *Military Information Systems: The Design of Computer-Aided Systems for Command.* New York: Praeger, 1964.

359

Bennis, W. G., et al. (eds.), *The Planning of Change.* New York: Holt, Rinehart, and Winston, 1961.

Benson, O., "A Computer Simulation of International Politics," *Midwest Conference of Political Scientists.* Columbia, Mo.: University of Missouri, May 12, 1961.

Benson, S. G., and H. H. Wilson, *Designing a Computer-Based Automated Hospital Information Processing System.* Santa Monica, Calif.: System Development Corporation, SP-1770, September 15, 1964.

Berkowitz, M., and J. Jaffe, *The Development and Uses of a Functional Model in the Simulation of an Information-Processing System.* Santa Monica, Calif.: System Development Corporation, SP-584, November 2, 1961.

Bertalanffy, L. von, "General System Theory: A New Approach to Unity of Science," *Human Biology,* December 1951, pp. 303–361.

Biel, W. C., et al., *Exercising Teams in Military Systems Through the Use of Simulation.* Santa Monica, Calif.: System Development Corporation, SP-1739, October 15, 1964.

Blumberg, D. F., "Computer Applications for Industry and the Military: A Critical Review of the Last Ten Years," *Proceedings of the 1963 Spring Joint Computer Conference,* Detroit, Mich., May 1963, pp. 179–190.

Bogdanoff, E., *An Epidemiological Game: Simulation in Public Health.* Santa Monica, Calif.: System Development Corporation, SP-1286, September 12, 1963.

Boguslaw, R., *The New Utopians: A Study of System Design and Social Change.* Englewood Cliffs, N.J.: Prentice-Hall, 1965.

Boguslaw, R., and R. H. Davis, *An Integrated Scientific and Engineering Manpower Information System: Some Problems and Recommendations.* Santa Monica, Calif.: System Development Corporation, SP-1385, October 18, 1963.

Borko, H. (ed.), *Computer Applications in the Behavioral Sciences.* Englewood Cliffs, N.J.: Prentice-Hall, 1962.

Borko, H., "The Information System of the Future," *STWP Review,* 12:4, October 1965, pp. 2–4.

Boulding, K. E., "General Systems Theory: The Skeleton of Science," *Management Science,* April 1956, pp. 197–208.

Boulding, K. E., "Where Are We Going, If Anywhere?" *Human Organization,* **21,** No. 2 (Summer, 1962), 162–167.

Brady, R. A., *Organization, Automation, and Society: The Scientific Revolution in Industry.* Los Angeles: University of California Press, 1961.

Buchanan, G. N., *Man-Computer Cooperation in Tasks Involving Pattern Structuring and Recognition in Military Command/Control Systems.* Santa Monica, Calif.: System Development Corporation, SP-1139, November 1, 1963.

Burck, G. (and the Editors of *Fortune*), *The Computer Age and Its Potential for Management.* New York: Harper and Row, 1965.

Bushnell, D. D., *The Automation of School Information Systems,* National Education Association, Monograph No. 1, 1964.

Bushnell, D. D., "Computer-Mediated Instruction—A Survey of New Developments," *Computers and Automation,* 14:3, March 1965, pp. 18–25.

Caffrey, J. G., et al., *Application of Electronic Data Processing Methods in Education: Preliminary Report.* Santa Monica, Calif.: System Development Corporation, TM-1754, March 9, 1964.

Carter, L. F., *The System Development Corporation and the System Training Program*. Santa Monica, Calif.: System Development Corporation, SP-52, February 6, 1959.

Carter, L. F., *Command and Control Research*. Santa Monica, Calif.: System Development Corporation, SP-2185, August 25, 1965.

Carter, L. F., and H. Silberman, *The Systems Approach, Technology and the School*. Santa Monica, Calif.: System Development Corporation, SP-2025, April 1, 1965.

Case, H. M., and S. R. Quincey, *A Unified Approach to System Development: An Application to Wildland Fire Control*. Santa Monica, Calif.: System Development Corporation, SP-294, May 9, 1961.

Chapman, R. L., et al., "The System Research Laboratory's Air Defense Experiments," *Management Science*, **5**, No. 3 (April 1959), 250–269.

Chenzoff, A. P., *A Review of the Literature on Task Analysis Methods*. Valencia, Pa.: Applied Science Associates, Navy, TDC, Technical Report: NAVTRA-DEVCEN 1218-3, June 22, 1964.

Christie, L. S., et al., *Systems Development of Command and Control Systems*. Santa Monica, Calif.: System Development Corporation, SP-182, October 3, 1960.

Churchman, C. W., *Does Operations Research = Systems Science?*, Symposium on Operations Research. Santa Monica, Calif.: System Development Corporation, March 27, 1963.

Churchman, C. W., et al., *Introduction to Operations Research*. New York: Wiley, 1957.

Cogswell, J. F., et al., *New Solutions to Implementing Instructional Media Through Analysis and Simulation of School Organization*. Santa Monica, Calif.: System Development Corporation, TM-1809, March 24, 1964.

Cohen, K. J., and E. Rhenman, "The Role of Management Games in Education and Research," *Management Science*, **7** (January 1961), 131–166.

"Command and Control Issue," *Armed Forces Management*, July 1963.

"Command/Control: Strategic and Tactical," *Data*, March 1964.

"Command and Control Systems in the U.S.A.," *Interavia*, June 1964, pp. 854–859.

"Computer-Based Management for Information and Control," *AMA Management Report No. 30*. New York: American Management Association, 1963.

Configuration Management During the Definition and Acquisition Phases, Air Force Systems Command, AFSCM 375-1, January 1, 1964.

Connelly, J. J., "Information Systems for Business and Industry," *Technical Session Proceedings*, National Symposium on Information Display. Santa Monica, Calif., February 1965, pp. 61–96.

Coons, H. G., *Recent Computer Applications in Medical Research*. Santa Monica, Calif.: System Development Corporation, FN-6995, November 13, 1962.

Corbato, F. J., et al., "An Experimental Time-Sharing System," *Proceedings of the Spring Joint Computer Conference*, San Francisco, May 1962, pp. 335–344.

Corbett, L., "Scientific Information and a National Reference Centre," *Library Association Record*, 67:5, May 1965, pp. 151–156.

Coulson, J. E., *Computers in Programmed Instruction and Educational Data Processing*. Santa Monica, Calif.: System Development Corporation, SP-950, January 20, 1963.

Cuadra, C. A., et al., *An Information Center for Law Enforcement.* Santa Monica, Calif.: System Development Corporation, TM-1670, January 2, 1964.

Culliton, J. W., "Age of Synthesis," *Harvard Business Review,* September-October 1962.

Daniels, A. E., "Some Observations Concerning Large Programming Efforts," *Proceedings of the 1964 Spring Joint Computer Conference,* Washington, D.C., April 1964, pp. 231–238.

"Data Processing Today: A Progress Report," *AMA Management Report No. 46.* New York: American Management Association, 1960.

Davidson, M., and E. Scott, *Simulation Techniques and Their Application.* Santa Monica, Calif.: System Development Corporation, SP-1133, July 19, 1963.

Davis, R. H., "The Computer Revolution and the Spirit of Man," *Proceedings of the 1964 Spring Joint Computer Conference,* Washington, D.C., April 1964, pp. 161–167.

Davison, R., *The System View and the Disenchanted Executive.* Santa Monica, Calif.: System Development Corporation, SP-1523, November 16, 1965.

Dearden, J., "How to Organize Information Systems," *Harvard Business Review,* March-April 1965, pp. 65–73.

DeFlorio, G., "Intelligent Automata and Man-Automaton Combinations: A Critique and Review," *Electrical Engineering,* March 1963, pp. 200–203.

de Latil, P., *Thinking by Machine: A Study of Cybernetics.* Boston: Houghton Mifflin, 1957.

Demaree, R. G., et al., *Development of Qualitative and Quantitative Personnel Requirements Information,* Wright Patterson AFB, Ohio, Behavioral Sciences Laboratory, 6570th Aerospace Medical Research Laboratories, Report No. AMRL-TDL-TDR-62-4, December 1962.

Desmonde, W. H., *Real-Time Data Processing Systems: Introductory Concepts,* Englewood Cliffs, N.J.: Prentice-Hall, 1964.

de Sola Pool, I., "Simulating Social Systems," *International Science and Technology,* March 1964, pp. 62–70.

Development of a Personnel Subsystem for Aerospace Systems, Department of the Air Force, Washington, D.C., AFR 30-8, November 14, 1962.

Diebold, J., "ADP—The Still-Sleeping Giant," *Harvard Business Review,* September-October 1964, pp. 60–65.

Diebold, J., *Automation: The Advent of the Automatic Factory.* Princeton, N.J.: Van Nostrand, 1952.

Diebold, J., *Beyond Automation: Managerial Problems of an Exploding Technology.* New York: McGraw-Hill, 1964.

Donegan, J., et al., "A Real Time Computing System for Supporting Manned Space Flight," *Computers and Automation,* October 1964, pp. 22–25.

Doyle, L., *Library Science in the Computer Age.* Santa Monica, Calif.: System Development Corporation, SP-141, December 17, 1959.

Dubinin, M. M., "Exchanging Scientific Information," *Bulletin of the Atomic Scientists,* October 1962, pp. 13–15.

Dunlop, J. T. (ed.), *Automation and Technological Change.* Englewood Cliffs, N.J.: Prentice-Hall, 1962.

Ebersole, J. L., *An Operating Model of a National Information System.* El Segundo, Calif.: North American Aviation, Report No. GO-IPS-1, February 5, 1965.

Ebersole, J. L., and J. M. Worth, *A Description of the North American Aviation Technical Information Processing System.* El Segundo, Calif.: North American Aviation, Report No. GO-IPS-2, April 24, 1965.

Eckman, D. P. (ed.), *Systems: Research and Design.* New York: Wiley, 1961.

Eckstein, M. E., *Sociological Perspective in the Analysis and Design of Large-Scale, Man-Machine Systems.* Santa Monica, Calif.: System Development Corporation, SP-1576, July 31, 1964.

Eckstein, M. E., *Some Organizational Problems in the Transition From Manual to Automated Systems.* Santa Monica, Calif.: System Development Corporation, SP-1577, August 25, 1964.

Edwards, N. P., "On the Evaluation of the Cost-Effectiveness of Command and Control Systems," *Proceedings of the Spring Joint Computer Conference,* Washington, D.C., April 1964, pp. 211–218.

Egbert, R. L., *System Design for a Continuous Progress School: Part II Surveillance and Detection System.* Santa Monica, Calif.: System Development Corporation, TM-1493/104/00, March 13, 1964.

Egbert, R. L., and J. F. Cogswell, *System Design for a Continuous Progress School: Part I.* Santa Monica, Calif.: System Development Corporation, TM-1493/103/00, February 28, 1964.

Electronic Systems Acquisition Process. Bedford, Mass.: The MITRE Corporation, TM-69, October 31, 1963.

Ellis, D. O., and F. J. Ludwig, *Systems Philosophy.* Englewood Cliffs, N.J.: Prentice-Hall, 1962.

Empey, S. L., *Computer Applications in Medicine and the Biological Sciences Bibliography.* Santa Monica, Calif.: System Development Corporation, SP-1025, November 9, 1962.

Engler, R. E., Jr., *Applied Social Research and the Development of Human Resource Systems.* Santa Monica, Calif.: System Development Corporation, SP-1438, July 24, 1964.

Englund, D. E., and D. P. Estavan, *CLASS—The Automated Classroom.* Santa Monica, Calif.: System Development Corporation, SP-544, November 6, 1961.

Evans, M. K., and L. R. Hague, "Master Plan for Information Systems," *Harvard Business Review,* January-February 1962, pp. 92–103.

Ewell, J. M., "The Total Systems Concept and How to Organize for It," *Computers and Automation,* X, No. 9 (September 1961).

Farr, L., *A Description of the Computer Program Implementation Process.* Santa Monica, Calif.: System Development Corporation, TM-1021/002/00, February 25, 1963.

Farr, L., and B. Nanus, "Cost Aspects of Computer Programming for Command and Control," *Proceedings* (PTGMIL 64), National Winter Convention on Military Electronics, Vol. III, February 1964.

Feigenbaum, E. E., and J. Feldman (eds.), *Computers and Thought.* New York: McGraw-Hill, 1963.

Fein, L., "Automation, Unemployment and Utopia," *Datamation,* January 1964, pp. 35–37.

Feld, M. D., "Information and Authority: The Structure of Military Organization," *American Sociological Review,* 24, No. 1 (February 1959), 15–22.

Feuers, M. M., *Scheduling and Phasing of Management Decisions in an ADP*

(*Automated Data Processing*) *Cycle*. Santa Monica, Calif.: System Development Corporation, SP-918/001/00, January 10, 1963.

Fitzgerald, W. P., *An Introduction to SAGE*. Santa Monica, Calif.: System Development Corporation, TM-490, May 18, 1960.

Fitzpatrick, R., *Toward a Theory of Simulation*. Santa Monica, Calif.: System Development Corporation, SP-1007, November 15, 1962.

Flagle, C. D., et al. (eds.), *Operations Research and Systems Engineering*. Baltimore: The Johns Hopkins Press, 1960.

Flood, M., *The Systems Approach to Library Planning*. Chicago: University of Chicago Press, 1965.

Folley, Jr., J. D., *Guidelines for Task Analysis*. Valencia, Pa.: Applied Sciences Associates, Navy, TDC, Technical Report: NAVTRADEVCEN 1218-2, June 22, 1964.

Forrester, J. W., "Common Foundations Underlying Engineering and Management," *IEEE Spectrum*, 1, No. 9 (September 1964), pp. 66–77.

Forrester, J. W., *Industrial Dynamics*. New York: Wiley, 1961.

Fredkin, E., "The Time-Sharing of Computers," *Computers and Automation*, 12, (November 1963), pp. 12–20.

Freed, A. M., "Human Interactions in Man-Machine Systems," *Human Factors*, 4, No. 6 (December 1962), pp. 389–396.

Freiberger, W. F., and W. Prager (eds.), *Applications of Digital Computers*. Boston: Ginn, 1963.

Gagné, R. M. (ed.), *Psychological Principles in System Development*. New York: Holt, Rinehart, and Winston, 1962.

Gardner, J. F., et al., "Inquiry into Methods Used to Obtain Military Information Requirements," Armed Forces-National Research Council Vision Committee, Report No. ESD-TDR-62-302, May 1962.

Garfunkel, I. M., and J. E. Walsh, "Method for First-Stage Evaluation of Complex Man-Machine Systems," *Naval Research Logistics Quarterly*, 7, No. 1 (March 1960), pp. 13–19.

Gass, S. I., et al., "Project Mercury Real-Time Computation and Data-Flow System," *Proceedings of the Eastern Joint Computer Conference*, Washington, D.C., December 1961, pp. 47–53.

Gay, L. G., *Stages in the Design and Development of an Information Processing System*. Santa Monica, Calif.: The System Development Corporation, SP-1023, November 9, 1962.

Geisler, M. A., "The Simulation of a Large-Scale Military Activity," *Management Science*, 5 (July 1959), 359–368.

Gerard, R. W., "Intelligence, Information, and Education," *Science*, 148, No. 3671 (May 7, 1965), 762–765.

Ginzberg, E., and E. W. Reilley, *Effecting Change in Large Organizations*. New York: Columbia University Press, 1957.

Glaser, E. L., and F. J. Corbato, "Introduction to Time-Sharing," *Datamation*, November 1964, pp. 24–27.

Glass, B., "Information Crisis in Biology," *Bulletin of the Atomic Scientists*, October 1962, pp. 6–12.

Goode, H. H., and R. E. Machol, *System Engineering: An Introduction to the Design of Large-Scale Systems*. New York: McGraw-Hill, 1957.

Green, J. C., "The Information Explosion—Real or Imaginary?" *Science,* 144, No. 3619 (May 8, 1964), 646–648.

Greenberger, M., "Banking and the Information Utility," *Computers and Automation,* 14:4, April 1965, pp. 28–31.

Greenberger, M. (ed.), *Management and the Computer of the Future.* New York: Wiley, 1962.

Greenberger, M., et al., *Microanalysis of Socioeconomic Systems.* New York: Harper, 1961.

Greenfield, M. S., et al., *Designing Systems for Data Processing.* San Francisco: Automation Institute Publishing Co., 1965.

Guetzkow, H., "The Development of Organizations in a Laboratory," *Management Science,* 3 (July 1957), 380–402.

Guetzkow, H., *Simulation in the Study of International Relations: Developments for Research and Teaching.* Englewood Cliffs, N.J.: Prentice-Hall, 1963.

Gullahorn, J. T., and J. E. Gullahorn, *Approaches to Testing Theories of Organization Design.* Santa Monica, Calif.: System Development Corporation, SP-1238/000/01, January 3, 1964.

Gullahorn, J. T., and J. E. Gullahorn, "Computer Applications in Social Science," *American Sociological Review,* 30 (1965), 353–365.

Gustafson, C. E., and M. R. Rockway, *The Air Force Personnel Subsystem Concept,* a paper presented at the Southwestern Psychological Association meeting, Fort Worth, Tex., April 6, 1962.

Hake, D. L., "Improving the Information Flow," *Bulletin of the Atomic Scientists,* November 1962, pp. 21–22.

Hall, A. D., *A Methodology for Systems Engineering.* Princeton, N.J.: Van Nostrand, 1962.

Hall, J. A. P., *Computers in Education.* New York: Macmillan, 1962.

Hammond, P., *Organizing for Defense: The American Military Establishment in the Twentieth Century.* Princeton, N.J.: Princeton University Press, 1961.

Handbook of Instructions for Aerospace Personnel Subsystem Designers, Air Force Systems Command Manual 80-3, July 15, 1962.

Harman, H. H., *Simulation: A Survey.* Santa Monica, Calif.: System Development Corporation, SP-260, July 1961.

Harman, H. H., *Simulation as a Tool for Research.* Santa Monica, Calif.: System Development Corporation, SP-565, September 25, 1961.

Haverty, J. P., and R. L. Patrick, *Programming Languages and Standardization in Command and Control.* Santa Monica, Calif.: The RAND Corporation, RM-3447-PR, January 1963.

Hayden, R. F. C., "Computers and the Administration of Justice," *Proceedings of the 1963 Fall Joint Computer Conference.* Las Vegas, Nev.: November 1963, pp. 609–617.

Hayes, R. M., *The Concept of an On-Line, Total Library System.* Chicago: American Library Association, May 1965.

Head, R. V., *Real-Time Business Systems.* New York: Holt, Rinehart, and Winston, 1964.

Hearle, E. F. R., *A Data Processing System for State and Local Governments.* Englewood Cliffs, N.J.: Prentice-Hall, 1963.

Hearle, E. F. R., *Can EDP Be Applied to All Police Agencies?* Santa Monica, Calif.: The RAND Corporation, P-2454, October 1, 1961.

Hearle, E. F. R., *Electronic Data Processing for Cities—The Broad Look*. Santa Monica, Calif.: The RAND Corporation, P-2714, February 1963.

Hearle, E. F. R., *Information Systems for Urban Planning*. Santa Monica, Calif.: The RAND Corporation, P-2765, July 1963.

Heilprin, L. B., "On the Information Problem Ahead," *American Documentation*, 12, No. 1 (January 1961), pp. 6–14.

Heinze, K., et al., *Management of Computer Programming for Command and Control Systems*. Santa Monica, Calif.: System Development Corporation, TM-903/000/02, May 8, 1963.

Heyne, J. B., *New Directions in Management Control Systems Research*. Santa Monica, Calif.: System Development Corporation, TM-708/300/00, October 15, 1962.

Hill, M. V., and K. J. Lindsay, *Personnel Planning Information for the Air Force Satellite Control System*. Inglewood, Calif.: Space Systems Division, Air Force Systems Command, TDR-62-21, February 1962.

Hilton, A. M., "An Ethos for the Age of Cyberculture," *Proceedings of the 1964 Spring Joint Computer Conference*, Washington, D.C., April 1964, pp. 139–153.

Hopkins, R. C., "A Systematic Procedure for System Development," *IRE Transactions of Engineering Management*, EM-8, No. 2 (June 1961), pp. 77–86.

Huntington, S. P., *The Common Defense: Strategic Programs in National Politics*. New York: Columbia University Press, 1961.

Information System Design Techniques. Bedford, Mass.: The MITRE Corporation, SS-9, November 20, 1962.

Information System Performance Evaluation. Bedford, Mass.: The MITRE Corporation, SS-15, January 1964.

Isaacs, H. H., *Time-Sharing and User-Oriented Computer Systems: Some Implications for Public Administrators*. Santa Monica, Calif.: System Development Corporation, SP-1772, September 30, 1964.

Isaacs, H. H., and W. W. Herrmann, *Advanced Computer Technology and Crime Information Retrieval*. Santa Monica, Calif.: System Development Corporation, SP-1927, 1965.

Israel, D. R., *System Design and Engineering for Real-Time Military Data Processing Systems*. Bedford, Mass.: The MITRE Corporation, SR-124, September 1964.

Jackson, R. A., *Computer-Based Programs and Air Traffic Control*. Santa Monica, Calif.: System Development Corporation, SP-1103/000/01, August 12, 1963.

Janowitz, M., *The Professional Soldier*. Glencoe, Ill.: The Free Press, 1960.

Jarrett, H. F., *The Systems Concept and Its Application to Fire Service Problems*. Santa Monica, Calif.: System Development Corporation, SP-782, April 24, 1962.

Johnson, R. A., et al., *The Theory and Management of Systems*. New York: McGraw-Hill, 1963.

Jones, Jr., E. A., "Law and Electronics: The Challenge of a New Era," *Proceedings of the First National Law and Electronics Conference*, Lake Arrowhead, Calif., October 21-23, 1960.

Jordan, N., "Motivational Problems in Human-Computer Operations," *Human Factors*, 4, No. 3 (1962), 171–175.

Kahn, H., *On Thermonuclear War.* Princeton, N.J.: Princeton University Press, 1960.

Kahn, H., *Thinking About the Unthinkable.* New York: Horizon Press, 1962.

Karush, W., *On Mathematical Modeling and Research in Systems.* Santa Monica, Calif.: System Development Corporation, SP-1039, November 28, 1962.

Kast, F. E., and J. E. Rosenzweig (eds.), *Science, Technology, and Management.* New York: McGraw-Hill, 1963.

Kennedy, J. L., "The System Approach: Organizational Development," *Human Factors,* 4, No. 1 (February 1962), pp. 25–52.

Kepner, C. H., and B. B. Tregoe, "Developing Decision Makers," *Harvard Business Review,* 38, No. 5 (September-October 1960), 115–124.

Kibbee, J. M., et al., *Management Games: A New Technique for Executive Development.* New York: Reinhold, 1961.

Kirby, R. L., and H. L. Wright, "Information Systems Integration," *Proceedings* (PTGMIL 63), National Summer Convention on Military Electronics, September 1963.

Kraft, J. A., "A 1961 Compilation and Brief History of Human Factors Research in Business and Industry," *Human Factors,* 3, No. 4 (December 1961), 253–283.

Kroger, M., and L. S. Christie, *Command and Control in Limited War: Execution and Monitoring.* Santa Monica, Calif.: System Development Corporation, SP-1183, April 9, 1963.

Kroger, M., et al., "Computers in Command and Control," *Institute for Defense Analyses,* TR 61-12, November 1961.

LaBolle, V., *Management Aspects of Computer Programming for Command Control Systems.* Santa Monica, Calif.: System Development Corporation, SP-1000/000/02, February 5, 1963.

Laden, H. N., and T. R. Gildersleeve, *System Design for Computer Applications.* Wiley, 1963.

Lafferty, E. L., *The Role of Simulation and Data Reduction Programs in the Development of Real-Time Systems.* Bedford, Mass.: The MITRE Corporation, SR-125, December 1964.

Leavitt, H. J., and T. L. Whisler, "Management in the 1980's," *Harvard Business Review,* 36, No. 6 (November-December 1958), 41–48.

Ledley, R. S., and L. B. Lusted, "Computers in Medical Data Processing," *Operations Research,* 8, No. 3 (May-June 1960), pp. 299–310.

Licklider, J. C. R., "Man-Computer Partnership," *International Science and Technology,* No. 41, May 1965, pp. 18–26.

Licklider, J. C. R., "Man-Computer Symbiosis," *IRE Transactions on Human Factors in Electronics,* **HFE-1** (March 1960), 4–11.

Licklider, J. C. R., *The System System and Bridges over the Gulf Between Man-Machine System Research and Man-Machine System Development.* Cambridge, Mass.: Bolt, Beranek and Newman, January 1962.

Likert, R., *New Patterns of Management.* New York: McGraw-Hill, 1961.

Lippitt, R., et al., *The Dynamics of Planned Change.* New York: Harcourt, Brace, and World, 1958.

Lusted, L. B., "Data Handling, Computers and Diagnosis," *Proceedings of the Institute of Radio Engineers,* May 1962, pp. 1190–1194.

Maass, A., et al., *Design of Water-Resource Systems.* Cambridge, Mass.: Harvard University Press, 1962.

MacDonald, N., "Over 600 Areas of Application of Computers," *Computers and Automation,* XII, No. 6 (June 1963).

Malcolm, D. G., A. J. Rowe, and L. F. McConnell (eds.), *Management Control Systems.* New York: Wiley, 1960.

Mann, F. C., and F. W. Neff, *Managing Major Change in Organizations.* Ann Arbor, Mich.: Foundation for Research on Human Behavior, 1961.

March, J. G., and H. A. Simon, *Organizations.* New York: Wiley, 1958.

Meacham, A. D., and V. B. Thompson, *Total Systems.* Detroit: American Data Processing, 1962.

Meany, J., *The Automation of Psychotherapy.* Santa Monica, Calif.: System Development Corporation, SP-1050, December 12, 1962.

Meier, R. L., *A Communications Theory of Urban Growth.* Cambridge, Mass.: Massachusetts Institute of Technology Press, 1962.

Meier, R. L., "Explorations in the Realm of Organization Theory. IV: The Simulation of Social Organizations," *Behavioral Science,* **6**, No. 3 (July 1961), 232–248.

Meister, D., "The Measurement of Man-Machine Systems Under Field Operational Conditions," *Human Factors,* **3**, No. 4 (December 1961), pp. 245–252.

Meister, D., and G. F. Rabideau, *Human Factors Evaluation in System Development.* New York: Wiley, 1965.

Mesarović, M. D. (ed.), *Views on General Systems Theory.* New York: Wiley, 1964.

Michael, D. N., *Cybernation: The Silent Conquest.* Santa Barbara, Calif.: Center for the Study of Democratic Institutions, 1962.

Michael, D. N., *The Next Generation: The Prospects Ahead for the Youth of Today and Tomorrow.* New York: Random House, 1963.

Miller, J. C., "Conceptual Models for Determining Information Requirements," *Proceedings of the Spring Joint Computer Conference,* Washington, D.C., April 1964, pp. 609–620.

Miller, J. G., *General Behavior Systems Theory.* Pittsburgh, Pa.: Pittsburgh Psychological Association, April 1959.

Miller, J. G., "Information Input Overload and Psychopathology," *The American Journal of Psychiatry,* **116**, No. 8 (February 1960), 695–704.

Mottley, C. M., and T. G. Belden, *The Strategic Direction of the Armed Forces: Final Report.* Arlington, Va.: Institute for Defense Analysis, TR 62-18, August 1962.

Muller-Thym, B. J., "Cultural and Social Changes," *The Changing American Population,* Report of the Arden House Conference, 1962, pp. 85–96.

Nanus, B., and L. Farr, "Some Cost Contributors to Large-Scale Programs," *Proceedings of the Spring Joint Computer Conference,* Washington, D.C., April 1964, pp. 239–248.

Nelson, E., *Research Into the Management of Computer Programming: Some Characteristics of Programming Cost Data from Government and Industry.* Santa Monica, Calif.: System Development Corporation, TM-2704, November 12, 1965.

Nett, R., and S. A. Hetzler, *An Introduction to Electronic Data Processing.* Glencoe, Ill.: The Free Press, 1959.

Neuschel, R. F., *Management by System*. New York: McGraw-Hill, 1960.

Newell, A., and H. A. Simon, "Heuristic Problem Solving: The Next Advance in Operations Research," *Operations Research,* **VI** (January-February 1958), pp. 1–10.

Newell, A., and H. A. Simon, "The Simulation of Human Thought," *Current Trends in Psychological Theory*. Pittsburgh, Pa.: University of Pittsburgh Press, 1961, pp. 152–169.

Newell, A., et al., "Report on a General Problem-Solving Program," *Computers and Automation,* **8** (July 1959), 10–17.

Obermayer, R. W., "Simulation, Models, and Games: Sources of Measurement," *Human Factors,* **6**, No. 6 (December 1964), pp. 607–619.

O'Neill, J. W., Major-General, "O'Neill Takes Reins at ESD; Gives 'L' System Review," *Data,* October 1964, pp. 35–39.

Optner, S. L., *Systems Analysis for Business Management*. Englewood Cliffs, N.J.: Prentice-Hall, 1960.

Organizational Models for Command Post Information Systems. Bedford, Mass.: Electronic Systems Division, AFSC, Technical Documentary Report No. ESD-TDR-64-438, June 1964.

O'Toole, Jr., J. F., *Faculty Attitudes Toward Teaching Machines and Programmed Instruction*. Santa Monica, Calif.: System Development Corporation, SP-1178, April 12, 1963.

Overton, R. K., "Intelligent Machines and Hazy Questions," *Computers and Automation,* **14** (July 1965), 26–30.

Packer, R. E., "Computers, Education, and the Government," *Computers and Automation,* **14** (March 1965), 14–17.

Parker, R. W., "The SABRE System," *Datamation,* September 1965, pp. 49–52.

Parsons, H. M., *The Development and Installation of a System Training Program: The SAGE ECCM Example*. Santa Monica, Calif.: System Development Corporation, TM-537, September 28, 1960.

Peach, P., *Quality Control for Computer Programming: A Final Report on an Initial Study*. Santa Monica, Calif.: System Development Corporation, TM-2313/001/00, September 9, 1965.

Peach, P., *Simulation with Digital Computers*. Santa Monica, Calif.: System Development Corporation, SP-1390, October 28, 1963.

Peck, M. J., and F. M. Scherer, *The Weapons Acquisition Process: An Economic Analysis*. Cambridge, Mass.: Harvard University Press, 1962.

Perry, M. N., and W. R. Plugge, "American Airlines 'SABRE' Electronic Reservations System," *Proceedings of the Western Joint Computer Conference,* Los Angeles, May 1961, pp. 593–601.

Philipson, M. (ed.), *Automation: Implications for the Future*. New York: Vintage Books, 1962.

Pickering, G. E., et al., "Multicomputer Programming for a Large-Scale Real-Time Data Processing System," *Proceedings of the Spring Joint Computer Conference,* Washington, D.C., April 1964, pp. 445–461.

Pierce, J. R., "Communication as an Alternative to Travel," *Proceedings of the Institute of Radio Engineers,* May 1962, p. 643.

Porter, E. H., *Manpower Development: The System Training Concept*. New York: Harper and Row, 1964.

Proceedings of the IFIP Congress '65. Washington, D.C.: Spartan Books, 1965.

Proceedings of the Second Congress on the Information System Sciences. Washington, D.C.: Spartan Books, 1965.

Proceedings of the Symposium on Information Processing in Command and Control Systems. Santa Monica, Calif.: System Development Corporation, TR-4, June 1962.

Ramo, S., "Extending Man's Intellect by Electronics," *Proceedings of the Institute of Radio Engineers,* May 1962, pp. 640–643.

Rath, G. J., and W. P. Allman, "Computers: Applications to the Quantification of Human Behavior," *Human Factors,* 6, No. 6 (December 1964), pp. 585–605.

Ream, N. J., "On-Line Management Information," *Datamation,* March 1964, pp. 27–30.

Research and Development: Personnel Subsystem Program for Aerospace Support, and Command and Control Systems, AFSC Regulation No. 80-14, Headquarters, Air Force Systems Command, Andrews Air Force Base, Washington, D.C., May 10, 1963.

Resta, P. E., and C. P. Smith, *The Use of Electronic Data Processing in Corrections and Law Enforcement.* Santa Monica, Calif.: System Development Corporation, SP-1495, December 18, 1963.

Rhine, R. J., "Command-and-Control and Management Decision Making," *Human Factors,* 6, No. 1 (February 1964), 93–100.

Richardson III, General R. C., "The Stalemate in Concepts," *Air University Quarterly Review,* Summer 1960, pp. 2–13.

Riley, W. B., "Time-Sharing: One Machine Serving Many Masters," *Electronics,* November 29, 1965, pp. 71–89.

Roach, C. J., et al., "Medical Data Processing and Computer Automated Hospitals," *Datamation,* June 1962, pp. 25–28.

Rome, B. K., and S. C. Rome, *The Experimental Study of Large-Scale Organizational Structures.* Santa Monica, Calif.: System Development Corporation, SP-983, October 4, 1962.

Rosen, S., "Programming Systems and Languages: A Historical Survey," *Proceedings of the Spring Joint Computer Conference,* Washington, D.C., April 1964, pp. 1–15.

Rosenberg, A. M., *Group Communications and Program Interaction in Time-Sharing Systems.* Santa Monica, Calif.: System Development Corporation, SP-1386, October 14, 1963.

Rowell, J. T., and E. R. Streich, "The SAGE System Training Program for the Air Defense Command," *Human Factors,* 6, No. 5 (October 1964), 537–548.

Ryans, D. G., *An Information-System Approach to Theory of Instruction with Special Reference to the Teacher.* Santa Monica, Calif.: System Development Corporation, SP-1079, March 20, 1963.

"SABRE, a $30-Million Application," *Fortune,* April 1964, pp. 142–143.

Sackman, H., "Regenerative Recording in Man-Machine Digital Systems," *Proceedings* (PTGMIL 64), National Winter Convention on Military Electronics, Vol. III, February 1964.

Sackman, H., and J. B. Munson, "Investigation of Computer Operating Time and System Capacity for Man-Machine Digital Systems," *Journal of the Association for Computing Machinery,* II, No. 4 (October 1964), 450–464.

Samuel, A. L., *Time-Sharing on a Multiconsole Computer,* Massachusetts Institute of Technology, MAC-TR-17, March 1965.

Schaefer, W. C., *Information Management System Design for Public Welfare; The Role of EDP in Policy Decision and Administrative Planning.* Santa Monica, Calif.: System Development Corporation, SP-2202, September 24, 1965.

Schultz, L., "Management Communication Across Space and Time," *STWP Convention Proceedings,* 12th Annual, New York, May 19-22, 1965.

Schultz, L., *The Information System: Too Big and Growing.* Santa Monica, Calif.: System Development Corporation, SP-594, November 6, 1961.

Schwartz, J. I., et al., "A General-Purpose Time-Sharing System," *Proceedings of the Spring Joint Computer Conference,* Washington, D.C., April 1964, pp. 397–411.

Searle, L. V., *Configuration Management of Computer Programs for Information Systems.* Santa Monica, Calif.: System Development Corporation, TM-1918, June 2, 1964.

Seashore, S. E., "Field Experiments with Formal Organizations," *Human Organization,* 23, No. 2 (Summer 1964), pp. 164–170.

Shultz, G. P., and T. L. Whisler (eds.), *Management Organization and the Computer.* Glencoe, Ill.: The Free Press, 1960.

Simon, H. A., *The Shape of Automation for Men and Management.* New York: Harper and Row, 1965.

"Simulation and Gaming: A Symposium," *AMA Management Report No. 55.* New York: American Management Association, 1961.

Sinaiko, H. W., and E. P. Buckley, *Human Factors in the Design of Systems.* Washington, D.C.: Naval Research Laboratory, NRL Report 4996, August 29, 1957.

Singleton, J. W., *The Role of the Human Operator in Command-Control Systems.* Santa Monica, Calif.: System Development Corporation, SP-179, September 6, 1960.

Slavin, M., *Hospital Pharmacy and Automation.* Santa Monica, Calif.: System Development Corporation, SP-1041, January 10, 1963.

Smith, C. P., and P. E. Resta, "Computers and Correctional Agencies," *Data Processing Magazine,* 6 (July 1964), 22–24.

Smith, P. A., "Information Processing in Medicine: Design of a Multiple-Hospital Information Management System," *Bionics Symposium,* Dayton, Ohio, March 1963.

Smith, R. A., *Corporations in Crisis.* Garden City, N.Y.: Doubleday, 1963.

Staugas, L. W., *Report on 1963 Rochester Conference on Data Acquisition and Processing in Biology and Medicine.* Santa Monica, Calif.: System Development Corporation, TM-1412, August 7, 1963.

Steel, Jr., T. B., "Programmers and Cheap Computing: Effects of Batch Fabrication," *Datamation,* August 1965, pp. 58–67.

Steel, Jr., T. B., "The Fabulous World of Real Timeland," *Datamation,* March 1964, pp. 24–26.

Steele, G., and P. Kircher, *The Crisis We Face: Automation and the Cold War.* New York: McGraw-Hill, 1960.

Stoller, D. S., et al., *Design of a Management Information System.* Santa Monica, Calif.: The RAND Corporation, P-1362, November 22, 1958.

Strachey, C., "Time Sharing in Large, Fast Computers," *Information Processing,* Proceedings of the International Conference on Information Processing, UNESCO, Paris, 1960, pp. 336–341.

Striner, H. E., "Information Processing and Some Implications for More Effective Manpower Programs," *Proceedings of the 1964 Spring Joint Computer Conference*, Washington, D.C., 1964, pp. 155–160.

"Survey of Information Needs of Physicists and Chemists," *Journal of Documentation*, 21:2, June 1965, pp. 83–112.

Swanson, D. R., "Searching Natural Language Text by Computer," *Science*, 132, No. 3434 (October 21, 1960), pp. 1099–1104.

Systems Management: System Program Documentation. Washington, D.C.: Department of the Air Force, Air Force Regulation No. 275-4, February 12, 1962.

Systems Management: System Program Documentation. Washington, D.C.: Department of the Air Force, Air Force Regulation No. 375-4, November 25, 1963.

Systems Management: System Program Management Manual. Washington, D.C.: Headquarters, Air Force Systems Command, Andrews Air Force Base, Air Force Systems Command Manual 375-4, March 16, 1964.

Teeple, J. B., *System Design and Man-Computer Function Allocation*, Bendix Corporation, April 5, 1961.

Testing/Evaluation of Systems, Subsystems, and Equipment. Washington, D.C.: Department of the Air Force, Air Force Regulation No. 80-14A, April 13, 1964.

The Industry-Government Aerospace Relationships. Menlo Park, Calif.: Stanford Research Institute, May 1963 (2 volumes).

Thompson, F. B., "Fractionization of the Military Context," *Proceedings of the 1964 Spring Joint Computer Conference*, Washington, D.C., 1964, pp. 219–230.

Thompson, F. B., *Fundamentals Underlying Military Information System Design.* Santa Barbara, Calif.: TEMPO, General Electric Company, SP-183, November 1962.

Thurston, P. H., "Who Should Control Information Systems?" *Harvard Business Review*, November-December 1962, pp. 135–139.

Tilles, S., "The Manager's Job: A Systems Approach," *Harvard Business Review*, January-February 1963, pp. 73–81.

"Towards a World Information Centre," *Nature*, 206 (June 5, 1965), 967–969.

Von Buelow, R., *Techniques Used in Man-Machine Communication.* Santa Monica, Calif.: System Development Corporation, SP-1767, September 14, 1964.

Wagner, L. W., and E. G. Palola, "The Miniature Replica Model and Its Use in Laboratory Experiments of Complex Organizations," *Social Forces*, 42, No. 4 (May 1964), pp. 418–429.

Wallach, I. A., *A Functional Model and Its Utilization in the Design of a Complex System.* Bedford, Mass.: The MITRE Corporation, SR-48, Supplement 1, May 1963.

Waller, E. A., *The Feasibility of Time-Sharing as an Operational Concept for the NMCS.* Santa Monica, Calif.: System Development Corporation, TM-WD-121, May 19, 1964.

Walter, B., "Organizations, Computers, Logic," *General Systems: Yearbook of the Society for General Systems Research*, Vol. VII, 1962, pp. 261–267.

Ways, M., "The Era of Radical Change," *Fortune*, May 1964.

Weinwurm, G., and H. Zagorski, *Research Into the Management of Computer*

Programming: A Transitional Analysis of Cost Prediction Techniques. Santa Monica, Calif.: System Development Corporation, TM-2712, November 12, 1965.

Wiener, N., *Cybernetics: Control and Communication in the Animal and the Machine.* New York: Wiley, 1948.

Wiener, N., *The Human Use of Human Beings: Cybernetics and Society.* Garden City, N.Y.: Doubleday Anchor Books, 1954.

Wiener, N., "Some Moral and Technical Consequences of Automation," *Science,* **131** (May 6, 1960), 1355–1358.

Williams, R. H. (ed.), *Human Factors in Military Operations: Some Applications of the Social Sciences to Operations Research.* Chevy Chase, Md.: The Johns Hopkins University, Operations Research Office, TM-ORO-T-259, January 7, 1954.

Wilson, H. H., "System Design for Automating Patient Data in a Hospital," *Bionics Symposium,* Denver, Colo., March 1963.

Wilson, I. G., *Information, Computers, and System Design.* New York: Wiley, 1965.

Withers, C. R., et al., *Preliminary Design of an Information System for the Youth Opportunities Board of Greater Los Angeles.* Santa Monica, Calif.: System Development Corporation, TM-2036, August 31, 1964.

Wood, M. K., "The National Security Dilemma," *Management Science,* **7**, No. 3, April 1961, pp. 195–209.

Young, J. P., *A Survey of Historical Developments in War Games.* Bethesda, Md.: The Johns Hopkins University, Operations Research Office, March 1959.

Zuckerman, S., Sir, "Judgment and Control in Modern Warfare," *Foreign Affairs,* January 1962, pp. 196–212.

Index